THE ENGINE'S MOAN

American Steam Whistles

Edward A. Fagen
and members of the Horn & Whistle Enthusiasts Group

The Astragal Press

International Standard Book Number 1-931626-01-4
Library of Congress Control Number   2001095345

Published by
THE ASTRAGAL PRESS
5 Cold Hill Road, Suite 12
P.O. Box 239
Mendham, New Jersey 07945-0239

Cover design by Donald Kahn
Manufactured in the United States of America

UP 4017

Come; put your hand along my flank.
Remember me in that bright morning when
A hundred nameless sculptors in Schenectady, New York
Shaped me of iron and steel and singing bronze
And gave me life.

I bore the strength of armies in my frame.
Six thousand horses marched at my command.
I ruled the grassy uplands of Cheyenne; I warred
With gravity itself on Sherman Hill,
And did not yield.

What mountains could not do was done by men.
Mere words on paper overmastered me,
And stilled the mighty sinews of my thighs, and quenched
My belly's fire, and from my lungs withdrew
The living breath.

My years are spent in this black shed.
The air is still; the pigeons flap and drowse.
My kin are dead, and I am mute and cold, but I endure.
Now go; tell your race that once you knew
My sovereignty.

E.A.F.

Table Of Contents

Foreword

During the late fifties I traveled to Virginia's Blue Ridge Mountains. My quest was to witness the last years of the great steam parades that the Norfolk & Western Railway performed almost on an hourly basis, lugging a seemingly endless stream of loaded coal cars over the spine of the Blue Ridge Mountains to the port city of Norfolk.

My favorite spot alongside the tracks was a little glen located a scant 200 yards from the crest of the eastbound grade. The mountains beckoned with their sounds: the sing-song chatter of nearby crickets, the distant call of the crow. I felt calm amongst the undulating shapes that framed an evocative portrait of blacks and grays in the late afternoon summer haze.

Then I heard an unmistakably distinct sound, a distant deep hoot, blending with the moody spirit of the mountains. Then silence! Then the haunting hoot again, only louder. I felt change; something was happening.

Now I could hear the distant roar of a giant animal, mixing with the ever louder hoots. Like a loon's call in the lakes of the north country, the oncoming roar seemed part of the mountains, perhaps because I knew so well that the battle between machines and mountain grades had echoed at this spot for so long.

The roar was the beating exhaust of three huge Mallet locomotives; two at the front of the train and the third pushing. The hooting was the deep-pitched whistles that the Norfolk & Western was so fond of. Mostly the whistles sounded at road crossings, but engineers like to make music. I imagine there were more than a few extra blasts to salute a friend at trackside, or perhaps just for good measure.

The intent of the Norfolk & Western was to get as many tons of coal over the Blue Ridge as possible. Thus I knew that the locomotives were using every ounce of their enormous strength to crest the grade. These were titans at war with the force of gravity, and their sheer power, their sound, their smoke and steam, left me breathless. As the massive locomotives passed, I could feel the searing heat of their roaring

fires, the hot breath of the steam. The train crested the grade and the sound of the engine's exhaust began to subside, but the call of the whistles continued to echo in the mountains until it again became a distant hoot from far-off ridges. The sound of the crickets and the mountain haze returned.

Why do I retell the story of my encounter in the Virginia mountains years ago? Because Ed Fagen stood at my side, at least in spirit. I didn't know Ed in those days, but I do know that he would have had the same flood of experience and feelings that I did. Throughout his life Ed has found his own unique places of the spirit, to hear the steam whistle's call as it etched its own paths into his soul.

How does one become a whistle enthusiast? What motivates a man to undertake to write the definitive book on the American steam whistle? In Ed's case it appears to have been the confluence of three of the main currents in his life. In his Acknowledgments Ed credits his father with nurturing his interest in railroads, but in truth Ed sought out many of these early experiences by himself. He grew up a few blocks from the main line of the Chicago & Northwestern railroad. While still a schoolboy, he discovered that if he ran quickly to the Woodlawn Avenue overpass as soon as school let out, he could be peering down on the tracks as the northbound *Twin Cities 400* passed beneath, drawn by a splendid class E-2 Pacific. He claims that he can still recall the thrill of excitement as he received a blast of smoke in his face, while the whistle blew and the cinders rained down gently on his head.

The second main current was his profession. In adult life Ed was a physicist, whose hallmark as a scientist was an enduring interest in energy systems. He championed always a holistic view of such systems, one that considered not merely the component parts, but also the manner of their interconnection into larger systems. Thus when his attention turned at last to steam whistles, he was able to understand the whistle not merely as part of a larger and more complicated mechanical system, but also to explore its deeper significance as an icon of the industrial age. This breadth of perspective can be seen in his unique essay on the steam whistle in popular culture, which forms the fourth chapter of this book.

The third main current was his lifelong love of music. Music enabled him to reconcile the romantic side of his nature with the rational and skeptical habits of mind demanded by his profession. The meeting ground of science and art was the study of musical acoustics, which has engaged him as an amateur since his teens. In addition, his late wife Margery was a professional violinist and violin teacher, and he learned to love the sweet voice of the violin above all other instruments. It was only a few short steps from the love of orchestral instruments to a fascination with pipe organs, and thence to whistles in general.

What turned his attention to steam whistles in particular was the demise of the age of steam. As the curtains descended on the great machines that had so thrilled him in his boyhood, he found at last an outlet that united all three sides of his nature. He would have bought an entire steam locomotive if he could. Purchasing a 200 ton locomotive was an obvious absurdity, but the whistle itself was easily liberated from the condemned boilers, and could sometimes be purchased for the price of the scrap value of the brass. Thus Ed began his collection in 1972, almost the last possible moment in which steam whistles could readily be obtained from primary sources. His collection now numbers more than 140 whistles, and an equal number of steam era artifacts of other kinds.

Ed characteristically searches for the human experience that always lives one way or another in the machine. He knew that the age of steam and its voice had penetrated deep into the American culture and psyche. Thus, this is not just a book about whistles, but about America in the halcyon days of a steamy, smoky industrial revolution that lasted over a century, and then became a time and a culture that we will never know again, except through the words and images of history. The whistle's call then and now opens the doorway to a far larger portrait of ourselves.

Make no mistake about the whistle's utilitarian purpose. It was an essential mechanical device that warned, signaled and communicated. Locomotive engineers, ship captains, and factory masters knew well the need for the whistle's work. Consider, for example, the switchman's task of coupling and uncoupling freight cars in a dark railway yard. He absolutely had to know where the locomotive was, when it was going to move and in which direction. His life depended on the whistle's signal. Or consider the captain of a giant ship working in unison with tugboats in a fog-bound harbor. The whistle communicated when to push, to pull, to turn, and ultimately when to lead the great ship out into the open sea. In factory towns across America the blowing of the whistle determined when thousands worked or rested. The pace of community life depended on the timing of the whistle's call.

Sometimes tools evolve into something that they were not originally intended for. In the case of the whistle, ship captains, engineers, and many others quickly learned that they could make a sound so interesting that it was a form of musical expression. The celebrated Casey Jones, for example, had his own personal whistle that he changed from locomotive to locomotive depending on his assignment. His call, like that of many other engineers, was so well known that the people along the tracks that crisscrossed America knew who was at the throttle. The men of the locomotives and the people of the land spoke with one another.

Unlike the sweet sound of the violin, the steam whistle was not designed for concert halls. Rather the whistle belonged in the vast and robust landscape of America. The steam whistle was on the hooting Norfolk & Western Mallets in the Blue Ridge Mountains, and more than fifty thousand other locomotives in every conceivable geographic region of this country. Or it was the factory whistle in nearly every town in America, piercing the bone-chilling cold of a January morning. It was the deep moan of a Great Lakes ore boat driving tirelessly through the black night. From the prairies, to the forests, to the mountains, to the lakes and rivers, the whistle made music not merely for the privileged few, but for the masses. It was the music machine of our immense land.

Edward Fagen knows that the steam whistle has received scant attention over its 165 years of history. As he points out, the steam whistle has never

received
bland f
of the t
beeps
this nee
by pass
edge o

Alth
workin
ingly ra
the las
groan

ingly, we have to travel to museums or other pre-served industrial sites to hear a call that once was ubiquitous.

On that July day long ago, I was listening to the final calls of an era. Edward Fagen heard the same calls, and it has motivated him to make this gift to us in the 21st century. This book, *The Engine's Moan*, will reconnect us with the sound and the culture of a working world in another time.

I thank Ed because to omit the steam whistle from the history of technology and culture is to overlook something of decisive importance to the American past.

MARKLEY SMITH, Ed.D.
Editor Emeritus, *Locomotive and
      Railway Preservation Magazine*
Huntington, Vermont
September 2000

Preface

From the point of view of the industrial archaeologist or the historian of technology, the most remarkable thing about steam whistles is that no one has ever written a book about them. Despite a history extending over more than 165 years, despite their ubiquity as artifacts of the Industrial Revolution, despite their iconic significance in popular culture, and despite the millions of living persons who remember their sounds with varying degrees of affection, they have never had their chronicler. It is doubtful that one person in a thousand can name the inventor of the steam whistle, or the time and place of its invention, much less the circumstances which provoked its invention. One can search whole libraries in vain for a scientifically correct explanation of its manner of operation. It has never received one hundredth the scrutiny of meaner implements of communication, the soulless typewriters, telephones, and computers that dominate our age. Yet it richly deserves this documentation, and more.

There are, to be sure, a few books dealing with certain specialized applications of steam whistles, such as the calliope. And there is (and has been for more than a century) a continuing flood of books about steam railroading, both scholarly and popular, in which the locomotive whistle receives peripheral mention. There is also a small handful of anecdotal articles about whistles in railfan magazines and other ephemera. But to the best of my knowledge there has never been an extended work dealing in a cohesive way with the steam whistle itself in all its manifestations. It is this niche that I have attempted to fill.

As work progressed, I found it necessary to restrain my inclination to write an encyclopedia. It might be thought that resource materials would be hard to find in so recondite an area of investigation. On the contrary, a relatively small research effort yielded a rich harvest of archival materials. I found all of it interesting and wished to include it all. Wiser friends reminded me that my primary obligation was not to exhaust the topic but to deliver a marketable manuscript to the publisher.

In the end fatigue overcame ambition, as it inevitably must. Among the more notable omissions is any extended discussion of whistle valves and actuators, those essential accessories without which no whistle can be blown. There are several other areas in which collaboration with nationally recognized experts was denied me for reasons I found perfectly satisfactory.

The content of the book has been arranged so that the main body of the text may be read without specific preparation in science or engineering. As a former physicist, I am keenly aware of the shortcomings of the theoretical treatment of whistle operation presented here. Let it be said in my defense that many details of this operation have not yet been fully elucidated. The theory of turbulent sonic jets and their interaction with cavity resonators is extremely complex and remains an active area of investigation today.

Finally, in this era of exaggerated concern for political correctness, it may not be superfluous to remark that, to the best of my knowledge, everyone directly involved with steam whistles is male. It is this circumstance, and not male chauvinism or gender bias, that accounts for the exclusive use of masculine personal pronouns in the pages that follow.

Acknowledgments

My love of steam whistles was kindled by my father, who in 1934 at the Chicago World's Fair, held me up in the cab of the locomotive so that I could reach the whistle cord. Father was a traveling salesman who regularly rode the great passenger trains of the day, and he freely shared with me his affection for these conveyances and the marvelous machines that drew them. I have no fonder memories than of accompanying him to the stations of Chicago's Loop to witness his departure on the *Hiawatha*, the *Twin Cities 400*, or the *Twentieth Century Limited*.

My love lay dormant until 1972, when the late Bob Owen of Romeo, Michigan, a retired motorman from the Detroit Union Railways, blew for me his small collection of locomotive whistles. In that moment I became a whistle enthusiast, and before I left Bob's shop that day I had purchased my first whistle, Accession No. 1, a classically graceful 1883 Crane. My first mentor was Larry Simpson of Lynchburg, Virginia, who provided me with the nucleus of my collection and shared with me his vast knowledge of whistle lore in an exuberant correspondence extending over a decade. In 1977 I introduced Linsley Chapman of Wallingford, Connecticut to the hobby. The pupil quickly outstripped the master, and Lin rapidly became one of the leading American collectors as well as a cherished friend. His untimely death in 1999 ended a collaboration that would have greatly enriched this book. All that survives of our intended joint effort is Lin's historical review of the Lunkenheimer Co. and its products in Chapter 5, and the Glossary in Appendix A.

Above all, I am indebted to past and present members of the Horn & Whistle Enthusiasts Group, whose quarterly journal *Horn & Whistle* I have had the privilege of editing and publishing since 1994. These men have generously shared with me their private stores of historical and archival materials, as well as their vast anecdotal knowledge of steam whistles. Some of them deserve to be named explicitly as co-authors. John Bowditch, Curator of Industry at the Henry Ford Museum, was the co-author of Chapter 2 on the history of the steam whistle. David Fultz, the nation's pre-eminent whistle collector, was the co-author of the section on locomotive whistles in Chapter 3, and all of Chapter 6 on collecting. David also provided a critical review of Chapter 5 that resolved many troublesome issues and spared me much potential embarrassment. Harry Barry assisted me with the section on marine whistles in Chapter 3. Larry Spreckelmeier, the nation's foremost whistle restorer and a steadfast friend, was the co-author of Chapter 7 on conservation, and contributed many of the photographs in Chapters 3 and 7. David Fultz and Mark Phillips collaborated with me in the section on whistle-blowing artistry in Chapter 8. Bruce Cynar, historian of technology and tireless researcher, led the search for the whistle patents tabulated in Appendix B, assisted by Harry Barry, Gene Brady, Lin Chapman, Fred Dahlinger, and Richard Weisenberger. Other members, such as Ron Beberniss, Hyler Bracey, Tim Gautreaux, Eric Larson, Gareth McNabb, Ken Michelson, and especially Peter Ommundsen, one of the few people still pursuing experimental research on steam whistles, have assisted me in ways too numerous and varied to enumerate. Their interactions with me over the years are so tightly woven into the fabric of this book that it would be impossible to tease out passages which are exclusively theirs.

Among those outside the Horn & Whistle Enthusiasts Group, Theodore Teplow, former president of Crosby Valve, and Charles Beck, former sales manager of Buckeye Iron & Brass Works, furnished essential material regarding the histories of their respective corporations. Craig Bliss, also of Crosby Valve, discovered a large cache of corporate records long thought to have been destroyed, and took pains to make it available to me and to all members of the whistle fraternity. Tom Middleton obligingly lent me a catalog crucial to the history of the Union Brass Works. Steven Espenschied of Canton, Ohio generously provided me with a condensation of his book on the American steam calliope, material that forms the core of the section on steam calliopes in Chapter 3. Bert Wraith and Alexander D. Mitchell IV patiently tutored me on railroading in the United Kingdom. My friends and former colleagues at the University of Delaware, John Meakin, George Basalla, and Eugene Ferguson, have come to my aid on a variety of recondite matters. I am indebted to Mark Smith, founder and editor of the journal *Locomotive & Railway Preservation*, for writing the Foreword as well as for several stimulating and sympathetic discussions. Stanford Ovshinsky of Energy Conversion Devices, the most extraordinary man I have ever known, taught me much of what I know about the folkways of American heavy industry. The staffs of the Hagley Museum and Library in Wilmington, Delaware, the New York State Library in Albany, New York, and the library of Rensselaer Polytechnic Institute in Troy, New York, assisted my research in every possible way. Professor Samuel Elder of the United States Naval Academy at Annapolis, Maryland and Dr. John Coltman of Pittsburgh, Pennsylvania have favored me with critical reviews of the material on whistle science and technology. The blame for remaining errors and obscurities lies with me, not with them. Like all who deal with railroad-related matters, I am indebted to John White, former Curator of Transportation at the Smithsonian Institution and dean of American railroad historians, who made no direct contribution to this book, but whose writings provide a standard of scholarly excellence against which works of this nature will always be measured.

Finally, I owe a lasting debt to my editor, Lisa Pollak of The Astragal Press and all the members of her staff for their patience in dealing with one of the most dilatory authors in their stable, and for their skillful assistance in bringing to life a work that has spent nearly three decades in gestation.

1 *Introduction*

In the present age, when the conversion of chemical or thermal energy into mechanical work is effected largely by internal combustion engines and rotating machinery, it is almost impossible to recall the dominance once held by the reciprocating steam engine. From the beginnings of the Industrial Revolution until after World War II, a period of more than 150 years, it was the prime mover of industrialized society, the chief instrument, in Lewis Mumford's arresting phrase, of the era of "carboniferous capitalism."[1] The coal resources of the planet seemed inexhaustible, and the mere touch of a match sufficed to turn water into live steam, the vital fluid that animated every aspect of the newly mechanized world. Achievement could be measured in horsepower, and boundless optimism reigned as the nations of Western Europe rushed to transform their capital inheritance of fossil fuel into the manufacture of material goods.

The principal agent of this transformation was the steam engine. At first tentatively and then with increasing rapidity, it mastered and vastly multiplied the tasks earlier performed by the muscles of men and animals or by wind and water power. It pumped the seepage and hoisted the coal from the mines, spun the fibers into yarns, wove the yarns into cloth, ground the wheat into flour, sawed the timbers into planks, hammered the iron in the forge, and powered the very lathes and planers on which it was itself manufactured. In self-propelled form it dragged the barges along the canals, threshed the wheat in the farmers' fields, flung great iron ships across the world's oceans, and ultimately, as the steam locomotive, fathered the vast network of railroads that linked region to region and country to country. So pervasive was its influence, and so absolute was its sovereignty, that Lucius Beebe could write without the slightest suspicion of hyperbole, "The commanding and transcendent fact in the conquest of the American continent and the evolution of the United States as a nation is that water heated into steam occupies one thousand six hundred times as much space as it did in liquid form."[2] Even the dour historian Henry Adams, who found little enough to admire in any century later than the thirteenth, was compelled to acknowledge the "infinite force" of the steam engine, and to choose it as the central metaphor in his vision of the then-dawning twentieth century.[3]

In addition to its undeniable usefulness, the steam engine, and especially the steam locomotive, possessed a curious and largely aesthetic fascination. The breadth and durability of this appeal are attested by the number of antiquarian societies devoted to the preservation and celebration of the steam era, by the undiminished popularity of model railroading as a hobby, and by the ceaseless trickle of railroadiana from specialized publishing houses. No diesel engine, no turbine, no electric motor, none of the covert and anesthetic machinery of today, is the focus of such nostalgia. Although no wholly satisfactory account of the sources of this appeal has yet been given, it surely consists at least in part of a brute animism, a recognizable analogy to organic life and effort. The reciprocating steam engine had power one could *see*. The sources of its vitality, the articulation of its parts, the channels along which its energy flowed, were all so manifest as virtually to invite comparison with a living creature. It ate coal or wood, drank water, breathed air, and spewed waste. It had a belly, a heart, lungs, thighs, sinews, joints. It was at once subhuman and superhuman, an alien but docile giant. And to complete the catalog of resemblances, it had a mighty and sonorous voice, not merely the muffled bark of its exhaust, but a voice uniquely its own, used on no other engine before or since: the steam whistle.

Although the title of this book draws upon a familiar folkloric association between the steam locomotive and the steam whistle (and this is the context in which most of us remember them), it would be a mistake to assume that whistles were mounted only on locomotives. As the succeeding chapters will make clear, the steam whistle was first conceived and employed as an accessory to the steam boiler, independent of the steam engine. Regarded merely as a boiler accessory, it has no more intrinsic interest than other boiler accessories such as the feedwater pump, the sight glass, the pressure gauge, or the safety valve. Over the long history of the device, it is probable that as many whistles were used without engines as with them.

Where were all the whistles not associated with engines? These whistles were mounted on boilers that generated *process steam,* steam valued for its thermal energy rather than for its propulsive effort, an unsung and unglamorous usage virtually unknown to the general public. Process steam heated the fermentation vats in breweries and the drying drums in paper mills, vulcanized the rubber in tire factories, ripened the leaf in tobacco sheds, cured plastic castings in their molds, softened the molasses in the pipeline, steamed the clothes in laundries, bent the wood in shipyards and furniture factories, and warmed the very mills and plants and refineries in which this myriad of industrial processes was carried out. In general, process steam was generated at much lower pressures than steam intended for propulsion; nevertheless process steam boilers demanded the same range of accessories as boilers for high pressure steam, including low-water alarms and their attendant whistles.

It should also be remembered that the primary function of the steam whistle was not to please, but to summon or alarm. The whistle on the firehouse roof or on the boiler of the steam pumper signified incendiary disaster throughout urban America. In factory and mining towns, in railroad terminals and lumber camps, the whistle regulated the lives of workers as narrowly as the lives of monks were once ordained by the ringing of the canonical hours.

Its harsh call was in many respects the most characteristic and widely recognized sound of a burgeoning industrial society, far exceeding in pervasiveness and authority the church bells of an earlier age. Only rarely was the steam whistle given to any joyful purpose, as in the steam calliope beloved of circus fans, surely the loudest and most exuberant musical instrument ever devised by man.

A mere recital of the uses to which the steam whistle was put, however, conveys nothing of its extraordinary evocative power, particularly when associated with means of transportation. In folksong and story, the sound of the whistle often symbolizes the conveyance itself and, by extension, all the excitement, promise, and despair of journeying. At one time the familiar cry "Steamboat comin' round the bend!" heralded the arrival of the packet at innumerable towns along the nation's waterways. Similarly, no sound of modern times conveys anything like the connotative richness of the steam locomotive whistle. In countless ballads, including that from which this book takes its title, in poetry and the novel, and above all, in the hearts and minds of an older generation, the sound of the train whistle is invested with symbolic meaning far beyond anything the instruments of the acoustician might reveal. It is by turns a wailing banshee, a demonic shriek, a song of bewitchment, the spur to wanderlust, the voice of loneliness, the echo of solitude, the harbinger of grief, parting, and loss. It is inconceivable that a comparable wealth of association will someday be aroused by the nasal and expressionless blare of the air horn. The air horn merely warns its hearers to get out of the way, but the sound of the steam whistle beckons us to adventures that live only in the imagination.

The study of steam whistles must necessarily look forward as well as backward. As the reciprocating steam engine fades from our everyday consciousness, and the steam whistle slips inevitably into that realm of paleotechnic artifacts which future generations will regard with the same indifference they now accord to butter churns and muzzle-loaders, it seems more important than ever to salvage some remembrance of this remarkable device. The surviving whistles themselves are in no grave danger of disappearing, thanks to the durability of the copper alloys from which they were built. A significant fraction of all those manufactured is now in the hands of collectors, suffering neglect, perhaps, but largely immune to further loss or decay. What may well be lost in future years, however, is the *love* of whistles, that prideful affection which led their makers to shape and adorn and polish them far beyond utilitarian necessity, and their owners or proprietors to cherish them as they cherished no other component of the machinery under their command. It is the purpose of this book to rekindle some portion of that affection in those already sensible to it, and to elucidate it for the benefit of those who are not. It is in no sense the scholarly history nor the engineering treatise that the subject merits. No foreknowledge of either mathematics or mechanics is presumed on the part of the reader. We ask him only to join with us in paying fond tribute to steam whistles of all kinds, to explore briefly their marvelous diversity, and to share this small compendium of their lure and lore, in the hope of delaying for even a few more years the moment when their magical speech is stilled forever.

Portrait of Adrian Stephens, inventor of the steam whistle, in the Cyfarthfa Castle Art Gallery and Museum, Methyr Tydfil, England.

The Steam Whistle in Historical Context

2 The Steam Whistle In Historical Context *

The commanding and transcendent fact in the conquest of the American continent and the evolution of the United States as a nation is that water heated into steam occupies one thousand six hundred times as much space as it did in liquid form.

— Lucius Beebe

Historians these days do not write about things like locomotive whistles.

— George Basalla

A brief history of the steam engine

The reciprocating steam engine was the prime mover of the Industrial Revolution. Although the roots of this device lie in antiquity, its modern development began only at the end of the seventeenth century.[1] This development rested firmly on a foundation of capitalist avarice, and in particular, on the greed of the owners of Cornish tin mines and Welsh collieries (coal mines). These shallow mines were plagued with a tendency to flood, and for centuries water had been pumped from them with the aid of horse-driven pumps. But horses eat and require rest and eventually die, and the mine owners could scarcely have failed to observe that if the work of pumping were performed instead by some sort of machine, the cost of horses could be eliminated and their profits thereby increased.

The first person to achieve notable success in pumping water from mines by means of steam was a Devonshire engineer named Thomas Savery, who in 1698 patented "a new Invention for Raiseing of Water and occasioning Motion to all sorts of Mill Work by the Impellent Force of Fire, which will be of great Use and Advantage for Drayning Mines, Serveing Towns with Water, and for the Working of all Sort of Mills where they have not the Benefitt of Water nor Constant Windes."[2] Savery's pump contained no moving parts other than manually operated steam and water cocks. In order to draw water up from below, steam was first admitted to an empty copper reservoir and then condensed by a spray of cold water on the outside. This produced a partial vacuum which sucked water up into the reservoir. The inlet valve of the reservoir was then closed and steam admitted again, forcing the contained water up a long vertical pipe. The cycle could be repeated about four times per minute by turning the appropriate cocks. Savery installed two of these pumps in fashionable London manor houses, attaining a

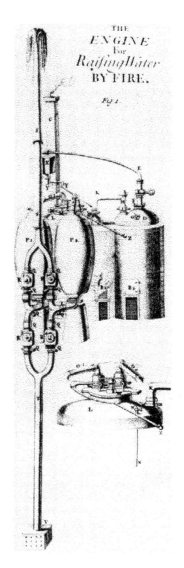

Savery's first working steam pump, as depicted in his book Miner's Friend of 1702. From Briggs, Ref.1.

Thomas Savery of Devonshire, inventor of the steam pump.

* In collaboration with John Bowditch

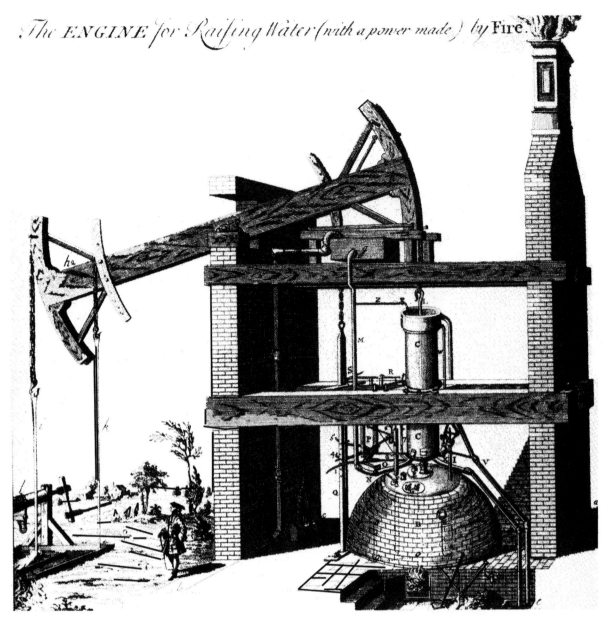

An early Newcomen atmospheric pumping engine, drawn by Henry Beighton ca. 1717. The man standing to the left of the pier indicates the scale of the device. The work output of the engine was probably just over five horsepower. From Briggs, Ref.1.

total lift of fifty-eight feet, of which sixteen feet were achieved by suction and forty-two feet by steam pressure. The latter figure corresponds to a gauge pressure of roughly 19 pounds per square inch. Savery's efforts to adapt the pump to mines several hundred feet deep ended in failure, however, because the flimsy copper boilers and copper piping of the day could not withstand the necessary steam pressure; they burst at the joints. These boilers were not fitted with safety valves, although such devices had already been invented and put to use on a

pressure cooker by Denis Papin more than a decade earlier. Thus to Savery goes the dubious distinction of the first recorded boiler explosion.

The next great milestone was the invention of the "atmospheric engine" by Thomas Newcomen, a Dartmouth ironmonger and inveterate tinkerer. Newcomen's engine had a true cylinder and piston, the first in any steam engine, and in this sense was the progenitor of all other piston engines. The cylinder was mounted vertically, and its upper end was open to the air. Steam was fed in under the piston and condensed by a jet of cold water playing inside. This produced a partial vacuum within the cylinder, permitting the pressure of the atmosphere to push the piston downward. The piston was connected by a chain to a pivoted beam, the other end of which operated a lift pump. Moreover the engine was fitted with auxiliary levers and cranks which worked its own valves— the first valve gear— making operation fully automatic. The first recorded engine of this type was installed in 1712 at a colliery in Tipton, near Wolverhampton in Staffordshire. The engine was the size of a small house, but modern engineers reckon its power output at about 5.5 horse-power. Hundreds of additional Newcomen engines were built, some of which still served nobly as late as the end of the eighteenth century.

Note that steam itself performs no thermodynamic work in Newcomen's engine; all work is performed by the pressure of the atmosphere acting on the outside of the piston. It fell to the Scottish instrument maker and surveyor James Watt to make the next great advance, an improvement so fundamental and far-reaching that he is still (erroneously) regarded by many school children as the inventor of the steam engine. Around 1765 Watt grasped that the abysmally low efficiency of Newcomen's engine was due to the thermal energy wasted in the repeated heating and cooling of the cylinder and piston. He therefore removed the cooling phase of the cycle to a separate condenser, so that the cylinder could remain hot at all times. He also closed the top of the cylinder and allowed steam to enter this closed volume at the appropriate moment, so that the pressure of the steam itself rather than that of the atmosphere drove the piston downward on the return stroke. These principles were embodied in a seminal patent issued to Watt in 1769, claiming "a new method of lessening the consumption of steam and fuel in fire engines."

1769, perhaps more than any other date, marks the beginning of the age of steam. In 1769 the Western world stood poised on the cusp of an unprecedented transformation. A Corsican couple named Buonaparte gave birth to an infant son Napoleon, who in the next half-century would redraw the political map of Europe forever. In the court of Catherine the Great of Russia, a blind Swiss mathematician named Leonhard Euler, the most prolific mathematician who ever lived, was laying the foundations of nineteenth century analysis. A thirteen-year-old prodigy named Mozart began to write his first string quartets. (He had already written an opera.) In Bonn, Germany, the following year, Maria Magdalena van Beethoven gave birth to a son Ludwig who would eventually overturn the world of Mozart and usher in the Romantic age of music. In England the poets William Wordsworth and Thomas Chatterton were born, Thomas Gainsborough painted "The Blue Boy," the printer John Newbury published a new book of children's verses entitled *Mother Goose's Melody*, and the first volumes of the *Encyclopaedia Britannica* were issued. A French engineer named Nicolas Cugnot, at least a generation in advance of his time, chugged down a Paris street in a two-cylinder self-propelled "steam carriage," stopping every ten or fifteen minutes to rebuild the fire.

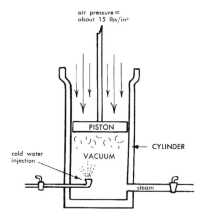

Piston and cylinder of a Newcomen atmospheric engine.

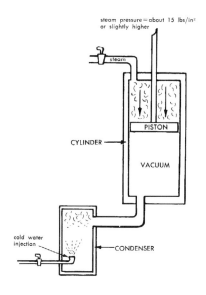

Piston and cylinder of a Watt single-acting engine.

And perhaps most pertinent to this narrative, the inventor James Hargreaves patented the spinning jenny, thus paving the way for Richard Arkwright and the establishment of the factory system. The production of cloth was no longer carried out in individual cottages but in vast mechanized mills. The seeds of mercantilism had been sown.

Further developments in steam engine technology followed at an accelerating pace. In 1774, following the bankruptcy of his original backer, Watt formed a partnership with the Birmingham entrepreneur Matthew Boulton, arguably the most important business alliance in the history of technology. In 1776 the firm of Boulton & Watt produced its first two large engines, one with a piston 50" in diameter(!) for the Bloomfield colliery in Staffordshire, and one with a 34" piston for Wilkinson's iron furnace. The difficulties of fabricating a cylinder of such size before the invention of the boring mill can scarcely be imagined. Watt was proud of his workmanship and boasted that "piston and cylinder were fitted so nicely that one could not insert a worn shilling between them."

By 1788 Watt had converted his original single-acting engine into a double-acting engine, with steam admitted to and condensed from the two sides of the piston in alternation. This gave two power strokes per cycle instead of only one. Since one cannot push on a chain, he also introduced a stiff parallel-motion linkage between the end of the piston rod and the beam. This made it possible in turn to convert the oscillating motion of the far end of the beam into rotary motion, and opened the way to innumerable applications in factories. Watt originally considered using a crank to perform the

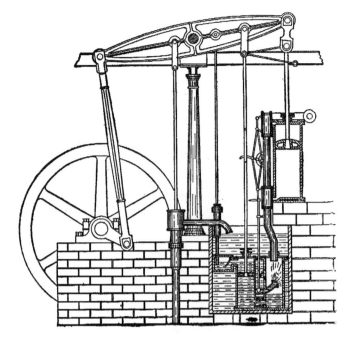

Watt's double-acting condensing engine of 1784. From N. Hawkins, New Catechism of the Steam Engine.

conversion, but another inventor, James Pickard, held the patent. Watt had already experienced bitter patent disputes and was unwilling to risk another. Therefore he chose to employ instead a rather complicated version of sun-and-planet gearing. Finally he adapted the familiar flyball governor, already in use on windmills, to the task of regulating the speed of his engines. By the end of the century several hundred of Watt's improved engines were in use, fifty-five of them in Cornwall alone. Ever the canny Scotsman, Watt knew his market, and advertised his engines in terms of the number of horses they would replace. Thus the term "horsepower" entered the language, where it lingers anachronistically in such remote areas as the specification of electric motors. Watt died in 1819, old and full of honors. His statue stands in Westminster Abbey amidst those of kings.

It had been evident from the time of Savery that the power output of a steam engine would increase in direct proportion to the steam pressure, all else being equal. Watt understood this thoroughly, but hesitated to use steam pressures much higher than atmospheric, believing them to be unwarranted and dangerous. Thus the next round of advances came from men who dared to experiment with higher steam pressures. Three inventors, working at the same time in England and the U.S., developed the first practical high-pressure steam engines. About 1800 the Cornish engineer Richard Trevithick began to design and build engines using steam pressures in the range 50 to 100 pounds per square inch gauge. Similar experiments were carried out on this side of the Atlantic by John Stevens of Hoboken, New Jersey, and by the inventor Oliver Evans of Philadelphia, more honored in Europe than in his native land. These new high pressure engines were more efficient and much smaller, cheaper, and lighter than the low pressure engines being built by Watt and others. But their most important advantage by far—and it is an interesting question whether their inventors foresaw its significance—was their portability. It must be remembered that the low pressure beam engines of the day were as large as houses; in fact the engine and the engine house were nearly one and the same, with the engine rooted to its site by many tons of foundationwork. Whatever else these earlier engines were, they were essentially immobile. But the high pressure engine was sufficiently small and compact so that it could be applied to transportation. It could propel itself along a roadway or waterway, and carry an additional load as well. These new engines were called "locomotive engines," from Latin roots meaning "to move from place to place." Eventually the the noun became superfluous, and the adjective alone took over its role.

Thus Trevithick, in 1801, having proved his compact high pressure engine at Cornish mines, took the radical step of building a full-scale road vehicle. In 1804 he went one step further and built the first true steam locomotive. Meanwhile in the United States, Stevens was experimenting with the use of high-pressure steam engines in small steamboats, an especially important development in a youthful nation that lacked proper roads and canals. In Philadelphia, Evans was building a self-propelled steam-powered

Oliver Evans, as he appeared in Henry Howe's book Memoirs of the Most Eminent American Mechanics, *published in 1844. The engraving was probably copied from an earlier oil portrait. From Ferguson,* op.cit.

dredge called the *Orukter Amphibolos*, or "amphibious digger," a machine even more ponderous than its name. This monstrous contraption lumbered through the streets of the city in 1805 on its way to the harbor. Once afloat, it paddled its way out to its working position and began dredging the ship channel. High-pressure engines were also well adapted to driving machinery in mills and factories. Thus, after about 1820, the use of high-pressure steam spread rapidly in both land and in water transport. By the late 1820's, truly practical steam locomotives appeared and the railway age began. In a very real sense, Trevithick, Stevens, and Evans had independently developed the prototypes for the type of steam engine that would drive the coming industrial revolution.

A high pressure steam engine, however, demands a high pressure boiler. In Savery's day, as we saw, such boilers did not exist. By 1800 much progress had been made, and in the years 1800 to 1840 tremendous inventive energy was applied to the design and creation of new types of boilers. Nevertheless, throughout most of the nineteenth century boilers exploded with appalling frequency, causing dreadful loss of life not merely among those who tended them, but also among innocent bystanders

A somewhat fanciful depiction of Evans' Orukter Amphibolos, *as it appeared in "The Mechanic," (Boston) 1834, many years after the event. Evans' straight-line engine of 1812 is correctly represented, but the remainder of the construction may be an artist's conception. From E.S. Ferguson,* Oliver Evans, Inventive Genius of the American Industrial Revolution.

The Hartford Insurance Co., among many others, was founded specifically to protect the railroads against the risk of boiler explosions.

and passengers. Great insurance companies were created to indemnify boiler users against claims of injury and death. The science of metallurgy and the art of boiler fabrication required nearly a century to advance to the point where the high pressure steam boiler became a thoroughly domesticated servant of technology, and boiler construction had been standardized and codified by the major engineering societies.

In truth, a working steam boiler (or a "fired pressure vessel" in the language of the American Society of Mechanical Engineers) is an awesome device. Only fools and ignoramuses are unafraid of it. The accepted margin of safety for American boilers is a factor of five; i.e., the boiler must withstand hydrostatic pressure equal to five times its working pressure. In nineteenth century France that factor was three. Of all high-pressure metal artifacts, only a gun barrel has a lower safety factor, usually in the neighborhood of two.

What makes boilers dangerous is the amount of stored energy they contain. Consider for example a rather small boiler rated at 25 horsepower, containing 3250 lbs of water, and producing saturated steam at 150 pounds per square inch gauge. A boiler of these modest specifications would be suitable for a traction engine. With the aid of steam tables one can compute that the energy stored within it, which would be set free to do destructive work in the event of an explosion, is approximately 54 million Joules. This in turn is approximately the energy contained in 26 pounds of TNT. On the basis of this small example, the reader may speculate how much energy is stored in the boiler of a late model steam locomotive, carrying perhaps twenty tons of water and producing superheated steam at a pressure of 275 pounds per square inch. These frightening numbers are the source of the old engineers' dictum, "To run is to die," signifying that the engineer who panics and abandons his machine in a moment of crisis will surely be killed by flying shrapnel.

A surprisingly small portion of the improvement in boiler construction was due to an increase in the inherent strength of materials. It can easily be shown that the internal pressure required to burst a homogeneous cylindrical shell is directly proportional to the tensile strength of the material of which it is composed. The primitive copper vessels of Savery's time had a tensile strength of roughly 30,000 pounds per square inch. The figure for ordinary wrought iron boiler plate, as used by Watt, is approximately 50,000 pounds per square inch. By the end of the nineteenth century, the best grade of cold-rolled mild steel plate had a tensile strength of 60,000 to 65,000 pounds per square inch. Thus in two hundred years the total improvement due to increased tensile strength amounted to little more than a factor of two.

The major contribution to boiler safety came from an improved understanding of fabrication techniques. Nineteenth century boilers seldom failed by bursting their walls; more often they burst their seams, the joints where the various plates were fastenened together. It took engineers some years to grasp, both in theory and in practice, that longitudinal seams are more likely to fail than circumferential seams, and to develop appropriate riveting techniques for each. The single riveted lap joint gave way to the double riveted lap joint, which yielded in turn to the double riveted butt joint with single cover plate, which was finally superseded by the double riveted butt joint with double cover plates (see next page). These advances in joint technology were matched by similar advances in staybolt technology, which is the art of bracing flat surfaces such as those surrounding the firebox. Early staybolts tended to pull their peened-over heads through the plate they were intended to support. The results were catastrophic, because when one staybolt failed, its neighbors were likely to fail too because of the increased load. This led to a chain reaction, like the falling of a row of dominoes or the unzipping of a zipper.

Boilers failed for other reasons too, having nothing to do with the adequacy of their design. Some explosions were traceable to the imperfect metallurgical knowledge and metal-working practices of the time. The metal might contain hidden inclusions or weak spots, or might be weakened by corrosion. Incipient stress cracks might have formed as a result of repeated heating and cooling. (Techniques of non-destructive testing lay at least a hundred years in the future.) But by far the largest causes of boiler explosions were human error, carelessness and neglect. Sometimes the neglect was willful, as when an early American locomotive, the *Best Friend of Charlestown*, blew up because its fireman had tied down its safety valve, the constant clacking of which disturbed his sleep. More often, however, the error was simply one of inattention. Particularly to be feared was "low water," the situation in which the level of water in the boiler fell below the crown sheet which formed the top of the firebox. This exposed the crown sheet to the full fury of the flames. Without water to carry the heat away it quickly softened and lost its strength, and a violent explosion ensued.

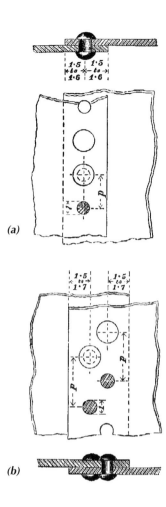

The inventor and the invention

It was explosions of this latter type which set the stage for the invention of the steam whistle.[3] We know that the inventor was a simple Cornish mechanic named Adrian Stephens, but many of the circumstances surrounding his invention remain cloaked in mystery. Stephens did not apply for a patent, being, as he later wrote, "neither in want of, nor caring for, money." (The concept of an invention as intellectual property seems not to have occurred to the working classes.) No contemporary published account of the invention exists, and there are significant discrepancies in later accounts, including the inventor's own recollections regarding the date and place of the invention and the event or events which provoked it. Even the inventor's name and date of death were in doubt until quite recently. All these uncertainties testify to the difficulty of reconstructing events many decades after their occurrence.

What is known is that Stephens was born in 1795, and early in the nineteenth century migrated with his younger brother James to the Merthyr Tydfil district of South Wales, there to take positions in the burgeoning ironworks industry. Initially Adrian was employed as chief engine operator at the Plymouth Ironworks, but left around 1827 to join the Dowlais Iron Company. He remained at Dowlais until 1837, in charge of the mill and the blowing engines. He then went to the Penydarren works, and still later returned to the Plymouth Ironworks in Pentrebach. His later years seem to have been spent in reduced circumstances, relieved only

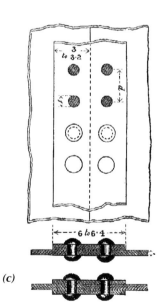

Boiler seams, in order of increasing strength: (a) single riveted lap joint; (b) double riveted lap joint; (c) butt joints with single and double cover plates.

by public subscription, and he died at his home in Merthyr Tydfil on Christmas day, 1876.

When and where did he invent the steam whistle? Charles Knight's *Cyclopaedia of Engineering*, published in 1851, states: "In 1826 the chief engineer of some works in Plymouth, Adrian Stephens, fitted a boiler in his charge with a whistle to give a clear audible signal of the escape of steam from the safety valve. He afterwards equipped boilers at Merthyr Tydfil with whistles." This account was widely reprinted in later editions of the *Cyclopaedia*. It contains no manifest inconsistencies, but is uncorroborated by other sources. In particular Stephens himself never claimed so early a date for the invention, nor did he cite the Plymouth Ironworks as the place.

Zerah Colburn, whose enormously influential treatise *Locomotive Engineering* was published posthumously in 1871, was the editor of the British journal "The Engineer." In the issue of December 20, 1861, he inserted a brief circumstantial account of the invention of the steam whistle, accompanied by several illustrations. The inventor's name was erroneously given as William Stephens, the place as the Dowlais Ironworks, and the year as 1833. Subsequent versions of this account gave various dates between 1832 and 1835. As with Knight, Colburn's account is not corroborated by other contemporary accounts.

Finally, there is the testimony of Stephens himself, in midlife, in later life, and as recollected by his son James. In a letter entitled "Account of the Explosion of a Steam Boiler at the Penydarren Works, South Wales," sent to the Institution of Civil Engineers on January 12, 1842, Stephens wrote:

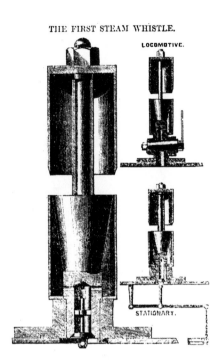

THE FIRST STEAM WHISTLE.

LOCOMOTIVE.

STATIONARY.

This is the only representation we have of Stephens' original invention. It is derived from a sketch made in 1835 by Thomas Turner, a mechanic employed by Sharp Bros. & Co. of Manchester, who had been sent to Dowlais Ironworks to put up some shafting. There he saw (and presumably heard) Stephens' whistle, and was sufficiently impressed to bring a sketch of the device back to his foreman. The foreman in turn showed it to a director of the Liverpool & Manchester Railway. This drawing, however, did not appear in print for another 26 years, until Zerah Colburn published it in "The Engineer" in 1861. From Lee, Ref.3.

"In the newspaper sent you herewith is a report of evidence given by me at the inquest at the conclusion of which there is an allusion to the verdict of the Jury recommmending *signal whistles* also an avowal on my part of having received directions to place them on these same boilers but unfortunately through having too many *irons* in hand this was not accomplished in time to prevent the lamentable accident.

"I shall perhaps be excused the liberty of here stating that these signal whistles were made by me and applied to several boilers at the Dowlais Works as far back as the year 1831 and although common in the neighbourhood are, I have reason to believe, but little used in other places. When properly constructed and attached whether to Locomotive engines as *signals of approach* or to stationary boilers as *low water alarms* they may be heard at a distance of (at all events in this vale) three or four miles, and might perhaps by increasing the size and varying a little the construction be heard at a much greater distance. They are *necessary* to the boilers of stationary engines. I believe them also applicable to steam boat engines not only to warn those on board of an insufficiency of water in the boiler but those at a distance of their approach at night or in foggy weather in the daytime . . ."

The Steam Whistle in Historical Context

Thirty years later, at the age of 77, Stephens wrote a charming letter to his niece:

"You desire me to give some account of the making of the first steam whistle. This I will endeavour to do, but scarcely think you will, when written down, feel enough interest in it to read it through, it being a rather dry subject. The whistle has been in constant use wherever there are railways and steam engines, for between thirty and forty years, without any improvement in the mode of action or intensity of sound. Somewhere about the year 1835 I was in the employ of the Dowlais Iron Company, having the charge of the mill and also the blowing engines . . . About the date above named one of the steam boilers got injured through a deficiency of water supply, luckily discovered in time to prevent explosion. It, nevertheless, showed strongly enough that something more certain and effective than the gauge cocks were required, and this something should not only be capable of warning the engine-tenter, or person in charge, of anything wrong in regard to the feed water, but should make itself heard by every person in the vicinity of the boiler.

"Now arises the question how or in what shape is this want to be supplied? I tried a whistle of the common sort, but larger; no good result. Tried the Dowlais House organ pipes, with no better success. Next made a short copper tube two inches in diameter, contracted one end to attach it to a steam boiler; closed the top and and made it in every possible respect as near as possible like the common boatswain's whistle; filed off the vent or opening and set it on the boiler. This was a decided improvement but too soft and weak. It served as a stepping stone nevertheless, for as in increase of size produced an augmentation of sound, why should not an increase in the vent or opening cause a further augmentation? This seemed plausible enough, and so it was tried at once, and I was gratified and very much pleased to find that I had made so much progress. I had got the harsh and unpleasant, though useful, sound at last. No improvement has been made, nor do I think there will be; none is required.. . ."

Although it differs in some significant details from the earlier account—did the boiler explode or not?—

this letter gives an astonishing insight into the inventive process. Stephens was clearly an empirical acoustician of genius, and his intuitive notions regarding the alterations necessary to increase the intensity of radiated sound are precisely in accord with modern acoustical theory. Noteworthy too is his insistence that the steam whistle needs no further improvement, and indeed it received none in British hands for the next half century at least. It remained for the Americans to develop the device in size, power and complexity, and to diversify its uses throughout the industrial world.

Yet a third account of the invention comes from a letter written by James Stephens, son of the inventor, in 1921. This letter is preserved in the Cyfarthfa Castle Museum of Merthyr Tydfil:

"My father, Adrian Stephens, was Chief Engineer of the Dowlais Works in the year 1835; when a boiler explosion occurred with one of the old non-tubular boilers, through the negligence of the stoker who had not kept up the proper supply of water in the boiler. The result was a loss of several lives.

"Sir John Josiah Guest sent for my father and enquired of him whether something could be done to prevent this happening again. After some further conversation and thought upon the subject, my father asked Sir John to procure for him some organ pipes from London. After considerable study my father produced the first Steam Whistle; and the same Steam Whistle is used all over the civilized world of today and has undoubtedly saved thousands of lives.

"One of the pipes was fixed at the top of the boiler in such a way that the end of it dipped in the water. A shrill whistle was attached to the top of the pipe, and immediately the water got too low in the boiler the steam rushed up the pipe and caused the whistle to blow, thus giving a warning to the man who was neglecting his duty."

James' understanding of the creative process is clearly less complete than that of his father, although he does confirm that commercially manufactured organ pipes played a role in it. Regrettably, neither account specifies whether these pipes were labial (flue) pipes or lingual (reed) pipes, nor whether they were constructed of wood or metal.

These distinctions will become important when we attempt to identify the antecedents of Stephens' invention.

In retrospect, what exactly did Stephens invent? George Basalla has argued persuasively that few if any inventions spring full blown from the minds of heroic individuals; instead they grow incrementally from prior art by a process akin to Darwinian natural selection.[4] Careful scrutiny of the Turner drawing, which we may take to be an accurate representation of Stephens' device ca. 1835, provides some answers. Certainly Stephens did not invent the whistle itself, whose origins are lost in pre-history. Mouth-blown flutes, such as the *Nay* flute of ancient Egypt, are pictured in the frescoes surrounding the tombs at Thebes, and surviving examples have been found in mummy cases. Nor did Stephens invent the organ pipe, the nearest relative of the steam whistle, in any of its numerous varieties. Hero of Alexandria described primitive bellows-blown organs before the Christian era, and the organ itself was fully perfected by the beginning of the seventeenth century.

Nevertheless, insofar as the Turner drawing can be trusted, Stephens seems to have borrowed numerous features of established organ flue pipe design. The bell or resonator is shorter and wider than any organ pipe; nevertheless it does not differ in principle from any capped cylindrical stop such as a Gedeckt or Bourdon. Like an organ pipe, the lip of the bell is precisely aligned over the emerging jet of steam, and is chamfered or tapered to a knife edge so as to split the jet precisely in two. Furthermore, the long tapered steam passage in the base or lower portion is also borrowed directly from the windway of wooden pipes of the flute family, where it enforces a regime of laminar flow essential to proper voicing at low wind pressures. Stephens did not know, nor could he have been expected to know, that flow at the steam pressures prevailing in his boilers was turbulent rather than laminar, and therefore all these borrowed features were unnecessary. Modern steam whistles have windways scarcely longer than they are wide; the diameter of the bell often exceeds the diameter of the steam slot, and the lip of the bell is frequently blunt or rounded rather than knife-edged.

Given these numerous debts to prior art, what are the "new and useful" features which would have earned Stephens a patent, had he elected to file for one? The truly novel feature of Stephens' design is its symmetry about a central axis. In contrast to an organ flue pipe, the windway and mouth extend entirely around the circumference of the device, exciting all portions of the bell or resonant cavity uniformly. Uniform excitation ensures in turn that this extremely broad-scaled resonator, less than twice as long as it is wide, operates in a purely longitudinal mode. Were a resonator of such proportions to be excited along a portion of the rim only, as in a conventional organ pipe, it would certainly result in the production of anharmonic overtones or "wolf notes." Finally, the short, squat resonator and large radiating area at its mouth contribute to the relatively high acoustic efficiency of the device, making it many times louder than an organ pipe of the same pitch. Thus all the parameters of Stephens' original design reinforce each other in mutually beneficial synergism. What is even more remarkable is that they rest on acoustical principles which were certainly unknown to Stephens, and which in fact were not elucidated until half a century later—further testimony to his secure intuitive grasp of acoustics.

Stephens was also the first to combine a whistle with a safety valve or a low-water sensor, thus endowing the operation of these devices with a distinctive audible alarm signal (see next page for illustration). Even if he had not invented the steam whistle itself, these combinations would be patentable. U.S. law allows the issuance of a patent on a novel combination of previously patented devices. (The best known example is the eraser on the end of the pencil!) On the other hand, Stephens is often wrongly credited with the invention of the locomotive whistle, whereas in fact he was not the first to apply a steam-operated signaling device to locomotives. In this he was preceded by the "steam trumpet" or "steam trombone." The story of this curious device is told at greater length in Chapter 3.

The second illustration shows another whistle, presumably built by Stephens himself, and preserved in the Art Gallery and Museum of Cyfarthfa Castle at Merthyr Tydfil. Unfortunately no date is given, but it is clearly of later origin than the whistle sketched by Turner. During the interim Stephens seems to have

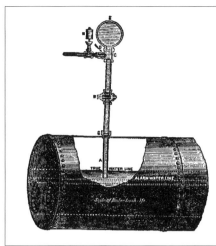

A steam whistle combined with a low water alarm to give an audible signal, ca. 1860. This was probably the first use to which Stephens put his newly invented whistle. Ashcroft later became one of the premier American manufacturers of boiler specialties, especially steam gauges.

A somewhat later whistle made by Stephens himself, and preserved in the Cyfarthfa Castle Art Gallery and Museum at Merthyr Tydfil. Unfortunately the bizarre display case obscures almost every detail, although the "egg cup" shape can be discerned within. From Lee, Ref.3.

grasped that the long transitional section within the base was superfluous, and the base was reduced to a simple bowl or cup. Uniform excitation around the rim permitted the bell to be shortened still further, raising its resonant frequency to a pitch nearer the maximum sensitivity of the ear and increasing the efficiency of the device. The flat top of the bell has been replaced with a graceful curve, probably for purely esthetic reasons. It now resembles an inverted egg cup, and indeed "egg cup" is the vernacular name given to whistles of this conformation. Thus little by little the steam whistle outgrew or abandoned its antecedents in the organ flue pipe and became a device *sui generis*. So successful was this design that it remained essentially unchanged on British locomotives for more than a century. Very similar whistles were manufactured in the shops of the Great Western Railway right up to the end of the steam era.

The triumph of steam

In the sixty-four years that elapsed between Watt's patent and Stephens' invention—less than the normal span of a human life—the nations of the West underwent a transformation more profound than any that had taken place in the previous two centuries. Popular revolts in the United States and France threw off the ruling monarchies, putting an abrupt end to the

Age of Enlightenment, but leaving behind such noble monuments as the American Declaration of Independence. The Congress of Vienna redrew the map of Europe once more, in a manner so irrational as to guarantee that unhappy continent would be ravaged by territorial disputes for generations to come. Perhaps most important from the point of view of this history, the factory system initiated by Arkwright and Hargreaves spread throughout Europe, making England the mercantile capital of the world and London the most important commercial city in the world.

At the very core of this revolution, in all its social, economic, and industrial dimensions, stood the steam engine. In the realm of transport, steamboats actually preceded steam locomotives, because waterways already existed whereas railroad rights-of-way did not. In 1802 William Symington operated the first steamboat, the *Charlotte Dundas*, on the River Clyde in Scotland. In 1807 Robert Fulton constructed the famous paddlewheel steamboat *Clermont*, using double-acting engines built by Watt and Boulton, and conducted pleasure cruises up the Hudson River from New York to Albany. We have already spoken of Trevithick's first steam locomotive in 1804. In 1829 the Rainhill Trials of the Liverpool & Manchester Railway were convincingly won by George Stephenson's *Rocket*, and the great age of railway building was

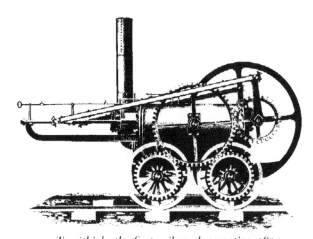

Trevithick: the first railway locomotive, 1804

The first railway locomotive, by inventor Richard Trevithick, 1804.

The great engineer George Stephenson, founder of the modern railway system. He began his career as a fireman at a shilling a day, and ended it as a multimillionaire capitalist, full of honors. His son Robert, an even greater engineer, carried on his work and was eventually knighted for his efforts. From N. Hawkins, New Catechism of the Steam Engine.

launched. By 1850 a network of railways had spread all over Europe and the United Kingdom. In a few short years the steam locomotive increased the maximum rate of land transport to approximately ten times what it had been in all previous centuries. Nowhere was the change of greater importance than in the United States, where it permitted continual westward expansion of the frontier while maintaining access to the capital at Washing-

The Stephensons' Rocket, 1829

George Stephenson's locomotive Rocket, decisive winner of the Rainhill trials in 1829.

ton. Already, in 1840, there were more miles of railroad track in the United States than in all the countries of Europe combined.

Amidst these world-shaking events there occurred another small event, beneath the notice of all but a few scholars. Yet it merits a digression because it teaches an important and little appreciated lesson regarding the evolution of technology. In 1824 a young French engineer named Sadi Carnot wrote an astonishingly prescient paper entitled *Sur la puissance motrice du feu* ("On the motive power of fire.") Using a false analogy between a steam engine and an overshot water wheel, he worked out the maximum efficiency theoretically attainable by any engine which converts heat into mechanical work. Despite its dubious origin, the argument has stood the test of time, and this efficiency is still called the Carnot efficiency in his honor. Carnot's analysis laid the foundations of the Second Law of Thermodynamics, arguably the most fundamental of all macroscopic laws of physics, and almost incidentally introduced the concept of the absolute zero of temperature. Incredibly, Carnot's paper preceded by nearly thirty years the exposition of the First Law of Thermodynamics, popularly but erroneously known as the law of conservation of energy. On the other hand, it followed Watt's steam engine by more than half a century. There exists a professional engineering society whose motto is "We turn ideas into reality." This is a historically inaccurate and needlessly restrictive view of the engineer's role in the growth of technology. As often as not, great

The Steam Whistle in Historical Context

inventions originate in the workshop, not the laboratory, and the task of the scientist is to turn reality into ideas. It was not nineteenth century science which drove the development of the steam engine; it was the steam engine which drove the development of the science of thermodynamics.

Sometimes inventions fail to flourish because they arrive too soon or too late. But the steam whistle was invented at precisely the right moment in the evolution of steam technology, and the timeliness of its invention does much to explain the rapidity with which it was adopted. Had it been invented earlier, in the days of low pressure steam, its voice would have been almost as soft and mellifluous as that of an organ pipe, hence virtually useless as an alarm. Had it been invented later, it would doubtless have been supplanted by some other form of acoustical signal and never attained currency. By 1835, no more than a year or two after its invention, it was applied to an English steam locomotive.[5] The circumstances which prompted its adoption make an interesting story, told at length in Chapter 3. Within another year it was employed on an American locomotive. Steam whistles were fitted experimentally to a few steamboats on our western rivers in 1843 or 1844.[6] By 1854 their use on steamboats was so widespread that it was made mandatory by the regulations governing navigation on western rivers. Adoption by ocean-going ships was slowed somewhat because these vessels used low pressure engines and salt water in their boilers. Nevertheless the *Great Eastern*, launched in 1858, was fitted with a whistle. Finally, in 1857, Messrs. Murry and Hazelhurst of Baltimore constructed a steam whistle foghorn and installed it at the Beaver Tail Light Station in Narragansett Bay. Thus, less than a quarter-century after its invention, the proliferation of the steam whistle was essentially complete. The industrial revolution had found its voice.

It would be a mistake, however, to assume that the coming of the steam whistle was universally welcomed. Its "harsh and unpleasant" quality, as Stephens himself acknowledged, offended many, and particularly those reluctant to embrace the new age of railroading. One of the first to complain was the poet William Wordsworth, who inveighed against the proposed Kendal and Windermere Railway and the aural and visual disfigurement he feared it would bring to his beloved Lake District:[7]

Hear Ye that Whistle? As her long-linked Train
Swept onwards, did the vision cross your view?
Yes, ye were startled; — and in balance true,
Weighing the mischief with the promised gain,
Mountains, and Vales, and Floods, I call on you
To share the passion of a just disdain . . .

Wordsworth's sentiments were soon echoed by Thoreau, only a few years after the coming of the railroad to Concord:[8]

"That devilish Iron Horse, whose ear-rending neigh is heard throughout the town, has muddied the Boiling Spring with his foot, and he it is that has browsed off all the woods on Walden shore; that Trojan horse, with a thousand men in his belly, introduced by mercenary Greeks! Where is the country's

In 1830 the Camden & Amboy was awarded a charter to build a railroad across New Jersey from New York to Philadelphia. Not all the citizens of Philadelphia were thrilled by the prospect, as this popular poster makes clear.

The image of an octopus was used repeatedly to symbolize the grasp of greedy robber barons. In this instance the cartoonist has applied it to an effort by the railroad monopoly to take control of New York wharves, thereby depriving local freight handlers of their livelihood. From O.L. Bettman, The Good Old Days—They Were Terrible.

"Then, faint and prolonged, across the levels of the ranch, he heard the engine whistling for Bonneville. Again and again, at rapid intervals in its flying course, it whistled for road crossings, for sharp curves, for trestles; ominous notes, hoarse, bellowing, ringing with the accents of menace and defiance; and abruptly Presley saw again, in his imagination, the galloping monster, the terror of steel and steam with its single eye, Cyclopean, red, shooting from horizon to horizon; but saw it now as the symbol of a vast power, huge, terrible, flinging the echo of its thunder over all the reaches of the valley, leaving blood and destruction in its path; the leviathan, with tentacles of steel clutching into the soil, the soulless Force, the iron-hearted Power, the monster, the Colossus, the Octopus."

champion, the Moore of Moore Hall, to meet him at the Deep Cut and thrust an avenging lance betwen the ribs of the bloated pest?"

By the turn of the century, the spread of the railroads over the young American nation was virtually complete, and the railroads themselves were in the grasp of the greedy robber barons who owned and operated them. Their attitude toward the public was perhaps best exemplified by William Henry Vanderbilt's response in 1882 to a reporter's questions about the public's needs: "The public be damned!" Here was a new form of tyranny, and protests against it took on an increasingly ominous tone. Nowhere was opposition to the railroad enterprise more eloquently voiced than in *The Octopus,* the first volume of Frank Norris' muck-raking trilogy:[9]

This perfervid passage is the very apotheosis of hatred for the railroad and its effects, as symbolized by the sound of the train whistle. A century after Norris wrote, when those who remember the sound of a train whistle are more inclined to nostalgia than loathing, it is difficult to imagine the animosity it once aroused.

Over the years, by a kind of cultural synecdoche in which the part came to stand for the whole, the steam whistle acquired iconic significance for both proponents and opponents of the industrial revolution. It represented not merely itself, but also the sweeping and often disruptive aspects of the new social and economic order wrought by the revolution. Furthermore the steam whistle rapidly gathered around itself a rich variety of symbolic associations in popular culture, extending to such diverse areas as literature, cinema, advertising art, folk song, and vernacular speech. These symbolic associations form a fascinating study in themselves, and we explore a few of them in Chapter 4.

In the final analysis, however, it must be admitted that the steam whistle by itself made nothing happen. It would be difficult to defend the claim that it advanced or retarded in any significant way the onrush of the mechanical revolution wrought by the steam engine. If it had never been invented, other forms of signaling and warning devices would doubtless have arisen to take its place. What it did do, however, was to give the revolution its voice, the authentic voice of live steam in action, an unforgettable music that resonated perfectly with the years of the ascendancy of steam, and which continues to haunt us today.

A hostler checks the installation of a six-chime Nathan steptop on the steam dome during the 1973 restoration of Michigan State's big Berkshire, Pere Marquette 1225. Photo by John B. Corns.

3 *The Applications Of Steam Whistles*

No sound is dissonant which tells of Life.
— Samuel Taylor Coleridge

The speciation of the steam whistle

At the time of its birth, the steam whistle was perfectly adapted to the task which provoked its invention, to wit, as a low water alarm. It was louder than all previous acoustic signals, but it was not overwhelmingly loud. It needed only to be heard at a distance of a hundred feet or less, not at ten miles or more. It was high pitched, rather near the range of maximum sensitivity of the human ear, so that its sound cut through the prevailing industrial din. Its operation was self-initiating, so that it needed no valve or other human intervention to make it work. And in all probability it was the only device of its kind within hearing range, and therefore needed no means to distinguish its signal from those of other sources of sound.

After its invention, however, the steam whistle underwent a process of rapid *speciation*. The word "speciation" is borrowed from biology, where it signifies the evolutionary process by which new species are formed. The analogy between biological evolution and technological evolution is due to George Basalla, who likened the manner in which various classes of artifacts flourish or perish over time to the workings of Darwinian natural selection.[1] Certainly the steam whistle was one of the artifacts that flourished, and very shortly after its invention it began to diversify into a multitude of forms adapted to specific applications and environments. The addition of a simple quarter-turn cock sufficed to adapt it to railway use, accounting for its rapid adoption by that industry. The process of speciation continued for at least the next sixty or seventy years, and probably reached its zenith early in the twentieth century. By 1910 a locomotive whistle did not look at all like a factory whistle, and a factory whistle in turn did not look at all like a marine whistle. Moreover, there arose certain types, such as the fire alarm and the calliope whistle, so specialized that they must be regarded as application-specific, and could scarcely be imagined in uses other than those for which they were designed.

It seems fair to assert that most of this speciation and differentiation according to application took place in the United States rather than Europe or the United Kingdom. A few distinctive types of whistles did originate abroad, notably the immense organ

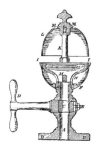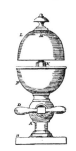

An English "egg cup" locomotive whistle ca. 1854, little more than Stephens' original egg cup (p.15) with the addition of a quarter-turn gas cock.

one or more mouths which embrace less than the full circumference of the bowl. A whistle whose pitch may be altered at will during operation is called variously a **piston whistle, mockingbird whistle, combination whistle,** or **fire alarm whistle**. Many more examples of named whistles may be found in the Glossary.

A whistle that sounds a single note, regardless of the richness of its overtone structure, is called a **plain** or **common** whistle. A whistle that sounds two or more notes simultaneously is called a **chime** whistle or **multi-tone** whistle. **Single-chime whistle** is an oxymoron, and its use marks the speaker as uninformed. If the chime is comprised of several plain whistles on a common manifold, it is called a **multiple-bell** chime. If the several resonators that comprise the chime are contained within a single bell, the whistle is called a **single-bell** chime. A single-bell chime which lacks a top plate, so that the exposed tops of the several resonating chambers resemble a spiral staircase, is called a **steptop** whistle.

The nominal size of a whistle is the outer diameter of its bell, usually rounded to the nearest inch or half-inch. By contrast, organ pipes are named in accord with the length of the longest member of the rank. The difference arises because the most important feature of an organ pipe is its pitch, which is governed by its length, whereas the most important feature of a whistle is its steam consumption, which is governed by its diameter. The second most important specification is the length of the bell. This length is conventionally measured from the lip of the bell in the case of plain whistles, and from the **spreader plate** or **languid** in the case of single-bell chime whistles. The length is frequently combined with the diameter of the bell; thus a 10" x 30" plain whistle has a bell 10" in diameter and 30" long. Whistles with bells less than twice as long as they are wide are generally called **short-bell**. Whistles with bells more than twice as long as they are wide are called **long-bell** or **extra long-bell**. The proportions of the bell are often expressed as the ratio of length to width; thus a "3X" bell is three times as long as it is wide.

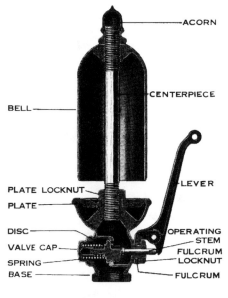

Plain Whistle with Valve

ACORN

CENTERPIECE

BELL

LEVER

PLATE LOCKNUT
PLATE

DISC
VALVE CAP
SPRING
BASE

OPERATING STEM
FULCRUM LOCKNUT
FULCRUM

pipe whistles and three-bell chimes used on large ocean-going vessels, but for the most part Americans developed a greater variety of whistles than other nations, and they developed them earlier. This may reflect an innate conservatism on the part of our transatlantic cousins, but more likely it reflects in some oblique way the expansive and improvisatory character of nineteenth century American life, with its vast spaces, its endless frontier, and its apparently limitless scope for enterprise and ambition.

What forces drove this speciation? Obviously utilitarian considerations were foremost. The whistle that sufficed for a traction engine was clearly too small for an ocean liner, nor would it serve for a heavyweight freight locomotive. In addition, much speciation arose from the desire to endow each whistle-bearing device with a distinctive sonic signature. Railroaders wished to distinguish a passenger locomotive from a freight locomotive, and the locomotives of one line from those of another. Similarly, seafarers found it important to distinguish the origin and tonnage of other vessels sight unseen, especially when navigating in fog.

Speciation among multi-tone whistles was further motivated by the desire to attain consonance. Among plain whistles, harshness of tone was generally regarded as a virtue, because it contributed to the urgency or attention-getting properties of the signal. But on trains and steamships, passengers soon made it clear that they preferred more harmonious tones. Manufacturers responded eagerly to these demands with advertisements proclaiming that their single-bell chimes were "less grating" or "more pleasing to the ear" than common plain whistles. This led in turn to the adoption of a great variety of chords and intervals, some of them quite contrary to the established practices of classical harmony.

On the other hand, two factors which might have been expected to spur development of diverse whistles seem to have played no role at all, or at most a very minor role. These are economy of manufacture and economy of operation. Numerous patents, such as the one-piece cast iron whistles of Barnes (U.S. 217,851) and the drawn bells of Ashley (U.S. 511,490), attest to the continuing efforts of inventors to produce whistles cheaply. In fact all such efforts failed in the marketplace, and the most widely sold whistles were among the most expensive. Similarly, many patents attempting to economize the use of steam failed of adoption. The steam whistle was a device of abysmally low conversion

The Applications Of Steam Whistles

efficiency; nevertheless live steam was generally regarded as a commodity so cheap and so plentiful in boiler rooms and engine rooms that efforts to minimize its use received scant attention.

As a final measure of the degree of diversification among steam whistles, we may compare their ranges of size and pitch with those of their nearest relation, the organ flue pipe, remembering that the development of organ pipes began at least four centuries earlier. Organ flue pipes range in size from the smallest member of a harmonic-corroborating mixture stop, thinner than a lead pencil and scarcely more than half an inch in length, to such monsters as the CCCC Double Open Diapason pipe in the pedal division of the great Wanamaker organ, 32 feet tall and weighing 1,735 pounds. Steam whistles do not span so great a range. The smallest steam whistles (apart from scale models) are probably low water alarms and safety valve signals an inch or less in diameter and an inch or two long. Several whistles contend for the title of largest whistle, including the nine-foot whistle from the former Long-Bell Lumber Co. mill, the seven-foot Star Brass whistle from a California oil company scrap yard, both still in existence, and the long-lost chime whistle from the street railway powerhouse in East St. Louis, Illinois, which allegedly consumed half a ton of coal per minute of blowing. The nominal pitches of organ flue pipes range from 16 Hz to more than 8 kHz, whereas whistles range from a mere 50 Hz or so to perhaps 4 kHz.

In the sections that follow we examine three of the environments in which steam whistles found widespread application, and therefore underwent a high degree of speciation: railroad applications, marine applications, and factory, industrial, or municipal applications. We conclude with a brief history of the only purely musical application, the steam calliope.

Locomotive whistles *

Introduction

Ask the man in the street to recall the sound of a steam whistle, and (if he is sufficiently old) the chances are overwhelming that the whistle that he brings to mind is the whistle of a steam locomotive. Certainly there are others for whom the whistle embedded in

memory is the whistle of ships in the harbor, or the whistle of the local mill or mine, but for the majority of Americans it is the never-to-be- forgotten wail of the locomotive whistle.

There are several reasons for this, but the chief one is certainly the iconic potency of the locomotive whistle. As will be discussed in Chapter 4, the sound of the locomotive whistle comes laden with connotative meanings and symbolic associations. It stands for travel and the excitement of journeying, the prospect of adventures yet to be tasted, enterprises yet to be undertaken. To the romantic imagination it can signify yearning and regret and loss, alienation and isolation, unfulfilled hopes and bygone passions. The listener endows it with whatever emotion fills his heart.

There are objective reasons as well. Locomotive whistles were not the most numerous of whistles, but they were by far the most widely heard. All other whistles, excepting only marine whistles, were stationary, but the locomotive whistle traveled and brought its sound to places that would otherwise never hear a steam whistle. Small towns in the Corn Belt that had no heavy industry whatsoever nevertheless had a creamery, where periodically the way freight would stop to pick up a reefer of milk. Other towns in the Great Plains had only a grain elevator, whence loaded hoppers of wheat would depart for the mills of the midwest. Even places where the train never stopped, the homes of the millions who lived along the railroad right-of-way, knew the sound of the locomotive whistle as it signaled for grade crossings and train movements. No other type of whistle had so large an audience.

It is surely relevant too that the American locomotive whistle was the most highly developed steam whistle in the world. Just as American steam locomotives were the largest in the world, so were American locomotive whistles. Few railway whistles of other nations were more than four inches in diameter, whereas American whistles were typically six inches in diameter. This gave the American whistle superior carrying power, befitting the vast expanses of our prairie and western states. Furthermore, no other nation made such widespread use of chime whistles, and those that did usually employed whistles with no more than three chambers. By contrast, the most common American locomotive whistles were the

* In collaboration with David Fultz

five- and six-chambered steptops. And no chime whistles anywhere offered the rich and idiosyncratic variety of musical chords of American chime whistles, some upbeat and cheerful, others wailing and mournful, all distinctive and unforgettable.

Finally, unlike whistles in all other applications, the locomotive whistle was a vehicle of self-expression for the men privileged to blow it. The art of whistle-blowing is discussed at length in Chapter 8. It is sufficient for the moment to say that the ability to make a whistle "talk" lent a further dimension to the unique sound of the locomotive whistle. Taken together, these considerations explain why the locomotive whistle exerts a fascination unmatched in scope by other types, and why "the voice of the iron horse" remains the quintessential voice of the age of steam.

Origin and early developments [2]

The use of whistles on steam locomotives can be traced to a collision at a railroad crossing between the towns of Bagworth and Thornton in England, where on May 4, 1833 the Leicester & Swannington Railroad locomotive *Samson,* built by the pioneer English locomotive designer George Stephenson, struck a farm wagon loaded with eighty dozen eggs and fifty pounds of butter, reducing eggs, butter, and wagon to a scrambled mess. It was apparent that some type of warning signal was needed to prevent further crossing accidents. The board of directors convened, and Ashlen Bagster, manager of the railroad, asked Stephenson if it were possible to apply a horn to a locomotive, one that could be operated by steam. Stephenson accepted the challenge and ten days later an instrument maker delivered a device called a "steam trumpet." No contemporary drawing of the device survives, but the engraving reproduced here appeared in the December, 1892 issue of *Railroad & Engineering Journal.* The steam trumpet was about 18 inches long, shaped like a megaphone, and equipped with a hand valve to admit steam. It was immediately applied to the locomotive *Comet* and proved to be a success.

It is evident from its shape that the steam trumpet was not a true whistle, yet it was the first steam-operated acoustic signaling device to be applied to a locomotive. Therefore some interest attaches to its mode of operation. One account says merely that the steam "agitated a diaphragm;" other accounts are even more vague. Recalling Stephens' early experiments with organ pipes sent up from London, it seems most likely that the steam trumpet was a version of a lingual or reed pipe, quite possibly one of the Trumpet stops which it strongly resembles. Inasmuch as exact pitch was not a consideration, the tuning wire and its attendant complication were apparently omitted from the construction, making the body of the trumpet very compact indeed. If so, there was no "diaphragm" in the sense that term is usually understood, merely a vibrating reed.

Ironically, 1833, the year of the *Samson*'s accident, was probably the same year in which Adrian Stephens was perfecting the true steam whistle, in which sound is produced without the aid of a moving mechanical part by passing a jet of steam over the lip of a resonant cavity. Stephens' whistles were intended only to provide an audible alarm in the event of boiler overpressure or low water. Others, however, were quick to appreciate its potential as a warning signal for moving engines, and in 1835 one Thomas Turner, a workman at Sharp, Roberts & Co., locomotive builders of Manchester, showed a sketch of Stephens' device to the locomotive superintendent of the Liverpool & Manchester Railway. This official immediately adopted the design for the engines of that road, whence it rapidly displaced Stephenson's steam trumpet on other English railroads.

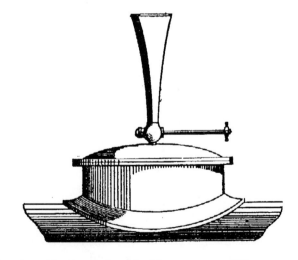

Drawing of Stephenson's original "steam trumpet." The accuracy of the drawing is questionable, however, since it did not appear until 59 years after the installation of the device. There is an unconfirmed story that the steam trumpet was designed by George W. Whistler, father of the artist James Whistler.

The Applications Of Steam Whistles

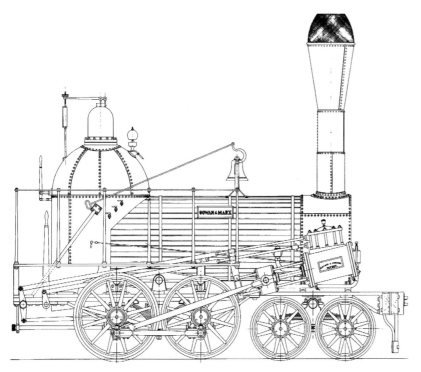

A very early American locomotive, the Gowan and Marx of the Philadelphia and Reading Railroad, built in 1839. The following year it pulled a 423-ton train of coal cars from Reading to Philadelphia, assuring it of a permanent place in American railroad history. Note the very short whistle with its nearly spherical bell. There was no need for a whistle lever or a whistle cord, since the whistle cock was within easy reach of the engineer as he stood on the rear platform. From White, Ref. 5 to Ch. 2.

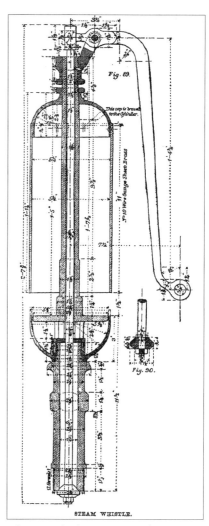

The standard passenger locomotive whistle of the Pennsylvania Railroad, ca. 1870. Note the unusually long bell and base.

According to White, the steam whistle first appeared on an American locomotive in 1836, scarcely a year after its first application to an English locomotive.[3] The locomotive was the *Susquehanna*, one of several built by the Locks and Canals Machine Shops of Lowell, Massachusetts. The same shops also fitted a steam whistle to the *Hicksville* of the Long Island Railroad. The following year, J. H. James, president of the newly organized Mad River & Lake Erie Railroad in Sandusky, Ohio, journeyed to the Rogers, Ketchum & Grosvenor Foundries in Paterson, New Jersey, to purchase a new locomotive. He was fascinated by the small steam whistle that the firm had mounted on the locomotive, and on a test run, blew the whistle so vigorously that scarcely enough steam remained to propel the engine. He purchased the locomotive, named *Sandusky* in honor of the railroad's hometown, where it was demonstrated on November 17, 1837. The *Sandusky* is sometimes credited as the first American locomotive to carry a steam whistle, a claim contradicted by White's tale of the *Hicksville*. The *Sandusky* was, however, the first steam locomotive to operate in Ohio.

These early steam whistles were small in size and, because of their short bells, produced a very shrill sound. Although effective as warning devices, they became increasingly unpopular with farmers whose livestock they frightened, and with others who lived sufficiently near the right-of-way to be irritated by them. The first major development, occurring near the end of the Civil War, was the lengthening of the bell to produce a sound of lower pitch. Old photographs show such a long-bell whistle applied to Pennsylvania Railroad locomotive No. 325, which pulled Abraham Lincoln's funeral train from Philadelphia to Springfield, Illinois. Railroad men sometimes referred to this style of whistle as a "bull whistle," because of the similarity of the sound to the bellow of a bull. Long-bell whistles were popular with the public, but some engineers still favored the short bell whistles, as many had become adept at playing simple tunes on them. (See Chapter 8 for a further discussion of whistle-blowing artistry.)

By 1870 the Pennsylvania Railroad, which prided itself on the degree of standardization of all its equipment, had developed a standard whistle for its passenger locomotives, a long-bell design with top-mounted lever and an inordinately long base (see previous page). This whistle was used to the exclusion of all others on the class C 4-4-0's. Shriller "egg-cup" whistles still prevailed, however, on the class H 2-8-0's, the PRR's standard freight locomotive of the era. The details of this PRR passenger whistle were so carefully worked out that the basic design endured for decades. In later years some of the plain bells were even replaced with chime bells in order to modernize them. The picture and description of the passenger whistle are taken from James Dredge's enormous folio *The Pennsylvania Railroad: Its Organization, Construction, and Management*, published in London in 1879. The book has a curious history. Dredge was an influential English engineer who set out to prove to a skeptical English public that their American cousins, far from being imitative bumpkins in the railroad business, were in fact well in advance of their British counterparts.

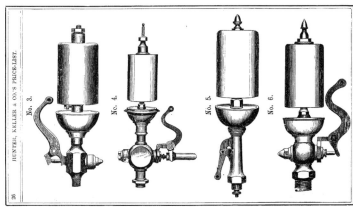

A selection of steam whistles offered in the 1868 catalog of Hunter, Keller & Co. of New York, jobbers of iron and brass specialties. The whistles themselves appear to have been manufactured by Hayden, Gere & Co. of New York and Haydenville, Massachusetts. Diameters range from 2" up to 6". American whistle design changed greatly between 1835 and 1865, and many "modern" features have appeared. Bells have lost their egg cup shape and taken the form of right circular cylinders, substantially taller than they are wide. Some of the fixing nuts at the tops of the bells have been elaborated into ornamental acorns. Bases have been fitted with horizontal or vertical levers, to permit remote actuation from an enclosed cab. On the other hand, much of the variation in design seems pointless, and there is still no hint of differentiation according to function or type of application.

The Barnes patent "mailbox" whistle of 1879, a one-piece iron casting. The valve is a separate item.

One of the peculiarities of the era of plain whistles was the Barnes patent steam whistle of 1879, manufactured exclusively by the Bass Foundry & Machine Works of Fort Wayne, Indiana. Machined from a one-piece iron casting in the shape of a mailbox, and possessed of a raucous monotone voice, it was arguably the least attractive whistle ever made, both aurally and visually. It was also cheap, exceedingly loud, and virtually indestructible, and its failure to attain widespread acceptance can only be explained on aesthetic grounds. Nevertheless, near the close of the nineteenth century it found brief favor among railroads serving northern Indiana, notably the Nickel Plate Lines and the Lake Erie & Western.

Although the locomotive whistle was born in England, British and European designs remained essentially stagnant for the next century, whereas locomotive whistles in the United States continued to evolve. This presents a puzzle for the historian of technology. It has been suggested that Americans were simply more inventive than their cousins across the ocean, but this chauvinist hypothesis is inconsistent with the high level of British achievement in other realms of science and

GUN METAL STEAM WHISTLES.

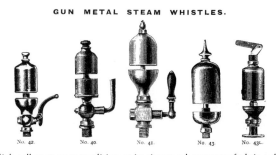

English adherence to tradition at its ripest: a bouquet of plain whistles excerpted from the 1910 catalog of James Gibb & Co., London. Some of the designs, e.g., No. 41, are essentially unchanged since the 1840's. Similar designs had vanished from the American market 30 or 40 years earlier.

The Applications Of Steam Whistles

technology. It has also been suggested that, in the libertarian tradition, American railroads placed fewer restraints on the use of locomotive whistles and thus gave license to innovation. It is true that, until the early part of the twentieth century, most railroad officials cared little how engineers used their whistles so long as they maintained their schedules.

A more plausible explanation for the continued evolution of the American locomotive whistle lies in the prevalence of grade crossings. In the densely settled portions of Great Britain and Europe, grade crossings are rare. The railroad right-of-way is almost totally enclosed, with vehicular and pedestrian traffic carried on overhead bridges. Hence the importance of the train whistle as a crossing signal was much diminished, and with it, the need to project an audible warning over great distances. The whistle served primarily to communicate with other members of the train crew, and for this purpose the shrill "egg cup" whistles of the nineteenth century sufficed. A further reason for the elaborate differentiation and speciation of whistles in the U.S. is that by the end of the nineteenth century many metropolitan areas were served by two or more railroads. Under these conditions, railroads understandably sought to equip their locomotives with distinctive 'signature' whistles that would identify them to the general public.

Multi-tone whistles

Just as railroad men were eager to distinguish one railroad from another, they were eager to distinguish railroad whistles as a class from whistles in other applications, such as factories, industries, and firehouses. One of the obvious means of doing this was to employ multi-tone or "chime" whistles, which sound two or three notes simultaneously. Such whistles had been used on ships since before the Civil War, but less commonly in land-based applications. These early chimes were merely assemblages of ordinary single-note whistles on a common manifold, actuated by a common valve. The size, expense, and susceptibility to damage by vibration of these multi-bell chimes stood in the way of railroad applications.

On January 30, 1877, however, John Einig of Jacksonville, Florida, was issued Patent No. 186,718 on a new type of whistle in which several resonant chambers were contained within a single bell. This is the fundamental patent on the single-bell chime, a design that would eventually sweep all others from the field. Einig did not initially assign his patent to the Crosby Steam Gage & Valve Co. of Boston; nevertheless Crosby seems to have acquired exclusive rights to manufacture the design. Moreover, it continued to re-assert its ownership rights by inscribing the date of the Einig patent on every chime whistle it ever produced. The single-bell chime brought multi-tone or chorded whistles to locomotive service. Crosby's 1888 catalog—the earliest to survive—proudly proclaims the "Patent Single Bell Chime Whistle" in three different versions, and goes on to say:

"The peculiar merit of this whistle consists in producing three distinct tones pitched to the first, third and fifth of the common musical scale, which harmonize and give an agreeable musical chord. It is more penetrating than the common whistle, and can be heard at a greater distance. It effectually destroys the harsh, disagreeable noise which has been a source of common complaint in other whistles and gongs. This whistle is rapidly coming into use on locomotives, and has been warmly endorsed by railroad men and by the traveling public wherever used, several lines having adopted them for their entire passenger service. They overcome one of the chief annoyances of railway travel, and serve to distinguish passenger from freight trains."

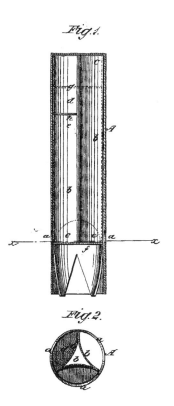

One whistle, three different notes. Drawings taken from U.S. 186,718, John Einig's seminal patent of January 30, 1877 on the single-bell chime whistle. Note that a flat top is maintained for the sake of appearance, even though the volumes above the tops of the chambers are functionless.

Crosby did not exaggerate. By the mid-1880's it was common to hear three-chime whistles on passenger locomotives. Short and long bell plain whistles never again enjoyed the popularity that had been theirs for nearly fifty years, although many survived up to the very onset of the diesel age.

Shortly thereafter Crosby introduced another important innovation, the compound automatic valve. As we have seen, the history of boiler development in the nineteenth century could be written largely in terms of ever-increasing operating pressure. By 1890 it had become quite difficult to open a conventional disc valve of large diameter against pressures of 150 PSI or more, regardless of the mechanical advantage provided by the lever and fulcrum. To this end Crosby produced a novel valve in which the opening of a small pilot valve released the pressure on the main disc valve. By this means the largest whistles could be operated with ease, and from 1897 onward all Crosby single-bell chimes were available in both "original" version with plain valve and "improved" version with compound automatic valve.

Although the compound valve did much to hasten the adoption of large chime whistles in factory and marine service, it was seldom employed on locomotive whistles. The reason is that it toggled abruptly from fully shut to fully open, depriving the engineer of any opportunity to modulate the flow of steam once he had cracked the pilot valve, and thus to display his artistry in making the whistle "talk." This was a degree of freedom that engineers were apparently unwilling to forego, and the conventional disc valve remained the standard throughout the heyday of the steam locomotive. Only in the twilight years of the steam era did the balanced valve, such as those made by the Lunkenheimer Co. of Cincinnati, begin to appear on locomotive whistles. In contrast to the compound valve, this type of valve assists in opening under high pressure but also retains the ability to vary the amount of steam reaching the whistle.

As Crosby's monopoly on the Einig patent expired, other manufacturers rushed to market with competitive single-bell chimes. One of the first to arrive was Lunkenheimer, which in its 1895 catalog offered an acornless three-chime whistle of its own design in three different versions. The first of these had a horizontal valve, the second was valveless, and the third, specifically identified as "locomotive style," had an upright or vertical valve with downward-hanging lever. Moreover, it was available only in diameters from four to six inches, the usual size of locomotive whistles. The vertical valve appeared to be the only concession to railroad service, for this version was otherwise identical to the other two. Neither Lunkenheimer nor any other manufacturer had yet grasped the need for exceedingly robust construction in order to withstand the constant pounding and vibration of service on a locomotive.

As usual Crosby led the way. Its 1900 catalog offered a new version of the single-bell chime whistle with horizontal valve and renewable valve seats. The accompanying text acknowledged for the first time the rigors of the railroad environment:

"This whistle is fully adapted to severe railway service. In the distribution of material and the uniting of the several parts, great care has been exercised in the designing and making of it, so that it shall resist successfully the jars and concussions that may arise in use on a locomotive. In all whistles, whenever the valve is badly worn, the rest of the whistle is of little use. To meet this condition, we have modified the valves so that the seats are the same as employed in the Crosby spring-seat valve.

"These seats can be renewed at a small expense whenever they are injured or worn, thus preserving the entire whistle for a very much longer time than formerly when in constant service. So constructed, they are furnished at no greater expense to the consumer than formerly.

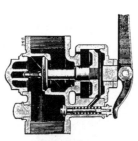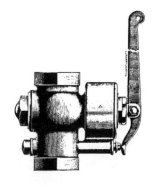

Sectional View.

The Crosby compound automatic whistle valve, from Crosby's 1897 catalog. The small valve at the bottom opens first, admitting steam to the right-hand side of the piston in front of the main valve disc. This counterbalances much of the force on the main disc, and permits it to be opened easily.

LUNKENHEIMER'S
Single Bell Chime Whistle.
IMPROVED AND RECONSTRUCTED.

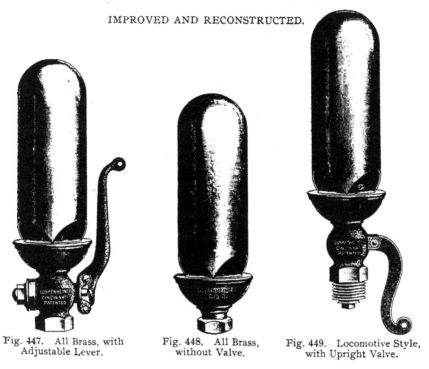

Fig. 447. All Brass, with Adjustable Lever. Fig. 448. All Brass, without Valve. Fig. 449. Locomotive Style, with Upright Valve.

Lunkenheimer's versions of single-bell chime whistles, from their 1895 catalog. The notation 'Locomotive Style' on Fig. 449 is another indication of the beginnings of differentiation according to application.

"The good qualities of this whistle have been so manifest that imitations of it, having the ordinary seats only, have been offered to the public, which should be avoided if the best is desired."

Crosby had successfully taken the measure of the railroad market, and its new heavyweight design rapidly displaced less durable whistles of lighter construction. Not the least of its attractions was its exceptionally long lever, which permitted extremely fine control of the steam input and facilitated "whistle talk." It was highly prized by engineers in the early part of the twentieth century, particularly in the southern United States, and remains a favorite of collectors today.

The Star Brass Manufacturing Co. of Boston was quick to follow. Star's 1904 catalog opened with a line of three single-bell chimes identical in every respect to the contemporaneous offerings from Crosby. Even the description that accompanies these whistles is word-for-word identical with that used by Crosby sixteen years earlier, suggesting a cooperative manufacturing or jobbing arrangement rather than mere plagiarism. But in addition Star Brass expanded the line

to include extra-heavy whistles specifically intended for railroad service. Figure 169 (next page) in the 1904 catalog depicted a squatty "Locomotive Style" chime whistle with special short bell and base:

"This whistle was designed for use on locomotives of extreme height, where only a limited space was allowable for the whistle. It is fitted with our special patent feature, namely an adjustment for the limit of the opening of the whistle valve. This feature is found only on our make of whistle, and especially commends itself for locomotive use where whistles are changed from one engine to another and consequently are used on different steam pressures. By use of this adjustment the tone of the whistle can be regulated and screeching or squealing prevented."

This whistle was available in a diameter of five inches. It was warranted for the highest pressures, and built extra heavy from the best "steam metal," a brass alloy rich in copper.

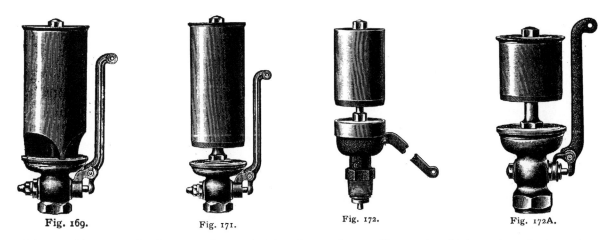

Fig. 169.   Fig. 171.   Fig. 172.   Fig. 172A.

Around the turn of the century, Star Brass moved aggressively into the manufacture of locomotive whistles, as shown by these selections from their 1904 catalog. Railroad service is now clearly differentiated from other types of service, and passenger locomotive service from freight locomotive service. The long actuating levers were intended to accommodate ever-increasing boiler pressures, as well as to facilitate "whistle talk."

Although by 1904 chime whistles had come to dominate both passenger and freight service, Star continued to cater to those railroads that preferred plain whistles. The Improved Extra Heavy Plain Locomotive Whistle, Figure 171 in its 1904 catalog, had the same valve adjustment feature offered on its single-bell chime whistle. It had a horizontal valve and was available in diameters of four, five, and six inches. Also available were two plain whistles designed for freight locomotives, one with a bell of normal length and the other a short ("Shrill Toned") bell. The standard bell model, Figure 172, featured a vertical whistle valve, and was available in 5-1/2-inch diameter. The short-bell model, Figure 172A, featured a horizontal whistle valve, and was available in diameters of three, four, five, and six inches. These two types were probably not in great demand, and few examples have survived. Nevertheless it is clear that by the opening years of the twentieth century the locomotive whistle had been firmly established as a separate breed, distinct from whistles intended for other applications.

With the exception of the highly idiosyncratic designs by the Kinsley Manufacturing Co. of Bridgeport, Connecticut, all the foregoing chime whistles had three resonant chambers and sounded a musical triad. Inevitably some enterprising tinkerer, seeking a unique whistle that could not be mistaken for any other, sought to expand the multi-tone whistle to a chord of five or six notes. Sometime in the late nineteenth century this anonymous inventor riveted six

different lengths of boiler tube together in a circular array to form a six-note whistle. The result looked rather like a panpipe bent round into a cylinder. Placed on a standard whistle bowl, it produced sounds that had never been heard before on a steam locomotive. Whistles of this type were usually built in railroad shops, often at the request of an engineer with long seniority. So far as we know, none has ever appeared in the catalog of a commercial manufacturer.

Undoubtedly the most famous whistle of this type was that owned by an Illinois Central railroad engineer named John Luther Jones, known to history as Casey Jones. Casey had a machinist make a six-note boiler tube whistle, and then tuned it to suit his tastes. It was said that he could make the whistle say prayers or scream like a banshee. Jones was killed in a train collision at Vaughn, Mississippi on the night of April 29, 1900, an event immortalized in the ballad that bears his name. The Illinois Central Railroad gave Casey's whistle to his widow Jane, who in turn gave it to her brother, who was an engineer on the Gulf, Mobile, and Ohio Railroad. It remains in the family to this day.

Casey gave his name to the entire species of multi-note boiler tube whistles, which are invariably known today as "Casey Jones" whistles. Many examples of the type were in use from the 1890's on, and no two were exactly alike. Innumerable pictures exist of steam locomotives with boiler tube whistles, undoubtedly replacements for whistles considered to have less individuality. Because of the popularity of these homemade whistles, practically all major

The Applications Of Steam Whistles

locomotive manufacturers began delivering engines with five-and six-note whistles. Some were made by the manufacturers themselves, while others were produced by companies that sold locomotive accessories.

Around 1905 there occurred a major improvement in the design of these multi-tone whistles. The circular assemblage of boiler tubes was replaced by a single five- or six-chambered casting of ingenious and distinctive design. Projecting ears or fins between the chambers minimized interaction between the resonant cavities. Unlike the three-chime single-bell whistle, which in most cases had a non-functional top plate and a decorative acorn nut, these five- and six-chime whistles were purely utilitarian. They had no adornments and made no concession to traditional appearance. Because the decorative top plate was absent, the top of the bell resembled a spiral staircase, the lowest step corresponding to the shortest chamber or highest note, and the highest step corresponding to the longest chamber or deepest note. Naturally this earned the design the name "steptop" whistle. Steptop whistles rapidly became the dominant form of American locomotive whistle, and were used in no other application.

Although the patent literature is rich with designs for multiple-bell chime whistles, there is a curious dearth of archival materials regarding the origins of the steptop whistle. A diligent search of the patent literature yields only the very peculiar Gillespie patent of 1891, U.S. 451,040 (see next page). The device depicted therein bears a superficial resemblance to a steptop whistle, but is in fact an assemblage of resonant vibrating reeds, of dubious efficacy and not a true aerodynamic whistle at all. The first verifiable appearance of a steptop whistle in a trade catalog was in the 1907 catalog of the Nathan Manufacturing Co. of New York, successor to Nathan & Dreyfus, an old-line maker of feedwater injector pumps. A similar design appeared in Star Brass Catalog No. 10 as Fig. No. 158, the Star Improved Five Tone Locomotive Chime Whistle. Unfortunately the date of issue of this latter catalog is in dispute, so it is not clear which firm had priority of manufacture. In any case, however, Nathan is the name indelibly associated with the locomotive steptop whistle. Nathan steptops were produced in five- and six-chime models, and were cast in both iron and brass. Some models combined a brass bowl with an iron bell, whereas in others the roles of the metals were reversed. All Nathan steptops were equipped with vertical valves, although the three-chime flat-tops had horizontal valves. These whistles were enormously popular with the railroads and the general public. It has been suggested that more modern steam locomotives were equipped with Nathan whistles than all other brands combined.

Persons with a knowledge of musical harmony will find it interesting to analyze the chords produced by multi-tone whistles, and especially those of locomotive whistles. As we have seen, most manufacturers of three-chime whistles initially stressed consonance, favoring simple major or minor triads in root position. Later these appeared in first or second inversions, although still in close or compact form. In the search for ever more distinctive whistle sounds, these consonant triads were eventually replaced with more dissonant diminished or augmented triads. Finally, with the advent of steptops

Casey Jones' whistle blows again in this faded old photograph, taken in the Illinois Central yards at Jackson, Tennessee. Looking on is Casey's son, Charles. Photo by Waymon Lacy.

A more modern home-built whistle in the Casey Jones style. Photo by David Fultz.

R. S. GILLESPIE.
STEAM WHISTLE.

No. 451,040.　　　　　Patented Apr. 28, 1891.

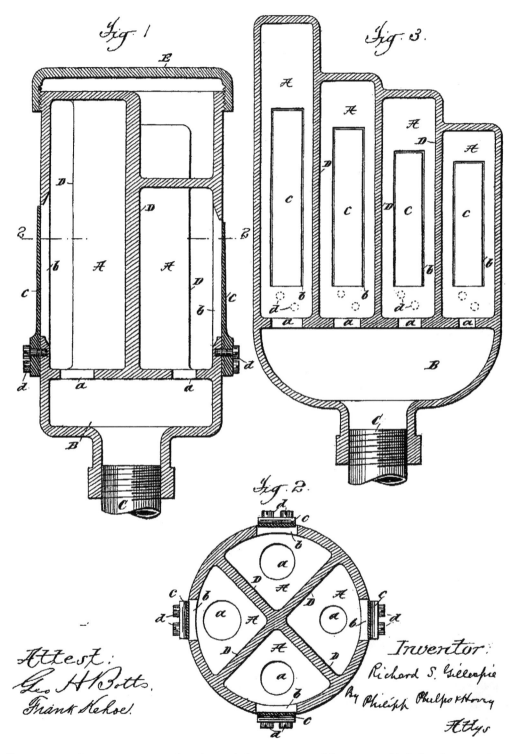

The bizarre Gillespie patent of 1891. It appears as though it might be a precursor of the steptop whistle, but this is not the case. In fact, contrary to the title, it is not a true aerodynamic whistle at all. Closer examination shows that the sound-producing elements are vibrating reeds!

having five or six chambers, the chords became increasingly complex, and often appeared in configurations quite contrary to harmonic practice in the classical period. Triads were replaced by jazzy sixth chords or mournful seventh and ninth chords, sometimes with bizarre inversions or doublings. With these unique harmonies the American locomotive whistle reached the zenith of its distinctiveness. No other type of steam whistle was so widely and readily recognized.

There appears to be only one compilation of multi-tone whistle chords in the open literature, and that is the one by Deane Ellsworth in *Live Steam Magazine.*[4] From Ellsworth's article we cite the following examples:

• Hancock "steamboat" three-chime: A-C-E. An A minor triad in root position, in a low register. Used by the Union Pacific, Illinois Central, Western Maryland, Southern Railway, and others.

• Nathan "steamboat" three-chime: B-D#-F#. A B major triad in root position, in a low register.

• Pennsylvania Railroad shop-built three-chime: E-G-B. An E minor triad in root position. This chord was later adopted by Nathan for its three-chime whistles.

• Southern Railway shop-built three-chime: A flat-C-F. An F minor triad in first inversion.

• Erie Railroad shop-built three-chime: G-C-D. One of the few three-note chords not based on a triad; difficult to analyze. Characterized (fittingly!) by hearers as "eerie."

• Union Pacific shop-built five-chime steptop: B-D-F#-G#-B. A B minor sixth chord with doubled root. Used on the 9000-class locomotives.

• Burlington shop-built five-chime steptop: G-B-D-E-G. A G major sixth chord with doubled root, in a high register. This whistle was renowned for its quilling ability.

• Canadian National shop-built five-chime step-top: G-B-D-F#-G. Substitution of the seventh for the sixth makes a pungent variation on the Burlington five-chime.

• Nathan six-chime steptop: D flat-E flat-F-A flat-B-E flat. A D flat major ninth chord in root position with doubled ninth. (The usually reliable Ellsworth notates this chord in the key of C# major, which has seven sharps and is unlikely to be used by a musician.) This is the standard Nathan six-chime, a much admired whistle used on New York Central Hudsons and Nickel Plate Berkshires, among others. A very similar version was built by the Southern Pacific in its Sacramento shops.

• Southern Pacific/Grand Trunk Western six-chime: D flat- E-flat-F-G-B flat-D flat. An E flat major ninth in third inversion with the seventh doubled. Again, Ellsworth notates this chord in the key of D#, which no musician would do if he had a choice.

A much larger compilation is the work of the indefatigable Peter Ommundsen of Salt Spring Island, British Columbia, who has recorded more than 300 whistle sounds from a variety of sources, subjected them to spectrum analysis, and characterized them in musical terms.[5] Regrettably,

TYPE 963-A-1030
Chime Whistle for Passenger Engines

Steptop whistles from the 1907 Nathan catalog, probably the first to be offered by an American manufacturer. These designs were so successful that they remained essentially unchanged for the next fifty years. For many of those years they were supplied as standard equipment to the American Locomotive Co.

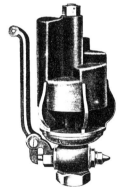

Fig. No. 158

The Star Brass version of a short-bell steptop whistle, ca. 1910(?). The date of first manufacture is uncertain, but it probably followed the Nathan designs (above) by a few years.

very little of Ommundsen's research has appeared in print, except for brief excerpts in a two-part review article by this author.[6] Ommundsen warns against the facile assumption that the same chord will be heard from the same whistle under all circumstances. He points out that variations in inlet pressure can not only transpose a chord to a different key, but can actually alter intervals within the chord, transforming it into another harmony. In one instance recorded by Ommundsen, an 8-inch Crosby that sounded a G minor triad in first inversion (B flat-D-G) at low pressure, rose a full tone to A minor (C-E-A) at higher pressure. In another instance, a 2-inch Crosby which sounded A-B-E flat at low pressure, sounded an A minor triad (A-C-E) at higher pressure. Slack manufacturing tolerances can further complicate this situation.

Shop-built whistles

As the foregoing tabulation indicates, the popularity of Nathan-pattern steptops led some railroads to cast imitative versions in their own foundries and shops, and many of these versions were tuned to alternative chords. Once again, the reason for this was to distinguish between railroads at places where two or more trains were present simultaneously. Even in the absence of markings, it is a relatively simple matter to distinguish a shop-built whistle from a commercially manufactured whistle. In the first place, most shop-built whistles had vertical valves, whereas most commercially manufactured whistles had horizontal valves. A vertical valve avoids the need for the intricate cored casting which a horizontal valve demands. In the second place, most of these vertical valves had top-mounted levers. The lever of a vertical valve necessarily hangs downward, so that it can be actuated by pulling horizontally on the cord. When a vertical lever operates through a slot in the base of the whistle, the length of the lever is added to the height of the whistle itself. This may cause the overall height of a vertically mounted whistle to exceed right-of-way clearances, and lead to collisions with bridges, tunnel mouths, and roundhouse doors. But a top-mounted lever lies neatly alongside the whistle itself, and adds nothing to its overall height. Hence a top-mounted lever is diagnostic. With the sole exception of the rare Lunkenheimer "Tri-tone" design, no commercial U.S.

manufacturer ever offered whistles with a top-mounted lever. Finally, many shop-built whistles had non-standard inlet threads, known as "boiler threads." These often had steep tapers and 12 threads per inch, regardless of nominal size. Folklore holds that this was done to discourage theft and diversion to unauthorized usage, but it may reflect nothing more than the standard practice of the railroad's own boilermakers.

The Southern Railway was perhaps the most prolific of all American railroads in the design and construction of shop-built whistles. It was the largest railroad in America that allowed engineers to use any whistle they chose, and therefore did not have a standard whistle. In consequence its shops produced almost every type of whistle that had ever been applied to steam locomotives. Most of these whistles were cast at the Southern's foundry in Lenoir City, Tennessee. Retired Southern machinists have said that these whistles were sent as unmachined pieces to the various system repair facilities, where they were assembled and readied for installation on the locomotives.

The most common whistle that the Southern built was a plain whistle made from a locomotive boiler superheater tube, 5-1/2" in diameter. These tubes were riveted to a bronze top cap, which was either flat or rounded. The bowl was made of bronze, and the vertical valve was actuated by a top-mounted lever. The usual length of the bell was between 12" and 15". Cheap to make and used extensively, this whistle was referred to by many Southern engineers as a "bootleg" whistle. The name suggests a certain defiance of, or at least disregard for, company regulations.

The Southern also built steptop whistles in three-, five-, and six-chime styles, all with top levers and valves. The five- and six-chime models, built entirely of iron, were apparently not very popular, and only a few survive today. The three-chime model was by far the most popular of the steptop designs. Practically all were made of bronze, although a few were cast in iron, probably during World War II when bronze was not readily available. This type of whistle, whose melancholy minor chord was tabulated above, was used on ex-Southern steam locomotive No. 4501 when the Southern began its well-known steam excursion program in 1966.

At one point, the Southern decided to create a deep-toned locomotive whistle for its passenger locomotives. It cast several 8" diameter three-chime whistles that had a distinct resemblance to those made by the Crosby Steam Gage & Valve Co. It is not known whether Crosby filed suit for patent infringement or the Southern was dissatisfied with the whistle itself, but in any event this model was soon discontinued. Still wanting a deep-toned whistle, the Southern then designed and built a 6" diameter three-chime whistle with a top-lever vertical valve. Made of bronze, it had an 18" long bell. It was immediately successful, and was applied to many of Southern's apple-green passenger locomotives. Southern locomotive No. 1401, on display at the Smithsonian Institution in Washington, is equipped with one of these whistles.

The Southern enjoyed one distinction that no other railroad in America could claim: it saved all its steam whistles when its locomotives were retired. Upon request these whistles were donated to on-line factories, fire stations, and historical societies. Many had their bowls stamped with the inscription "Gift of Southern Railway System." Because of their generosity and far-sightedness, more Southern Railway whistles survive today than those of any other railroad in the nation.

The Illinois Central Railroad also built a three-chime whistle that was used on many of its locomotives. It had an 18-inch long bell and was popularly known as a "steamboat" whistle; its chord is also tabulated above. These were cast at their huge facility in Paducah, Kentucky. It is said that the Illinois Central had proportionately fewer grade crossing accidents than any other railroad, in part because the pleasing sound of their whistles attracted the attention of the public. While the Illinois Central did not give away its surplus whistles at the close of the steam era, it did offer them for sale for the sum of $35.

The Reading Railroad also built many of its own whistles. Two of these, a plain whistle and a three-chime whistle, had vertical valves operated by a top lever. A third, and by far the most popular, was a six-chime whistle with a spring-loaded horizontal valve. It had a bell 12 inches long and was unique in that it had a top cap of traditional design, not the steptop pattern of Nathan and its imitators. Allegedly fewer than thirty of these six-chime whistles were built, and for this reason, as much as for its distinctive sound, many collectors regard this as the most sought after locomotive whistle in America.

Differentiation by region and class of service

There is no concrete evidence of institutionalized differences among locomotive whistles in various regions of the nation. Nevertheless there is some suggestion of a difference in preference above and below the Mason-Dixon line. Almost all the major railroads below the Mason-Dixon Line favored the use of plain or three-chime whistles, although five- and six-chime whistles were used as well. At least three large railroads, the Southern Railway, the Atlantic Coast Line Railroad, and the Louisville & Nashville Railroad, built three-chime whistles in their own shops. Engineers in the South took great pride in their ability to create "music" with their whistles, and plain and three-chime

Homely but serviceable, this short-bell top-lever plain whistle was built in the shops of the Reading Railroad for use on its freight locomotives. Photo by Lin Chapman.

MODERN LOCOMOTIVE WHISTLES

All photos by Larry Spreckelmeier

The renowned PRR three-chime whistle, usually associated with class K4 Pacifics, but also used on other classes, shown here with straight valve as used on class D16 4-4-0's. Marked "X 6532 A" on bell, "X 6524 C" on bowl.

The notorious PRR 'Banshee' plain short-bell freight whistle, well-adapted to 'wailing', as its name implies. It is shown here with angled valve mounting and curved casting to mate with steam dome. This same valve assembly was used interchangeably on the "K4" whistle. Valve casting marked "X12067."

The celebrated Norfolk & Western "hooter," only 5-1/2" in diameter but extremely powerful. Built in Roanoke shops for freight service and shown here at correct mounting angle, with distinctive lever. Top of bell was usually made of steel. Valve disc marked "NW;" valve housing marked "59545."

Southern Railway three-chime 'steamboat' whistle. Most long whistles of this kind were used on the CNO&TP division. Note the elaborate fulcrum and gland for top lever.

Southern Railway short-bell three-chime with top lever. Bell marked "EB2673," bowl marked "EB2671."

Baltimore & Ohio plain whistle with side mount, as used on class T3 4-8-2's. Bowl marked "L2243," fulcrum marked "L3568," spring cover marked "1737."

The Applications Of Steam Whistles

Baltimore & Ohio side-mounted three-chime with horizontal valve. Bell marked "L2051," bowl marked "L2243," spring cover marked "1737," fulcrum marked "A19435."

Close-up of a Baltimore & Ohio "tumor top" whistle. In this otherwise ordinary three-chime, the pitch of the longest chamber has been lowered by milling out its top and casting a new top plate with this excrescence over the opening.

Great Northern five-chime steptop, distinguished by the softly rounded shoulders on the bell and the unusually thick fins or ears between chambers. Bell marked "GN" and "11425," bowl marked "4166," neck marked with a lozenge-shaped logo.

Wheeling & Lake Erie five-chime steptop whistle with side mounting. Bowl marked "B2214," spring cover marked "B2215," bell marked "A1562."

AT&SF long-bell six-chime steptop, made by Locomotive Finishing & Manufacturing Co. of Kansas City (LFM). Bell marked "ATSF" and "LM540," bowl marked with LFM logo and "LS6826".

Even at the close of the steam era, the British never shared the American fascination with big steam whistles. This little "egg-cup" screamer, only slightly more than three inches in diameter, is from the London & North Eastern Railway (LNER).

whistles were better suited to this purpose than their five- and six-chime cousins. Certainly they were easier to modify when the engineer wished to alter the sound of his whistle. While this artistic endeavor was not encouraged by company officials, it was certainly tolerated, as long as it didn't result in too many complaints from trackside residents.

The opposite seems to have been true above the Mason-Dixon line. Practically all the major lines used five- and six-chime whistles, although there were occasional exceptions, notably the great Pennsylvania Railroad. The Santa Fe, which used primarily five- and six-note whistles on its locomotives, had strict rules regarding whistle use and discouraged unauthorized blowing. Nor were engineers allowed to tune these whistles. The following note appears on the blueprint of a Santa Fe five-chime, drawing No. 44-26: "Whistles are not to be tampered with for the purpose of changing the tone to suit individuals by partially filling one or more chambers of the bell with wood, babbitt, or other material."

For many years railroads made no particular distinction between freight and passenger whistles. Granted, long-bell plain whistles had been in use since the end of the Civil War, but this was done primarily as a concession to farmers and others who lived near the right-of-way and complained about the disagreeable sound of short-bell whistles. It was not until the first years of the twentieth century that long-bell whistles were regularly assigned to passenger locomotives and short-bell whistles to freight locomotives. The theory was that a long-bell whistle would be less likely to disturb passengers sleeping in Pullman cars on overnight runs, whereas passengers that might be disturbed by a short bell whistle on a freight train had in all probability not purchased a ticket, and therefore the railroad was not overly concerned for their comfort.

Some railroads, such as the Southern, had both plain and chime long-bell whistles available for use on their passenger locomotives, but as far as can be determined, the engineer had the final word on which type of whistle to use. No records can be found that specifically require a certain type of whistle be used on *any* Southern Railway steam locomotive, though many of the Ps-class passenger engines carried

the forementioned shop-built three-chime whistles with 18-inch long bells.

The Norfolk & Western Railway had a standard plain whistle that was used on all steam locomotives, until the Hancock Inspirator Co. of New York developed its well-known three-chime whistle. These deep-throated Hancock whistles were applied to all of the K and J class streamlined locomotives, as well as to several older passenger locomotives. This was the only chime whistle that the Norfolk & Western ever authorized for use during all the years it operated steam locomotives. It was also the only commercially manufactured whistle available in a version intended specifically for use with superheated steam at a pressure of 300 PSI. As historians of technology know, superheating of steam was the technological advance which made possible the development of the so-called superpower locomotives in the 1930's, and led to the final flowering of the American steam locomotive. But most superheated locomotives mounted their whistles on the steam dome and utilized saturated steam. Hence the design of whistles did not in general reflect the great twentieth century advances in the design of locomotives.

The distinction between freight and passenger engine whistles faded away during World War II. Every railroad in the country worked overtime to move men and equipment for the war effort, and if a locomotive was available to pull a train, it made little difference whether it was a freight or a passenger engine. After the war the diesel locomotive began rapidly to replace the steam locomotive, until almost every major railroad that still operated steam locomotives used them exclusively in freight service. Thus by the late 1950's, it was an air horn instead of a steam whistle that indicated whether a train was carrying passengers or freight.

The Foley experiments

A conventional steam whistle, provided it is not located very near reflecting or diffracting obstacles, radiates sound uniformly in all directions. This distribution pattern is far from ideal for railroad use. Sound radiated forward of the engine is useful to warn oncoming traffic, and sound radiated rearward is useful for communicating with other members of the train crew. But sound radiated to the sides serves primarily to annoy trackside residents and livestock, and sound radiated upwards is wasted. Furthermore, the locomotive engineer sits nearer the whistle than any other hearer, and hence is most susceptible to hearing damage from prolonged exposure. Worse still, in an effort to lessen the engineer's discomfort, the whistle was moved forward from the steam dome to a position just behind the stack. In this location, interference from the stack itself further diminished sound radiated in the forward direction. The overall result, attested to by engineers and trackside hearers alike, is that the sound of the whistle is less clearly audible in the forward direction than any other—precisely the reverse of what is wanted.

In 1925 these considerations led Professor Arthur L. Foley, chairman of the physics department at the University of Indiana, to undertake a series of measurements of the radiation pattern of a conventional locomotive whistle.[7] The immediate cause of Foley's investigation was a dreadful crossing accident on the Pennsylvania Railroad in which a school bus full of children had been struck in a dense fog, even though the bus driver had stopped short of the crossing and walked to the track to listen for the usual crossing signal. Measurements of radiation pattern are ordinarily performed by fixing the source of sound and moving the recording microphone around it in a wide circular arc. Foley had the rather clever notion of fixing the microphone and rotating the locomotive instead—a simple matter when one has access to a roundhouse turntable. His measurements decisively confirmed the popular impression that radiated sound energy is at a minimum directly in front of the locomotive. Foley's studies concluded with three recommendations: (1) the whistle should be mounted on the front of the locomotive to promote audibility and prevent the cloud of escaping steam from obscuring the engineer's vision, (2) the body of the whistle should be horizontal to prevent wind pressure from distorting the jet on the upstream side, and (3) the whistle should be fitted with a reflector or baffle to direct sound primarily in the forward direction.

Foley's recommendations were put to a practical test in the summer of 1926 by the Chicago & Eastern Illinois Railroad. A Pacific-type locomotive was fitted with two standard whistles, one located in the customary position in front of the cab, and the other located atop the smokebox and backed by a sheet metal reflector 30" wide and 24" high. Direct comparison of the two whistles under a variety of running conditions confirmed the greater effectiveness of the front-mounted whistle.

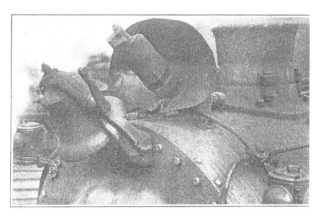

One of Foley's early experiments with whistle placement. The whistle is located forward of the stack, inclined because of clearance limitations, and fitted with a crudely shaped sheet metal "reflector."

Not long thereafter, Foley's design found a commercial embodiment in the Hancock type 4700 air whistle. This consisted of an exquisitely well-made single-bell chime whistle of 4" diameter, surrounded by a cast aluminum reflector (Hancock called it an "amplifier") resembling a wash basin tipped up on edge. The slot of this whistle was less than half the width of the slot of a conventional whistle, and fluid consumption was correspondingly reduced. For all its mechanical excellence, the Hancock 4700 did not find widespread favor among traditionally oriented railroad men. It didn't look like a whistle, and because it operated on compressed air rather than steam, it didn't sound like a whistle. The New York, New Haven & Hartford was one of the few railroads that purchased it in quantity, and they continued to use it on their diesel and electric locomotives well after the demise of steam.

The Hancock type 4700 air whistle, designed as a result of the Foley experiments.

The Applications Of Steam Whistles

Perennial favorites

Half a century after the disappearance of mainline steam, the locomotive whistle continues to exert its fascination. It is probably fair to say that no other type of whistle is so ardently pursued by collectors. Even within this general preference for locomotive whistles, there seem to be certain perennial favorites that regularly command the highest prices at auction. To say that a whistle is a perennial favorite is to ratify a popular taste, and taste is a notoriously treacherous basis for analysis of any kind. *De gustibus non disputandum est.* Nevertheless there seem to be two main sources of the affection in which collectors hold certain whistles.

The first of these is the beauty of the sounds they produce, coupled perhaps with great familiarity with, or nostalgia for, the memories they evoke. This is certainly the case with the melodious K-4 chime whistles, built in the Altoona shops of the Pennsylvania Railroad and in fact used on several classes of locomotive in addition to the K-4. Their haunting minor triad was familiar to millions of trackside hearers along the Pennsy right-of-way. It applies as well to the original 6" three-chime Crosby, a longtime favorite of "whistle artists" and the general public alike, because of the ease with which it could be made to talk. And it probably applies to steptop chime whistles of every description, both commercial and shop-built, which currently enjoy an enormous vogue. The five- and six-tone clusters which these whistles produce are unique to American railroading. Marked Nathans and Hancocks are always in demand, as are the products of certain railroad shops known for their unique tuning, such as the three-chime whistles built by the Baltimore & Ohio, the Reading, and the Southern Pacific. In particular, the six-chime long-bell steptops designed by David Joslyn and built in the Sacramento shops of the SP are regarded in some circles as the most desirable of all chime whistles.

The second source of favor appears to be association with a famous or much admired type of locomotive. This explains the popularity of the exceedingly powerful single-note "hooters" of the Norfolk & Western, forever associated in the minds of railfans with the immense class A and class Y-6 articulateds. Certainly there is nothing intrinsically lovable about the sound of these whistles, which is nothing but a stentorian honk, like a goose on steroids. Equally undistinguished are the sounds produced by the Southern "bootleg"

whistles, made from superheater tubing in the Southern's own shops and employed on many well known locomotives. Association rather than tonal beauty probably explains also the appeal of the Pennsylvania's standard short-bell plain whistle for freight service, popularly known as a "banshee" because of the eerie howling which a skilled engineer could elicit from it.

Decades from now the list of favorites might look quite different. What is unlikely to change is the enduring appeal of the steam locomotive whistle for both an older generation who remember it and a younger generation who thrill anew to its evocative voice.

Marine whistles *

From time immemorial seamen have communicated with each other by shouting, perhaps with the aid of a primitive megaphone or horn. For communication over greater distances, the human voice was supplemented by the use of signal flags, bells, lanterns, and cannon fire. In the 1830's, however, the new breed of steam-powered vessels began to compete vigorously with traditional sailing ships for supremacy of the waters. The availability of steam on board very quickly led to the use of the steam whistle as a means of communication, supplanting almost all others. The first American to install a steam whistle on a ship seems to have been Stephen D. Collins, who in 1837 fitted one to the *King Philip*, a small "tea kettle" plying between Fall River, Massachusetts and Providence, Rhode Island. Note that this was only one year after the first use of a steam whistle on an American locomotive (which Collins presumably had heard). Thus railroad applications and marine applications were very nearly coeval.

In common with most technological innovations, marine whistles then proceeded to evolve and differentiate along ever more specialized lines. By the beginning of the twentieth century, they constituted a distinct and readily identifiable type of whistle. By the late 1930's, however, newly constructed ships were increasingly fitted with air or steam horns rather than whistles, and the use of steam whistles in marine applications began its slow decline. Fortunately the

* In collaboration with Harry Barry

vessels themselves were relatively long-lived, and many marine whistles survived into the 1970's and 1980's before their parent ships were scrapped. After more than a century of ascendance, nowadays they are a great rarity, cherished mainly by antiquarians and hobbyists.

"Form follows function," was the guiding dictum of twentieth century architecture, and the design of marine whistles was similarly governed by their usage. Two principal considerations dominated: the need to be heard over great distances and the need to distinguish one ship from another. The first consideration led to the choice of whistles of large size and low pitch, and the second consideration led to the choice of multi-tone whistles sounding several notes simultaneously.

The audibility of a whistle at a remote location depends on the sound power it produces, its distance from the hearer, the nature of the intervening terrain, and on atmospheric propagation effects. At distances of several miles or more, the dominant propagation effect is atmospheric absorption, which increases markedly with frequency. The precise amount of loss depends strongly on the relative humidity, but in all cases the range of audibility is extended by lowering the frequency. On this basis alone, marine whistles should have the lowest possible pitch.

This is not the whole story, however. In addition to atmospheric loss, which is a purely physical phenomenon, there is a countervailing effect known as the Fletcher-Munson effect. This is a purely psychoacoustic effect occurring entirely within the human ear. Loosely speaking, the Fletcher-Munson curves represent the average frequency response of the ear. They say (among much else) that a low frequency sound of given intensity is *perceived* as less and less loud as the frequency is lowered. This argues for the use of higher frequencies, nearer the midrange of human hearing at 2000 to 3000 Hz. When the effects of atmospheric loss are added to the Fletcher- Munson effect, it emerges that maximum audibility is achieved when the pitch is low, but not too low. Shipbuilders had long known empirically that optimum frequencies lie in the range 50 to 300 Hz, and indeed this is where the majority of marine whistles are pitched. Pitches in this region have the further advantage that they are less annoying to passengers than higher pitches.

Whistles intended for general use typically had bells twice as long as they were wide, or thereabout. If this proportion were maintained in marine whistles of low pitch, the result would be bells of absurdly large diameter. Hence marine whistles tended to be tall and thin, a property described by builders of organ pipes as "small scale." Strictly speaking, the scale of an organ pipe is the ratio of its diameter to its length, a number less than one. Whistle builders, on the other hand, use the reciprocal of this ratio, the ratio of length to diameter, and denote the length as a multiple of the diameter. Thus, if conventional whistle bells have a shape factor near 2X, the bells of marine whistles tend to have shape factors in the range 3X to 6X. This conveys an additional advantage. Whistles of large shape factor tend to be richer in upper harmonics, because the end correction is smaller and does not choke off the overtone sequence so rapidly. These upper harmonics in turn give security to the pitch and promote audibility at normal distances. A large shape factor also incurs a penalty, however, in that the acoustic output is smaller than that of a whistle of the same diameter but lesser length. In compensation, marine whistles tend to be large in diameter as well as in shape factor.

In the preceding section, we saw that locomotive whistles tended to evolve along different lines for freight and passenger service. Furthermore, some effort was made to distinguish the whistles of one railroad from those of another. But except in rare cases, differentiation did not proceed to the level of the individual locomotive. This is in contrast to the maritime environment, where encounters among ships at sea are relatively infrequent, and it is useful to distinguish one vessel from another in the absence of visual identification. At the simplest level, this consideration led to the assignment of whistle pitch in rough accord with the tonnage of the vessel. For example the Leslie Co. of Parsippany, New Jersey, recommended fundamental frequencies in the range 247 to 440 Hz for small vessels and intra-compartment signals, 156 to 233 Hz for vessels between 1000 and 6000 tons, 110 to 129 Hz for vessels between 6000 and 15,000 tons, and 54 to 87 Hz for vessels over 15,000 tons. A roughly equivalent criterion is contained in the 1972 version of the International Regulations for Prevention of Collisions at Sea, which mandated frequencies

A typical owner-built multiple-bell chime whistle on a small craft: two plain whistles of differing parentage mounted on a manifold of ordinary pipe fitting. The interval may not have been consonant, but it was certain to be distinctive. This is the stack of the 30-foot steam yacht Julia Bulette. Such relatively fragile construction would never have survived the rigors of railroad use. Photograph by owner David Fogg.

Steam Whistle Chime.

A three-bell Lunkenheimer chime or "Lunk triple," the characteristic whistle of American riverboats. This is a relatively early version of this perennially popular whistle, ca. 1890, with flat tops on the whistles and a gracefully curved cast manifold. A number of later versions are pictured in Chapter 5.

in the range 250 to 700 Hz for vessels of length up to 75 meters, 130 to 350 Hz for vessels more than 75 but less than 200 meters in length, and 70 to 200 Hz for vessels exceeding 200 meters in length.

Further differentiation among vessels of the same tonnage class was achieved by using various combinations of plain whistles to produce a chord of several tones. This practice dates back at least to the Civil War, and initially was carried out in a wholly unsystematic way. The captain or chief engineer simply mounted anywhere from two to five plain whistles on a pipe manifold with a common valve, in total disregard of the consonance or dissonance of the result. Whatever it was, it was at least distinctive. These makeshift arrangements can still be seen on numerous small boats, and especially those built or equipped by their owners.

Manufacturers quickly recognized the marine market as one they could not afford to ignore, and by 1890 almost every major manufacturer offered a harmoniously tuned three-bell chime intended primarily for use on ships. Lunkenheimer led the way with a handsome cast bronze manifold made expressly for its "triples," whereas most other makers merely assembled three of their plain whistles on a manifold of ordinary pipe fittings. In addition to Lunkenheimer, only Ashton cast a manifold specifically for use on its triples, and these never attained the popularity of the Lunkenheimer version. A large Lunkenheimer triple is among the most impressive of all steam whistles, both visually and aurally. A few Lunk triples found their way onto factory roofs and mineheads, but by and large it was marine usage that earned them their fame. They found immediate favor among the riverboats that plied the Ohio-Mississippi-Missouri system, and may be regarded as *the* characteristic whistle of America's inland waterways during the nineteenth century. A distant second in favor was the two-bell chime or "gong" whistle, in both vertical and horizontal versions.

No type of ship ever captured the popular imagination to the same extent as the great trans-Atlantic passenger liners of the early part of the twentieth century. These were the vessels that gave new meaning to the expression "first class" above decks, while below decks they transported the masses of immigrants hoping to find freedom and fortune in the New World. Beginning with the ill-fated *Lusitania* in 1897, German and English shipbuilders engaged in a see-saw contest to produce the largest and fastest vessels. National pride was at stake. A century later it is difficult to recapture the awe with which each new liner was greeted, or to appreciate the magnitude of the engineering achievements that they represented. The new breed of trans-Atlantic liners were the largest and heaviest mobile man-made objects, and in fact were larger than most stationary man-made objects, including the Eiffel Tower and the tallest skyscrapers. Each of them was fitted with several immense three-bell chimes. It would be a pleasure to report that some of these whistles were of American manufacture, but none were. Ships of British registry usually bore the mighty three-bell chimes manufactured by Smith-Hyson of Nottingham, England. The

The Applications Of Steam Whistles

SMITH BROTHERS AND COMPANY (HYSON), LTD.

" HYSON "

Triple Bell Super Whistle

INSTALLED ON THE WORLDS LARGEST LINERS

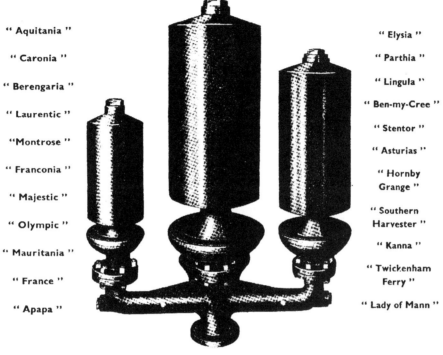

" Aquitania "	" Elysia "
" Caronia "	" Parthia "
" Berengaria "	" Lingula "
" Laurentic "	" Ben-my-Cree "
"Montrose"	" Stentor "
" Franconia "	" Asturias "
" Majestic "	" Hornby Grange "
" Olympic "	" Southern Harvester "
" Mauritania "	" Kanna "
" France "	" Twickenham Ferry "
" Apapa "	" Lady of Mann "

Fig. 186

Fitted with Patent " Willett Bruce " Electric Control.

These Whistles are made in sets of three, tuned in harmony, and have the greatest carrying power in the world, in the largest size.

Recommended sizes when used in conjunction with the " Willett Bruce " control are as follows :—

Fig. 186A. 15-in. × 12-in. × 9-in. dia. Bells.
Fig. 186B. 12-in. × 10-in. × 8-in. ,, ,,
Fig. 186C. 12-in. × 9-in. × 6-in. ,, ,,
Fig. 186D. 10-in. × 8-in. × 6-in. ,, ,,

Prices on application.

Hyson Green Valve Works NOTTINGHAM . ENGLAND

The enormous three-bell chimes made by the Hyson Green Valve Works of Nottingham, England, and fitted to many of the world's most famous ocean liners in the first third of the 20th century. No American firm offered a comparable whistle.

largest of these had bells 9", 12", and 15" in diameter, stood 50-1/2" tall, and weighed 775 pounds. They were fitted to such famous liners as the *Aquitania, Mauretania, Normandie, Ile de France, Olympic, Britannic,* and *Titanic.* The *Titanic* had one set on each of her two forward funnels, and enough parts have been recovered from the wreck to reconstitute one of them. This reconstituted whistle is now the property of RMS Titanic, Inc. and is currently on tour of the United States. A similar chime from the *Mauretania,* and a somewhat smaller chime from the *Lady of Mann,* survive today in private collections. After the *Normandie* burned at a Hudson River pier in 1942, her whistle went to the Bethlehem Steel mill in Bethlehem, Pennsylvania. There it signaled shift changes until 1952, when its valve stuck open for two hours, to the annoyance of residents of the Lehigh Valley. It was removed from service and lay forgotten in the mill for more than three decades, until rediscovered in 1985 by marine historian Frank Braynard. Bethlehem then donated it to the proposed Ocean Liner Museum in Manhattan. After several more peregrinations, this whistle is now in the custody of Conrad Milster of the Pratt Institute in Brooklyn.

Harry Barry of North East, Pennsylvania, stands beside the whistle from the Canadian Pacific passenger ship Assiniboia, which he painstakingly restored. This whistle, one of the largest plain whistles ever put to marine use, is made entirely of cast iron and has a bell 12" in diameter and 48" high. The Assiniboia's sister ship Keewadin carried an even larger whistle, 12" in diameter and 60" high. Photo by Marlene Barry.

An even larger three-bell chime was allegedly offered by Steven & Struthers, shipfitters of Glasgow. The center whistle of this combination was reputed to be 18" in diameter. It is not known whether a whistle of this size was ever built and installed on a ship, much less whether an example has survived. By the early 1930's the use of steam whistles on large ocean-going ships had essentially ended. When the *Queen Mary* was launched in 1934, she carried three immense jacketed steam horns, Tyfon model T-575-DVEK, manufactured by Kockums Mekaniska Verkstads Aktiebolag in Sweden. When the ship was reconditioned as a stationary tourist attraction in 1970, these horns were converted to compressed air operation at lower pressure.

When the single-bell chime was invented in 1877, it quickly came to dominate railroad service, but it did not immediately attain comparable acceptance in the world of marine service. There is some objective justification for this, inasmuch as a three-bell chime has greater radiating area than a single-bell chime sounding the same notes, and hence is louder. Perhaps the most widely recognized single-bell chime in marine service was the 8" Crosby used on New York City tugboats, fireboats, and ferries. Nevertheless 10" chimes by Lunkenheimer and 12" chimes by Crosby were also employed in marine service, and the deep, throbbing sound of these great whistles was widely admired.

The turn of the century was also the heyday of large organ pipe whistles in marine service. As their name indicates, these whistles were modeled on organ flue pipes, except that they were closed at the top and thus sounded only odd harmonics. Their distinctive feature was a mouth, or more likely two mouths, each subtending only about 90 degrees of the cir-

This majestic device, awaiting its fate in a West Coast scrapyard, is a Tyfon T-575, the largest of all steam horns. From World War II onward, horns of this type replaced steam whistles on the largest ocean-going vessels, including battleships, aircraft carriers, and passenger liners. Photo by Zidell Explorations.

The Applications Of Steam Whistles

cumference of the bell. The bell was narrow, of length typically five or more times the diameter. Small whistles of this type, based on British prototypes and up to 4" in diameter, were offered by many domestic manufacturers, including American, Ashton, Crosby, Morrison, and Star Brass. These smaller whistles had been in use for decades as factory whistles and alarms, and were also much favored for use on private yachts. It was British manufacturers, however, who popularized the use of very large organ pipes on large vessels. The Scottish brassfounders Steven & Struthers of Glasgow furnished organ pipes up to 10" in diameter, and these were adopted as standard by the British Admiralty for ships of the line. The pitch of these large organ pipes was low indeed, but they were not especially loud. Unfortunately, the large ratio of the emitted wavelength to the dimensions of the mouth made them rather inefficient radiators of sound. Thus, although they were thrilling to hear at close range, in the final analysis they lacked the carrying power of conventional plain whistles.

By the second decade of the 20th century the proud tradition of a distinctive whistle for every ship had begun to fade away. This was due at least in part to the emergence of large classes of nearly identical ships. There now existed, for example, a more or less standardized Great Lakes freighter for the shipment of bulk cargo such as iron ore, taconite pellets, grain, and cement. Not surprisingly, it was fitted with a more or less standardized plain whistle, with a bell 10" in diameter by 36" long, and an integral balanced valve. This length was intermediate between the 30" (3X) and 40" (4X) lengths regularly offered by makers such as Lunkenheimer, Powell, Star Brass, and Ashton, and seems to have been chosen precisely to give these freighters a distinctive sound. It produced a throbbing bass growl in the neighborhood of 90 Hz. Four makers produced the majority of these whistles, the American Shipbuilding Co., the Great Lakes Engineering Works, the American Steel Barge Co., and the Chicago Shipbuilding Co. The products of the first three bear a strong family resemblance, with copper bells, waterfall tops, and cast iron bowls. The Chicago Shipbuilding whistle, on the other hand, is utterly distinctive, with a bell of seamless brass tubing and a large and ornate top cap and acorn of cast brass.

No type of ship was more thoroughly standardized than the Liberty Ships and Victory Ships of World War II, and they carried a standardized 8" x 32" (4X) plain whistle with balanced valve. There is some confusion about who manufactured these whistles. The majority carry the bold intaglio markings of the Star Brass Co. of Boston on their top plates. Occasionally, however, the top plate is unmarked and one finds instead a valve

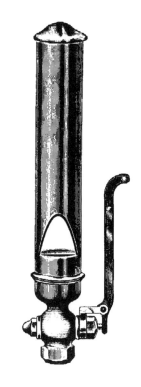

An Ashton organ pipe whistle, ca. 1918. American-made whistles of this type were widely used on small craft such as yachts and launches, and were characterized by a soft, mellow tone, small diameter, and semi-elliptical arch mouths. British firms, on the other hand, built them up to ten inches in diameter, usually with square or rectangular mouths, and applied them to the largest vessels.

a b c d

Whistles of the Great Lakes freighters, as furnished by their builders. (a) American Shipbuilding Co., (b) Great Lakes Engineering Works, (c) American Steel Barge Co., (d) Chicago Shipbuilding Co. All have 10" x 36" bells. Photos by Harry Barry.

Heavy intaglio markings on the top plate of a Star Brass Liberty Ship whistle. Photo by the author.

Detail of the bowl and balanced valve of a Star Brass Liberty Ship whistle. Photo by the author.

cover marked by the Ballou Service and Instrument Co. of New York, Durkee Marine of Staten Island, or Benson Electric. So far as is known, none of these firms manufactured whistles of its own, so either they were jobbing Star Brass whistles or they had been pressed into manufacturing by wartime exigency. Very rarely one encounters a Liberty Ship whistle with no markings at all. It is alleged that some of these were made by Lonergan or Crosby, and if so, the reluctance of these makers to identify their products remains a mystery.

Because the Liberty Ships were well known to, and well loved by, the generation of World War II, a considerable body of folklore has grown up around them. Some of this folklore bears on their whistles. It is rumored, for example, that every Liberty Ship carried a second whistle in Stores in case the first one was shot away. Any shot that carried away the whistle is likely to have damaged the stack as well, probably rendering the ship inoperable, but this consideration does not seem to trouble the tale-bearers. In 1996 an unused 8" x 30" Star Brass whistle came to market, still in its original crate. This may be the source of the rumor that some Liberty ship whistles were never put into service, although the non-standard length makes it clear that this particular whistle was intended for some other purpose, probably as a municipal fire alarm. It is also rumored that ca. 1942 all brass whistles were replaced by iron or steel whistles, in order to conserve precious copper. But no iron or steel whistles of the appropriate size are known to have survived, and there is no documentation to support this anecdote.

Much useful information about marine whistles on our inland waterways can be found in the *S & D Reflector*, a monthly publication of the Sons and Daughters of Pioneer Rivermen, with headquarters in Marietta, Ohio. See also *Steamboat Bill*, a quarterly publication of the Steamship Historical Society of America, headquartered in Providence, Rhode Island. There are several museums that feature steam whistles as a part of their historical presentations, and some of these concern ship and steamboat whistles. Two of the most notable are the Marine Museum of Upper Canada, located in Toronto, and the Ohio River Museum in Marietta, Ohio. The Marine Museum has a large collection of ships' whistles, mostly from Great Lakes vessels. Many of the whistles on display are connected to a low pressure air supply, and can be activated by simply pushing a button that opens a solenoid valve. This interactive presentation affords the visitor a splendid opportunity to experience the sound of various whistles.

The Ohio River Museum is dedicated solely to riverboats that navigated on the Mississippi and Ohio Rivers. This collection contains a large number of steamboat whistles, many of which are on display. Beside each whistle is a short history of the ship on which it served, as well as a picture of the ship itself. Many of these whistles were heard during the first organized whistle blow at Sistersville, West Virginia in the early 1960's. Since then they have been sounded several other times, most recently at the museum site. On these occasions one can sit back and imagine the scene a century ago when hundreds of these old steamboats, each with a different whistle, plied the length of the nation's longest and greatest waterway.

Industrial and institutional whistles

Like railroad and marine applications, in which the design of whistles underwent progressive evolution and refinement in accord with the unique needs of these areas, industrial and institutional applications also spawned certain distinctive types of whistles. The difference, however, is that these innovative designs did not displace pre-existing types; they merely supplemented them in certain specialized areas. The overwhelming majority of factory whistles were chosen from the conventional offerings of commercial whistle manufacturers, and their chief characteristic was their diversity. There is scarcely a type of whistle that was not employed in one industrial application or another. Choice among the vast range of available whistles was more or less at the whim of the plant manager or stationary engineer. Virtually the only general principle that can be discerned is that small establishments tended to use small whistles and large establishments tended to use large whistles. Needless to say, this minimal regularity followed from the fact that small installations usually had small boilers whereas large ones usually had large boilers.

It is also pertinent that industrial and institutional whistles, unlike railroad and marine whistles, served in fixed locations. Hence limitations on size, weight, and portability, as well as requirements for resistance to vibration, simply did not apply. This led to the employment of certain whistle types of imposing size and apparent fragility, as will be discussed below. Furthermore, industrial and institutional whistles tended to be located in cluttered urban environments, in contrast to the open or nearly open environments of most railroad and marine whistles. This led to a radiation pattern (and hence a zone of audibility) governed by essen-

tially unpredictable reflection and diffraction effects, rather than by the inverse square law that obtains in an unobstructed space. It has been said that on occasion the whistles of the smelters in Tacoma, Washington could be heard on Vashon Island, many miles away across the open waters of Puget Sound, when they could not be heard amidst the industrial clutter of Tacoma itself.

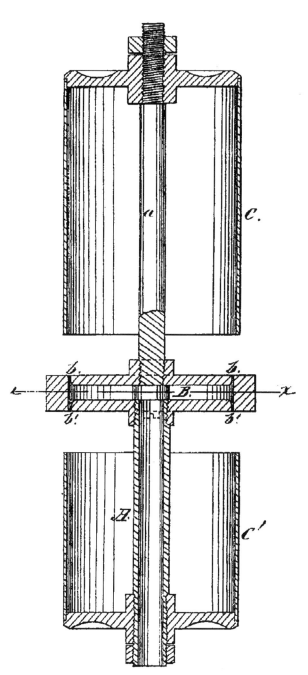

A figure from Fitts' original patent of 1865, showing two opposed bells of different lengths, one on either side of a central bowl (next page).

At the lower end of the size spectrum, including whistles up to about 4" in diameter, the well-established conventional offerings from Buckeye, Crosby, Lonergan, Lunkenheimer, Powell *et al.* filled most applications. Tens of thousands of plain and chime whistles—there seems to have been no systematic preference for one type over the other—were fitted to sawmills, laundries, breweries, machine shops, foundries, collieries, mine heads, generating stations, pumping stations, paper mills, vulcanizing plants, steam shovels, hoists, gantry cranes, traction engines, etc., in fact wherever a boiler was used to power an engine or to provide process steam. During the heyday of the steam whistle, whistles used in industrial, mining, forestry, and agricultural applications greatly outnumbered railroad and marine whistles, and it is these sources that provide the majority of whistles available to the collector today.

What then were the truly innovative designs in the industrial/institutional sector and where were they used? The first major innovation was the opposed-bell chime or "gong" whistle, patented in 1865 by Abraham Fitts of Worcester, Massachusetts as a boiler alarm or fog signal (U.S. 48,921). Previous chime whistles consisted of two or more plain whistles mounted side by side on a transverse manifold. Fitts had the notion to align two bells coaxially, one bell on either side of a common bowl, thus making a compact and economical two-bell chime. He also gave the device its name, but its meaning remains obscure. One theory holds that "gong" harks back to the fire alarm gong that typically hung in the center of town and was struck with a hammer to summon the fire brigade.

The design proved quite popular. Commercial versions were shortly offered by the Union Water Meter Co. of Worcester, Massachusetts[8], by Pitkin Brothers, and by the James Morrison Brass Manufacturing Co. of Toronto, and found immediate service as factory whistles, fog signals, and fire alarms. They also spawned some variants. These are of two basic types, superficially resembling each other. The first type was simply a Fitts vertical gong with the addition of a third bell on top, fed coaxially through the center of the middle bell. Thus the top two bells opened downward while the lowest bell opened upward. The largest of these three-bell gongs had bells 12", 12" and

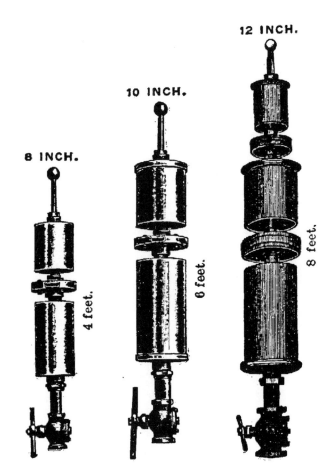

Commercial embodiments of the Fitts patent, as manufactured by the Union Water Meter Co. of Worcester, Massachusetts, ca. 1906. These were widely used as factory whistles, fog signals, and fire alarms. The three-bell version had bells 12, 12, and 8 inches in diameter, and stood almost eight feet tall.

8" in diameter, dwarfing all other whistles excepting only the conventional three-bell chimes of ocean liners. A three-bell Union Water Meter gong, topped with its trademark spire and ball finial, was a compelling structure almost eight feet tall. In the two-bell and three-bell "vertical chimes," however, all bells opened downward, contrary to Fitts' original design. Each bell had its own bowl assembly and the upper bells were fed coaxially through the centers of those below. Morrison Brass also offered two-bell gongs of both types. These too were available in large sizes. A 12" Harmonium resides in a private collection. A 14" version was also offered, but no whistles of this size are known to have survived.

The Applications Of Steam Whistles

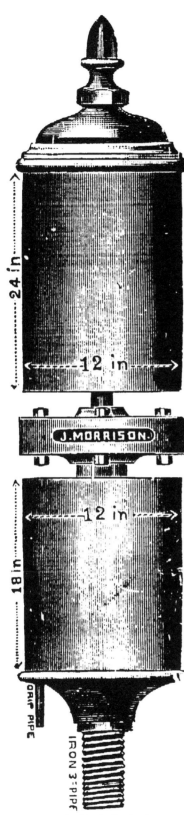

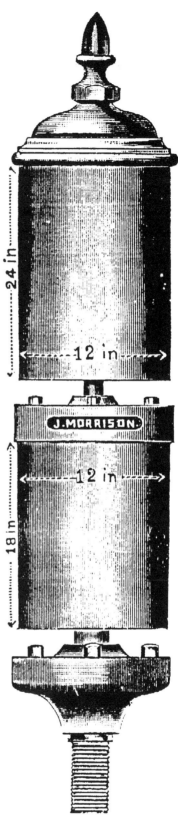

A Morrison 'Harmonium' double bell whistle, ca. 1905. Note that the two bells are opposed, and fed from a common bowl. Hence this is another version of the Fitts vertical gong whistle, despite the name. As the dimensions indicate, these too were available in enormous sizes.

A Morrison double bell chime whistle, ca. 1905. Note that the two bells face the same direction and each has its own bowl, the upper one being fed coaxially through the lower one. This is a compact alternative to side-by-side mounting on a manifold. These too were available in sizes up to 14" in diameter.

A Crane No. 5 Saw-Mill Whistle, ca. 1887, not yet truly differentiated. Although labeled and sold for sawmill use, it scarcely differs from a conventional freight locomotive whistle of the day.

A two-bell horizontal "gong" whistle, made by Sinker-Davis of Indianapolis. These cast iron whistles were extremely loud and used primarily in logging camps, but found occasional service on ships.

Cutaway view of a Lunkenheimer "mockingbird" whistle, ca. 1912. The movable piston E is pulled upward by a spring D and downward by a light chain which runs over a pulley system F, terminating in a ring. An earlier version of this whistle will be found in Chapter 5.

The opposed-bell gong whistle found application in yet another area, and that was in logging and lumbering operations. The whistle at a logging camp was preferably very loud, very robust, and very inexpensive. The first of these considerations dictated a short, wide bell, because acoustic efficiency is proportional to the area of the mouth and inversely proportional to the wavelength generated. The last two considerations suggested a plain whistle made of cast iron, requiring as few machining and finishing operations as possible. The first firm to produce a whistle based specifically on these criteria was the Crane Brothers Manufacturing Co. of Chicago, whose No. 5 Saw-Mill Whistle, available in diameters from 4" through 8", appeared in catalogs as early as 1887. Although manufactured in quantity, they were probably left behind to rust away when the timber ran out. Hence they are quite rare today, and it is a fortunate collector who has one.

Sometime around the turn of the century, the Sinker-Davis Co. of Indianapolis, Indiana, realized that the Fitts gong could be adapted to logging operations. In Fitts' original patent the two bells were aligned on a vertical axis, but Sinker-Davis aligned them on a horizontal axis and fed the bowl from its edge. (This configuration is called a horizontal gong, to distinguish it from Fitts' original vertical gong.) Like the Crane Saw-Mill whistle, the Sinker-Davis gong was made of cast iron, with rough external surfaces and minimal machine finishing, in sizes up to 12" in diameter. It was just as cheap as the Crane, just as robust, and because it had two bells rather than one, other things being equal, it was twice as powerful. Its enormous acoustic output and carrying power earned it the nickname "bull-of-the-woods" whistle among lumberjacks. Sinker-Davis gongs are also highly prized by collectors.

Another class—perhaps the only other class—of task-specific whistles was developed for use as municipal fire alarms, air raid alarms, and storm and flood warnings. These were plain whistles whose pitch could be varied by the operator during use, and their whooping portamentos were intended to distinguish them at first hearing from ordinary factory whistles. Their common feature was an internal piston which varied the length of the bell and hence its frequency of resonance. They differed, however, in the means whereby this piston was actuated. In the "mockingbird" whistles offered by Lunkenheimer, the piston slid longitudinally on a central support rod, and was automatically drawn to the top of the bell by an internal spring. A thin wire cable extended from the piston through a pair of pulleys to a handle that the operator held in his free hand. By pulling on this handle he could counteract the upward pull of the spring to any desired degree, and thereby raise the pitch of the whistle. Lunkenheimer mockingbirds were available in 3-1/2", 5" and 8" diameters, and adorned thousands of city halls and fire stations. At least one 5" mockingbird crossed the line into railroad service, however. Now in the author's collection, it was the personal whistle of Cody Burdette, an engineer on the Cass Scenic Railroad of West Virginia.

The Applications Of Steam Whistles

A similar type of variable-pitch whistle was the so-called "fire alarm" or "combination" whistle, offered by Lunkenheimer, Crane, and others. In these the piston was actuated by a stiff central rod extending downward through the base of the whistle. This required in turn a rather complex offset valve and base assembly in order to clear the rod. Moreover, this pitch-changing mechanism did not lend itself to remote operation, as did the mockingbird design. These too were manufactured in diameters up to 8", and are much prized by collectors. Lunkenheimer conscientiously reserved the name "mockingbird" for its cable-actuated piston whistles, but other manufacturers were careless or indifferent to the use of this name. In particular Crane called its piston whistles "mockingbirds" although in fact they were rod-actuated "combination" whistles according to Lunkenheimer's designation.

Beyond these examples, it would be difficult to identify a particular design with a particular industry. Some whistles seem to have wandered very far indeed from their usual realms of employment. A large three-bell chime of the type traditionally associated with river packets was used at a coal mine in Millersburg, Indiana. One of the few surviving Powell three-bell chimes was discovered by a collector atop

Cutaway view of a Lunkenheimer combination or fire alarm whistle, ca. 1912. The movable piston is worked up and down by a stiff rod that runs down the axis of the whistle and emerges at the bottom through a packing gland. Earlier versions of this whistle will be found in Chapter 5.

the Hudson River Psychiatric Center in Poughkeepsie, New York. And the only 12" Crosby single-bell chime still in service, a type more usually found on large vessels, sits atop the General Electric plant in Erie, Pennsylvania.

Calliopes *

Origins and early history

The calliope, the loudest and most exuberant musical instrument ever devised by man, has somewhat clouded origins.[9,10] An article in the April 1, 1851 issue of the *Dayton Journal and Advertiser*—presumably not an April Fool's joke—asserts that William Hoyt of Dupont, Indiana had "invented a plan whereby music can be produced on steamboats, of the softest (*sic!*) and most pathetic character by the agency of steam." Hoyt described his device as consisting of a horizontal pipe into which were screwed seven or more whistles of various sizes and tones, the whole operated by a set of keys. This would appear to constitute a steam calliope in every essential respect, but there is no proof that Hoyt ever built such a device, nor did he ever apply for a patent.

Thus the invention of the calliope is generally credited to Joshua C. Stoddard of Pawlet, Vermont. (There is no evidence that Hoyt and Stoddard were aware of each other's work.) Stoddard was born in 1818, the first son of Nathan Ashbel and Ruth (Judson) Stoddard. He was reared on his father's farm, where he developed a special interest in bee culture and honey production. After his marriage to Lucy Maria Hersey in 1845, he moved to Worcester, Massachusetts, where he continued to keep bees, devoting his spare time to tinkering with various inventions in typical Yankee fashion.[11] By 1845 the locomotive steam whistle was in fairly common use, and Stoddard was intrigued by its sound. He conceived the notion of combining a number of such whistles into a stentorian musical instrument which would call the faithful to worship—an aim consistent with his own evangelical beliefs and those of his New England neighbors. His first instrument consisted of fifteen (some authorities say thirteen) whistles of graduated sizes mounted in a row atop a steam chest. Another of Stoddard's aims was to obviate the need

* In collaboration with Steven Espenschied

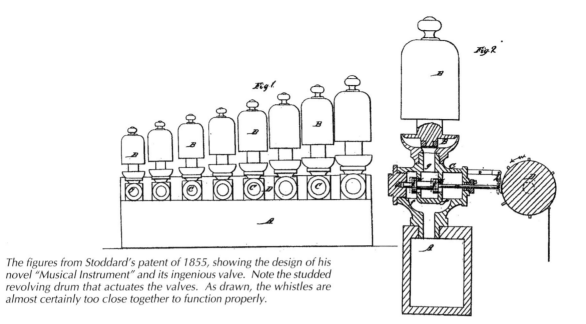

The figures from Stoddard's patent of 1855, showing the design of his novel "Musical Instrument" and its ingenious valve. Note the studded revolving drum that actuates the valves. As drawn, the whistles are almost certainly too close together to function properly.

for a musician to play the instrument. To this end he adapted the technology of the Swiss music box. The whistle valves, of a particular type that Stoddard called a "puppet" valve, were actuated by pins or studs mounted on a rotating cylinder.[12] Unlike Hoyt, Stoddard understood the importance of patent protection, and on October 9, 1855 he was granted U.S. Patent No. 13,688 for an "apparatus producing music by steam or compressed air." The first claim of this patent covers the instrument, and the second covers the peculiar construction of the valves themselves, which are an elementary form of balanced valve. Stoddard seems to have been well aware that a whistle that ordinarily required the brawny arm of an engineer to actuate it was unlikely to respond to the pressure of a single finger, and he was at pains to ease the task of the performer. In this he was less than completely successful, as the subsequent experience of calliope players demonstrated.

On July 5, 1856 Stoddard gave the first public demonstration of his invention on Worcester Common, with his daughter Jennie turning the cylinder. The instrument was an immediate sensation, even though it had to compete with ongoing July 4th festivities. A few days later the calliope made an excursion by train to a political meeting at Fitchburg, Massachusetts. The instrument astonished the residents of the county, playing music that could be heard for miles as the train moved along. The instrument continued these excursions over the rails of the Boston & Maine. Not

everyone was pleased. To Stoddard's dismay, the city of Worcester passed an ordinance forbidding the playing of his calliope within city limits.

Shortly thereafter Stoddard and others organized the American Steam Music Company. (By this time the rotating cylinder had been replaced with a keyboard.) The firm manufactured calliopes for riverboats and private yachts, and even sent an instrument to London for exhibition in the Crystal Palace. A contemporary account relates that models were made with steam pressures ranging from 5 PSI to 150 PSI, the latter audible twelve miles away. Unfortunately the fledgling company was riven by internal factionalism. In 1860 Stoddard was removed as president by one of the co-founders, the financier Henry A. Denny, and in 1865 Stoddard was forced out entirely.

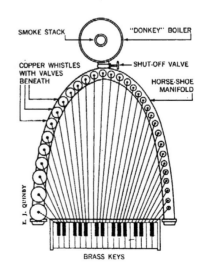

Plan of an old-time 32-note calliope, after E. J. Quinby. The traditional horse-shoe-shaped or V-shaped manifold, open end toward the calliopist, was dictated by the need to run pull wires directly from each whistle valve to the keyboard, a mechanical action similar to the tracker action of Baroque organs. From Jensen, Ref. 9.

Uses of the calliope

Although conceived as a musical instrument, the steam calliope never satisfactorily filled that role. It was simply too loud, trying the endurance of its hearers after a short while. Instead it survived and flourished in an entirely different role, as a purveyor of ballyhoo in the entertainment industry. Three such venues account for almost all the uses of the steam calliope during its lifetime: the steamboat, the showboat, and the circus.

Quite soon after its invention, the calliope was engaged in providing music upon the waterways of America. The first marine exhibit of the calliope was given by Stoddard's company in the waters around New York City on August 6, 1856. The company mounted an instrument on the large side-wheeler tugboat *Union*, which it had chartered for the purpose, and offered two or three excursions each day around the river. During this time the calliope was operated for the pleasure of the passengers, and also to bring it to the notice of the owners of other passenger steamboats.

S. H. Townsend, owner of the independent steamer *Glen Cove*, which was having an unsuccessful season on the Hudson River, became the first owner of a waterborne calliope. The reason for Mr. Townsend's poor season was the public's disinclination to board a vessel whose engine had been taken from the ill-fated *Henry Clay*, which had lost sixty passengers in a disastrous fire. Soon after the calliope was installed, however, the daily passenger load was doubled, for people were eager to ride with the new "floating music box." By 1858, however, the *Glen Cove* was competing with another showboat, the *Armenia*. Not only did the latter have a calliope, but it was an improved version, made especially for boats and twice the size of the original model. It consisted of 37 whistles with bells ranging from 1" to 6" in diameter, and a piano-like keyboard. It was located on the promenade deck in the main saloon. Problems arose, however, because the calliope robbed steam needed for propulsion, making the boilers harder to fire. The owners of the *Armenia* concluded that the novelty of the calliope did not justify the added expense and operating problems, and junked their calliope by 1870.

Eighteen years after the installation aboard the *Armenia*, a new calliope was heard on eastern waters. In 1876, at the Philadelphia Centennial Exposition, an improved version with modified steam intake was shown. This instrument was later installed on the excursion steamer *General Sedgwick*, owned by the Briggs Excursion Company. Other calliopes were installed aboard the sidewheelers *Canonicus* and *New World*, operating out of New York. An amusing story is told about the rivalry between these several riverboats:[13]

> The crafty skipper of the vessel which had the advantage of a calliope on board would order that the instrument be played just as his rival drew abeam and was about to pass him. Although the precious steam required for the music robbed his engines of some of their speed, it was a shrewd investment, for the passengers on the other steamer's decks would invariably crowd the rail on the side toward their rival's music, with the result that the ship would bury her paddlewheel on that side and hoist the other clear of the water. Immediately the hapless vessel would be left behind executing an unmanageable circle, to the intense delight of those aboard the vessel sporting the calliope.

On the Upper Mississippi, Captain James Ward installed an early model on the side-wheeler *Excelsior*, running between St. Louis, Missouri, and St. Paul, Minnesota. Many of the steamboats of this period were virtually floating hotels, competing for passengers by offering various attractions. The calliope persuaded many travelers to board the steamers, but it was soon found that they never returned, because they grew tired of the whistles before the trip was over. Later, the cabin orchestra replaced the calliope.

With the onset of the Civil War, the calliope from the *Excelsior* traveled west in order to escape destruction by the Confederate Army. It found a new home in California, where several steamboat owners pooled their boats in the California Steam Navigation Company to control river traffic between Sacramento and San Francisco. They were eager to equip their steamers with any means of attracting passengers. The largest of the instruments constructed for these steamboats had 34 whistles ranging from 1" to 6" in diameter. The smallest had 13 whistles, while some had 20 or 27. They were operated from a keyboard as well as from Stoddard's original studded cylinder, although the smaller ones had cylinders only.

The second great use of the calliope was aboard showboats, which thrived on the Ohio, Mississippi, and Illinois rivers and their tributaries throughout the last half of the nineteenth century and well into the early years of the twentieth. These boats were basically floating theaters, painted in gaudy colors and operated with a flair for showmanship. Folks in the small river towns of the Midwest regarded them as palaces of entertainment and gleefully welcomed their arrival. Early showboats were voiceless, possessing only a trumpet and a few handmade posters to tell of the rich cargo of drama they carried. Most showboats, however, were not self-propelled, but were pulled along their routes by small towboats. Showboat operators realized that these towboats provided a convenient source of steam that could be piped aboard to operate a calliope. The calliope changed everything. It became the showboat's characteristic voice, the means of announcing her presence to the potential audiences remote from the river landings. *Roger's Floating Palace* had a calliope as early as 1858, probably the first showboat to do so. She was followed by *Sensation*, carrying a calliope built by the Van Duzen Foundry in Cincinnati. During the heyday of these vessels at least fifteen more showboats carried calliopes, including the *Goldenrod, Princess, American, Bryant's New Showboat, New Era, New Sensation, Majestic, Wonderland, Water Queen, Floating Theatre, Fun Boat, Temple,* and *Lulubelle.*

Like the Civil War, World War I hurt the showboat industry badly. With the return of peace and the advent of the nickelodeon and talking pictures, the boats largely disappeared from our rivers. But in 1927, when there were only a dozen or so boats remaining, the business experienced a brief and unexpected renaissance. Audiences suddenly doubled in number and "S.R.O." signs were posted once again. On the strength of new profits—the highest in twenty-five years—many boats were enlarged and renovated, and some owners even felt safe in raising admission prices. The crash of 1929 put an abrupt end to this Indian summer of the showboat.

Surprisingly, the showboat made one final appearance, this time in the hands of amateurs. In 1948 a group of drama students from Kent State University hired the former showboat *Majestic* and refitted it. They cruised up and down the Kanawaha and Ohio rivers, doing a grueling repertoire of three shows on alternate days of the week and resting on the seventh day. Making one-night stands at small towns, they packed the house; and at larger towns they often stayed a week. Some of the spectators still affectionately remembered river theater, and others welcomed it as a fascinating novelty. The venture was not only a financial success, but provided great experience for the young theater students, who had found a huge and appreciative audience. In 1951, the *Majestic* was again cruising the rivers, this time for Hiram College, Ohio. Under owner and captain Tom J. Reynolds, a veteran of showboating, the vessel called at some thirty river towns along the Ohio and its tributaries.

As the age of the showboat came to an end, another age came to life in the form of the excursion steamboat. Calliopes played a prominent role in the success of these excursion boats. Daily playing of the calliope proved to be a more effective advertising tool than all the posters and columns of space in daily newspapers. Among currently operating excursion boats, the best known is the *Delta Queen,* inaugurated in 1948. Originally she had no calliope, an omission that drew the interest of one E. J. Quinby, whose hobbies were pipe organs, trolley cars, and steamboats. Quinby learned that a fine calliope built in 1890 by Thomas J. Nichol of Cincinnati had been aboard the showboat *Water Queen,* when it sank, instrument and all, in the Kanawah River in 1937. The former calliopist of the

A portion of the Frisbee calliope on the stern rail of the excursion boat Natchez. *The globes behind the whistles contain colored lights that illuminate the plume of vapor from the whistle in use. Photo by Harry Barry.*

The Applications Of Steam Whistles

Water Queen, "Crazy Roy" Choiser, had salvaged the contraption and played it at carnivals until his death. It was subsequently acquired by the King Brothers Circus, and when that enterprise folded, it joined the collection of circus veteran Ellsworth "Slim" Somers of Waterbury, Connecticut. Somers was persuaded to part with the instrument after receiving assurances that it would be played again, which of course was Quinby's goal all along.

Quinby made various improvements that benefited both the player and the instrument. He set the keyboard a safe distance from the steam whistles, which he arranged in a straight line. The ivory keys were furnished with a mercury contact to activate the whistles electrically. Solenoid valves opened and closed the passages that sent the steam to the stops. Other improvements included a handy steam pressure gauge and a foot pedal to increase or lower the amount of steam to the instrument. But Quinby's most successful innovation was the "aurora effect," a series of colored lights hidden under the whistles which illuminated the plumes of escaping steam.

The last major American-made steam calliope was also intended for an excursion boat. It was built in 1975 by the Davis Calliope Works of Seattle for the newly launched *Mississippi Queen.* Its 44 whistles of gold-plated brass extend from C below middle C to G three-and-a-half octaves above, making it the world's largest. Among the novel features introduced by the builder was an electronic playback system that permitted the performer to record the keyboard signals on a digital cassette recorder, and then play them back over the calliope itself. After completion of this masterwork, the Davis Calliope Co. survived for another decade or so selling small do-it-yourself calliopes to amateurs. It was then dissolved and all its assets sold.

The third great use of the steam calliope was in circuses, and its adoption there took place almost contemporaneously with its adoption on steamboats and showboats. P. T. Barnum, the circus magnate, envisioned a great future for the instrument and obtained rights for its use in shows. It is believed that he first employed a calliope in a circus parade in 1859. Another smaller circus, the Sands & Co. Circus, also installed a calliope in their parades about the same time as Barnum. Soon the calliope, mounted in an elaborately carved and decorated wagon, became a familiar part of every circus parade. Because of the distinctiveness and volume of its music, the calliope was eventually installed as the last vehicle in the parade. When the spectators saw the circus "whopper" coming, they knew the parade was over. But the placement of the calliope at the end also indicated that a much bigger show would take place that afternoon. Barnum's idea was so successful that the calliope's position at the end of the parade became traditional. Use of the calliope in circus parades gradually declined after 1950 due to increasing traffic problems and widespread introduction of traffic signals at intersections. These combined to make it almost impossible to keep a parade organized and moving together. The demise of this colorful spectacle saddened many circus fans.

Beginning around the turn of the century, the compressed air calliope gradually began to replace the steam calliope. The air calliope lacks the volume of the steam calliope, and its tones are not as distinctive, but it obviates the nuisance and hazard of maintaining and firing a boiler. Furthermore, it is easier to tune and, once tuned, it will stay in tune. This makes it better suited to accompany a band, and hence to participate in parades. Among the better known manufacturers of air calliopes were the Rudolph Wurlitzer Co. of North Tonowanda, New York, maker of the "Calliola" model, the Tangley Co. of Muscatine, Iowa, whose products were generally sold under the name "Calliaphone", the Pneumatic Calliope Co. of Newark, New Jersey, the National Calliope Corporation of Kansas City Missouri, and Artizan Factories, Inc. of North Tonowanda, New York. Some of these models still appear on the antique market occasionally.

Today, only a few steam calliopes can be either seen or heard. With the exception of those on excursion boats, the instrument that crowned and symbolized America's entertainment industry for ninety years can now be found only in museums, theme parks, and private collections.

Calliopes and their whistles

The calliope whistle was a specialized type of steam whistle, and hence calliope manufacture was a specialized branch of whistle manufacture. So far as is known, no maker of calliopes ever made steam whistles for other purposes, and no maker of steam

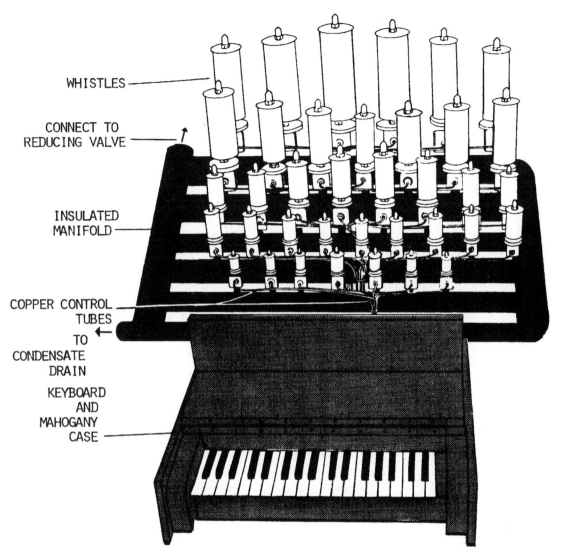

WHISTLES

CONNECT TO
REDUCING VALVE

INSULATED
MANIFOLD

COPPER CONTROL
TUBES
TO
CONDENSATE
DRAIN

KEYBOARD
AND
MAHOGANY
CASE

Plan of a modern 37-note steam calliope, as manufactured by the Davis Calliope Works of Seattle, ca. 1980. In this calliope the valves are operated by compressed air, controlled in turn by DC-operated pilot valves. This permits the whistles to be arranged in tiers like the seats in a grandstand, obviating the need for a horseshoe-shaped or V-shaped manifold required by the old tracker actions.

whistles for general use ever made calliope whistles. The reason of course is that the whistles form only a part of a functional calliope, and must be completely integrated with all other parts. The calliope maker was also obliged to provide the manifold on which the whistles were mounted, the whistle valves and keying mechanism, the keyboard, and more often than not, the donkey boiler that energized the whole affair. He did not, however, provide the wagon in the case of circus calliopes. This was the province of dedicated wagon-builders such as the Ohlsen Wagon Co. of Cincinnati.

Because most calliopes operated at pressures significantly lower than normal boiler operating pressures, calliope whistles usually took the form of other low-pressure whistles, characterized by shallow, flat-bottomed bowls. (Compare for example the Lunkenheimer low pressure whistles in Chapter 5.) Curiously, this seems to be more a matter of tradition than mechanical or hydrodynamic necessity. There does not seem to be any fundamental reason why a low-pressure whistle should have a shallow bowl. Conversely, there does not seem to be any fundamental reason why a high-pressure whistle should have a hemispherical bowl. Indeed, the Hancock three-chime "steamboat" locomotive whistle, specifically designed for use with superheated steam at 300 PSI, higher than any other regularly manufactured whistle, had a flat shallow bowl.

Among other distinctive features, calliope whistles

The Applications Of Steam Whistles

sometimes had a reverse taper on the outer edge of the spreader plate and the inner edge of the rim of the bowl. This produced a divergent nozzle or "velocity nozzle" for the escaping jet of steam, in contrast to conventional whistles in which the taper, if any, was such as to produce a converging nozzle. This may have been done in an effort to compensate for the low inlet pressure. The acorn, if any, was likely to be functional rather than ornamental. Finally, because the whistle was a component of a musical instrument, it was fitted with some means of adjusting its pitch. Sometimes this took the form of an adjustable stopper, as in an organ flue pipe; sometimes an adjustable collar or sleeve was fitted to the lower edge of the bell, but most often tuning was accomplished merely by adjusting the lip height, as in a conventional plain whistle.

Perhaps surprisingly, the proportions of calliope whistles were governed by principles laid down by north European organ builders as early as the 15th century. As mentioned in the discussion of marine whistles, the *scale* of an organ pipe is the ratio of its width to its length. By extension, a *scaling law* is the rule whereby the scale changes as the fundamental frequency of the pipe changes. For technical reasons, a pipe of small scale, i.e., a tall skinny pipe, is rich in overtones, whereas a large-scale pipe, i.e., a short, fat pipe, emits a purer, flute-like tone. It might be imagined that pipes of identical scale would be wanted throughout the entire range of a musical instrument, but this is not the case. The human ear does not like a uniform overtone structure all up and down the musical scale. High in the treble, especially in the region between 2 and 3 kHz where the ear is most sensitive, a very simple harmonic structure suffices. Indeed, if harmonics beyond the fifth were present, they would be inaudible to most people. Low in the bass, by contrast, the ear becomes increasingly insensitive, and demands a rich spectrum of harmonics in order to improve audibility and give security to the apparent pitch. In other words, from a musical standpoint, long skinny whistles are wanted at low frequencies and short fat whistles are wanted at high frequencies.

In a pipe organ, the necessary balance is achieved by letting the diameter of the pipe decrease more slowly than its length as the fundamental frequency increases. The length of the pipe necessarily decreases inversely with the first power of the frequency. In other words, each pipe is half as long as its counterpart an octave lower. This is called "halving on the twelfth note." (The first or bottom note is not counted.) But the width of the pipe is made to decrease more slowly. It might, for example, be half the diameter of its counterpart one-and-a-half octaves lower. This is called "halving on the eighteenth note." So refined was the musical judgment of early organ builders that they even specified different scaling laws for different types of pipes. Flue pipes such as diapasons typically halved in diameter on the eighteenth or twentieth note, whereas reed pipes typically halved on the twenty-second or even the twenty-fourth note.[14]

How are calliopes actually built? The author has analyzed the mechanical specification of the Davis calliope, built in 1982 for the *Delta Queen*.[15] There is some lumpiness in the data because this modern builder was constrained to used commercially available sizes of seamless drawn brass tubing, whereas organ pipes are traditionally made by rolling flat sheets to precisely the desired diameter. Nevertheless the analysis clearly shows that the whistle diameter decreases as the 2/3 power of its length. In other words, the diameter halves on the eighteenth note, because 2/3 = 12/18. Thus the empirical scaling law established by the organ builders of North Europe centuries ago has reverberated down through the ages to govern the design of this modern calliope.

Calliopes were notoriously difficult to keep in tune. The pitch of the entire instrument depended on the boiler pressure, which depended in turn on the diligence of the fireman and the volume of steam expended in loud climaxes. Early calliopes were required to operate at any steam pressure the boiler provided. If tuned at a steam pressure of 75 PSI and played at 60 or 90 PSI, they went grievously out of tune. Later a reducing valve was employed to reduce the boiler pressure to a uniform value in the neighborhood of 10 PSI. Furthermore, if tuned at a given ambient temperature, a calliope went out of tune at a higher or lower temperature, owing to differential thermal expansion of its parts. The longer it was played the warmer the entire instrument became, owing to continuing immersion in steam, and this drove it further off pitch. Finally, the first time a note was sounded there was a pronounced initial chirp of speech as the air contained within the bell was displaced by steam. These musical subtleties, which would have driven an organ voicer to distraction, seem not to have troubled the less critical hearers of a circus or showboat calliope.

Calliopes were also notoriously difficult to play. In Stoddard's early instruments the valves were actuated by a direct mechanical linkage to the keys, a scheme known for centuries to the makers of Baroque pipe organs as a "tracker" mechanism. But whereas the keys in organs worked against air pressures of a few inches of water, the keys in calliopes worked against many pounds of steam pressure. This made them almost impossible to depress with the fingers. It is alleged that half a dozen conventionally trained organists attempted to play one of Stoddard's early instruments and did not succeed. Early performers (who preferred to be called "calliopists", although they were invariably addressed as "Professor"), often had to hammer on the keys with their fists, a difficulty which effectively excluded women from the profession. Beyond the need for sheer physical strength, moreover, the job was beset with numerous other hazards. Every performance began with a deluge of hot water as the whistles cleared themselves of condensate. The keys themselves were initially made of brass, so that they quickly became as warm as the instrument itself, even to the point of blistering the player's hands. In order to keep the steam line short, the donkey boiler was usually placed directly behind the calliope, whence it showered the performer with sparks, blazing embers, and soot. If the wind direction was unfavorable, he played the entire performance enveloped in clouds of steam and water vapor. At the end of the performance, it has been said, the poor calliopist was both broiled and parboiled.

Relief was half a century away, and awaited the development of electro-pneumatic and all-electric (solenoid) valve actuating mechanisms for pipe organs. When these were at last adapted to the calliope, the instrument became playable by persons of less than superhuman strength. For the first time women achieved a reputation as calliopists. Among the most celebrated women performers were Nelly Donnigan, who played for the Ringling Bros. for many years, and Nellie King of the old Mighty Haag Shows, who earned the name "Queen of the Calliope" by popular acclaim.

There does not seem to be any way in which a collector can acquire a single authentic calliope whistle, since restorable calliopes are far too precious to be disassembled for parts. Any competent machinist can make a reasonable facsimile of a calliope whistle, however, because castings are not necessary, strictly speaking. Construction drawings suitable for the amateur machinist have been published.[16] On the other hand, the wealthy or persevering collector might reasonably hope to acquire an entire calliope, although it will almost certainly be operated by compressed air rather than steam. But this brings us to the boundary of another realm altogether, the world of fair and carousel organs and those who admire and collect them.

The Wreck of the Ol' 97, lithograph by Thomas Hart Benton, 1944.

The Steam Whistle in Popular Culture

4 *The Steam Whistle In Popular Culture*

The switchman knew by the engine's moans
that the man at the throttle was Casey Jones.
— *The Ballad of Casey Jones*

The cultural significance of the steam whistle

In the preceding chapter we discussed the steam whistle from a utilitarian point of view, in terms of the environments in which it served as an acoustical signaling or warning device. These included railroad, marine, industrial, and institutional applications, as well as the somewhat anomalous role of the calliope as a source of musical entertainment. In this chapter we explore the steam whistle in terms of its cultural significance. What role (or roles) did it play in everyday life? What meaning (or meanings) did it convey to the people who hearkened to it during the long years of its prominence? It will emerge that the steam whistle was a cultural icon of surprising connotative richness, embedded in an extensive web of widely shared associations and responses.

Before we begin, however, let us remark some largely self-evident properties of whistles and whistle-blowing. Note first that the steam whistle was intended primarily for one-way communication. One whistle toot did not ordinarily answer another, as birdsong answers birdsong in the world of nature. (The only significant exception was marine applications, in which fogbound ships identified each other by the exchange of signals.) Information flowed unilaterally from a single whistle-blower to a plurality of whistle-hearers, and this had important sociological consequences. It implied the existence and the acceptance of a stratified or hierarchical community, in which only those in authority were privileged to blow the whistle. All others were expected to hear and obey. In short, a whistle was a profoundly undemocratic—even anti-democratic—instrument, quite the opposite of the nearly contemporaneous telephone, with its almost limitless ability to facilitate two-way communication and blur class distinctions.

Second, the repertoire of messages which could be explicitly conveyed by a whistle was extremely limited. In railroad and marine applications these messages were strictly codified, and permitted neither alteration nor extension. (See Chapter 8.) In this respect the whistle was even more constrained than the telegraph. It is true that early in this century the British navy engaged in what it called "whistle telegraphy," using the Morse code. Absent a repertoire of brief coded messages, however, such as that used by radio amateurs, this method of communication must have been tedious beyond endurance. In general, there was no widely accepted convention for delivering a message of arbitrary content by whistle. Once again, the world of the steam whistle was structured in advance, governed by pre-established rules. So rigid and well established were these rules that departures from them almost invariably signified disaster. No sound was more terrifying to the members of a tightly knit mining community than the prolonged and unscheduled shrieking which announced a cave-in or explosion at the mine.

Third, it scarcely needs to be pointed out that the evocative power of a steam whistle resided in its sound, not its appearance. The sight of a whistle, either as an image or in reality, was at best a surrogate for its sound. Thus the cultural significance of the steam whistle was predominantly—although not exclusively—an aural phenomenon. Furthermore, what was important about the sound of a whistle was not the sound itself but the connotations which that sound carried. Great pipe organs are remembered for the sound they produced, but whistles are remembered for what their sound symbolized. And finally, like virtually everything else connected with the industrial age, these symbolic connotations and associations of the steam whistle are gradually fading from memory. The whistle as symbol is kept alive only within the memories of an older generation and by the activities of antiquarian societies, without which it would soon be lost.

The cultural significance of the steam whistle manifested itself in four principal areas. Like all such classification schemes, the boundaries between classes are approximate, and a given instance may well embrace more than one area. Broadly speaking, however, the steam whistle served: (1) to regulate the lives of the working classes, (2) to herald a coming event, (3) to establish setting or atmosphere, and (4) to convey emotional states. We turn now to examples from each of these major areas:

The steam whistle as regulator of the workday.

One of the first persons to grasp the importance of the steam whistle as the timekeeper of the community was Thoreau. As much as he disliked railroads in general, he was compelled to acknowledge their beneficial effect on the ordering of daily life:[1]

> "The startings and arrivals of the cars are now the epochs in the village day. They go and come with such regularity and precision, and their whistle can be heard so far, that the farmers set their clocks by them, and thus one well-conducted institution regulates a whole country."

The trend that Thoreau so presciently discerned in 1854 quickly became ubiquitous. At the zenith of the industrial age, in mill towns and mining towns and railroad terminals and lumber camps, a pocket watch was superfluous. Here is testimony from Albert Murray's quasi-autobiographical novel *Train Whistle Guitar*, about the boyhood of a black youth in Gasoline Point, Alabama during the 1920's:[2]

> "It was as if you had been born hearing and knowing about trains and train whistles, and the same was also true of sawmills and sawmill whistles. I already knew how to mark the parts of the day by sawmill whistles long before I learned to read time as such from the face of a clock."

As Lewis Mumford pointed out long ago, the plant or factory whistle regulated the lives of the laboring classes as narrowly as the ringing of the canonical hours once regulated the lives of monks.[3] The rigidity of such a mode of life could quickly become oppressive. The supremacy of the time clock and the fundamental asymmetry of communication by whistle are both revealed with frightening candor in the illustration on the facing page. This is the frontispiece of the 1957 catalog of the Toots-E division of Lovsted, Inc., makers of industrial signal systems. The artwork may be amateurish but the message is unmistakable. The principal occupant of the office is not the homunculus behind the desk, but the enormous time clock that looms menacingly over him, dominating the room. The manager is merely the agent of the clock; he exists to serve it, not *vice versa*. He in turn commands the workers by means of his imperative finger on the whistle button. There can be no doubt of the route by which orders flow at this plant.

By contrast, a considerably more benign—indeed, positively roseate—view of the role of the steam whistle in reinforcing the work ethic is reflected in these excerpts from Catalog 900-W, issued in 1955 by the J. E. Lonergan Company, a prominent whistle manufacturer.

"The STEAM WHISTLE as an Investment in Plant Efficiency and Community Good Will.

"Every now and then we get letters from old-time customers, inquiring whether Lonergan still makes whistles. In one of these letters our customer wrote interestingly about the factory whistle in his home town where he lived as a boy . . . how the town scheduled itself by that big whistle. . . how it was tooted for big celebrations. And now our friend saw an opportunity to be of

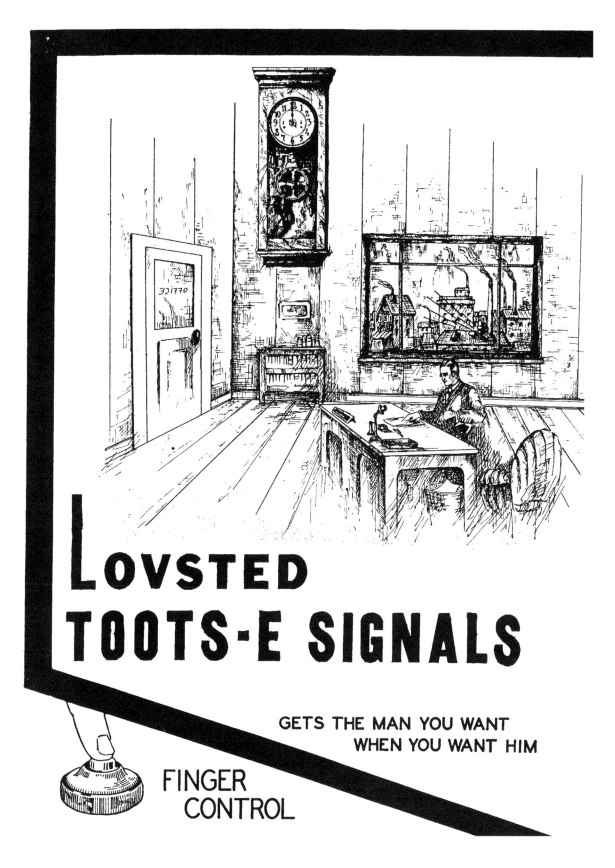

The frontispiece of the 1957 catalog of the Toots-E division of Lovsted, Inc.

service to his present business and community by installing a whistle on the new power plant which his company was building . . .

". . . In following this inquiry with a personal call, we found out more things about the value of a factory whistle. For instance—*as an aid to plant efficiency.* No matter what kind of signal is used to start up operations in the morning and afternoon, there is a certain amount of lost motion until each worker gets into the swing of his job. Our friend expressed the opionion that a factory whistle cuts down this slack . . . men respond and get adjusted to their jobs quicker when the whistle blows, and gongs, sirens, or loud speakers do not equal a whistle in this respect. He said—'There's something about the sound of a big steam whistle that is associated with the urge to get going.'

"But, by the same token, we reasoned that if a whistle helped the force to get going, it would work in reverse at quitting time! To the contrary, our friend argued, when you have a whistle on the factory, there is less tendency for employees to watch the clock.

"Finally, our friend pointed out that a whistle is a good-will builder. It serves as a constantly repeated 'ad,' identifying the company as the means of livelihood for friends and neighbors . . . and it helps to give the community a certain *rhythm* or *tempo.*"

Whatever the merits of the arguments expressed here, such concern for labor relations and community good will was a rarity in the matter-of-fact world of boiler accessory manufacture.

The steam whistle did more than regulate the work day in a literal sense. It also served as an icon of the work ethic itself. The Coca Cola Co., always a leader in advertising art, cleverly exploited this association in an ongoing series of advertisements (see color insert). The first of these dates from 1941, and merely superimposes the Coke bottle on a blowing factory whistle, leaving the mind of the viewer to supply the connection. The second dates from 1950 and is considerably more elaborate. Against a background of Chicago area landmarks (including no less than four Coca-Cola vending

machines), the smiling denim-clad workman holds a Coke in one hand, while with the other he blows the plant whistle. The juxtaposition of the bottle and the whistle is of course intended to suggest that the pause for the soft drink, like the blowing of the whistle, punctuates the rhythm of the workday and relieves its monotony. The nine years which separate these two advertisements testify to the durability of the association.

The steam whistle as herald or harbinger.

The well known lyric "Steamboat comin' round the bend" manifestly does not refer to sighting the riverboat but to hearing its whistle, that magisterial booming through hill and valley that preceded the arrival of the packet at innumerable river towns. The whistle not only announced the imminent arrival of the boat; it also heightened the anticipation of it. The use of the calliope probably belongs in this category too. Although calliope-lovers are loath to admit it, the sound of their instrument is virtually unendurable for extended periods at close range. The saying "distance lends enchantment" was never more true than when applied to the calliope. Only the most hardened enthusiast would find pleasure in a prolonged "concert" by a stationary calliope a few feet away. (This was put to the test at the inauguration of the new Davis calliope on the reconstructed river steamboat *Delta Queen.* Within a few minutes the captive passengers were imploring the crew to turn the damned thing off.) Hence all calliopes were mounted on moving vehicles, so that they were heard only in passing. Thus the real function of the calliope was not to play music, but to announce the coming of the showboat or the end of the circus parade.

Hollywood has exploited the premonitory function of the steam whistle in countless films. In the classic 1952 western *High Noon*, all events lead up to a crucial moment, the very cusp on which the plot hangs, the arrival of the noon train carrying the gunman who has vowed to kill sheriff Gary Cooper. After a long interval of mounting suspense, the silence is shattered by the train whistle, and the film's denouement begins to unwind. In the equally famous 1969 western *Butch Cassidy and the Sundance Kid*, an extreme closeup of a steptop locomotive whistle in action prefigures the explosive emergence of the bandit gang from the boxcar. The fact that the steptop locomotive whistle had not yet been invented is of scant concern to most movie-goers.

Occasionally the mere image of the whistle is sufficient to foreshadow disaster. At the beginning of this chapter, in Thomas Hart Benton's swirling and rhythmic 1944 lithograph *Wreck of the Ol' 97*, the plume of steam from the furiously blowing whistle mimics the plume from the stack of the doomed locomotive. One can almost hear the final scream as the engine strikes the broken rail and plunges to its end.

The steam whistle as establisher of mood, setting, or atmosphere.

In this area, the significance of the steam whistle is almost entirely symbolic. It depends for its effectiveness on responses that originate within and draw upon culturally acquired connotations. For example, the grimy industrial locations in which Shaw's *Major Barbara* takes place are symbolized by the recurrent blowing of a factory whistle. Similarly, there is scarcely a harbor or waterfront scene in a Hollywood movie that does not have a variety of marine whistles overlaid on the sound track to lend ambience. Think too of Alfred Hitchcock's *The Lady Vanishes*, in which an English locomotive whistle becomes an instrument of nameless menace, as its high-pitched scream carries us from scene to scene with ever-heightening suspense.

To the delight of whistle cognoscenti (and the disinterest of almost everyone else), Hollywood often gets its background sound effects wrong. In the 1989 film *Glory*, about a black regiment during the Civil War, the regiment trains in a railroad yard to the accompaniment of locomotive chime whistles. Unfortunately, the single-bell chime whistle for locomotive use was not invented until 1877. In a National Geographic documentary entitled "Secrets of the *Titanic*" the sound of the ship's whistle, which was in fact an immense Smith-Hyson three-bell chime, is replaced by the nasal and expressionless blare of a steam horn. This disregard for historical accuracy is characteristic of numerous commercial films. It appears that the Foley editors in these cases simply reach into their stock libraries of sound

effects without doing the necessary background research.

The steam whistle as metaphor for emotional states.

Here too the significance of the steam whistle is almost exclusively symbolic. As might be expected, examples are found primarily in creative writing, although occasionally in music. In *September Song* William Humphrey writes, "No sound was so sad and lonesome as the whistle of a departing train to one left behind."[4] Indeed, the adjective most often applied to American locomotive whistles is "lonesome." Obviously it is not the whistle itself which is lonesome, nor even the train, but the listener, in whose breast the sound of the whistle arouses feelings of longing, despair, regret, separation, or isolation. Here are two more testimonials to the affective power of the steam whistle from Albert Murray's *Train Whistle Guitar*.[5]

> "Nor can I remember when I had not yet heard him playing the blues on his guitar as if he were also an engineer telling tall tales on a train whistle, his left hand doing most of the talking including the laughing and signifying as well as the moaning and crying and even the whining, while his right hand thumped the wheels going somewhere.
>
> "Not to mention his voice, which was as smoke-blue sounding as the Philamayork-skyline-blue mist beyond blue steel railroad bridges. Not to mention how he was forever turning guitar strings into train whistles which were not only the once-upon-a-time voices of storytellers but of all the voices saying what was being said in the stories as well."

Finally, on rare occasions the mere image of a whistle suffices to elicit the desired state of mind. An example is shown in this advertisement for a brand of bourbon whiskey named "Rebel Yell." Rebellion is symbolized by the Confederate flag and epaulets in the foreground, while the soldiers' defiant battle cry is represented by the three-bell chime of a Mississippi River steamboat in full voice. (See color insert.)

In addition to the foregoing functional analysis, it is also possible to examine the cultural significance of the steam whistle in terms of the medium whereby these functions were transacted. These media include the written word, illustration and advertising, movies, music, and everyday speech. We do not pretend to exhaustiveness. What follows are merely a few examples from a vast and largely unexplored field. Note that the great majority of these examples are drawn from the world of railroading. This far exceeds the proportion of railroad whistles among the population of steam whistles as a whole, but the world of railroading exerts a special hold on the popular imagination. The steam locomotive in particular has an appeal virtually unmatched by other artifacts of the industrial age. No one thrills to the sound of a low water alarm, a few persons thrill to the sound of a factory whistle, a few more persons thrill to the sound of a ship's whistle, but almost everyone thrills to the sound of a train whistle. Thus it is not surprising that railroad-related examples dominate our survey.

Whistles in print: protest and affirmation

Chapter 2 gave us a few glimpses of popular resentment against the railroads as a whole, but additional protest was directed quite specifically against the sound of the steam whistle itself. We have already heard Thoreau's complaint about the "ear-rending neigh" of the Iron Horse. Throughout the next hundred and fifty years these complaints were a perennial fixture of newspaper squibs and letters to the editor. Here, for example, is a two-sentence notice from a late 19th century engineering journal, summing up what must have been the feelings of thousands who lived in the shadow of mills and factories.[6]

> "A big steam whistle that can be heard for ten miles has been placed on Weidmann's Mill at Paterson, New Jersey. The people who are awakened by it at 6:20 o'clock every morning are indignant."

At their most virulent, protests against the sound of the steam whistle took on paranoiac overtones. Hearken to these excerpts from a 1905 broadside by Edward S. Morse, entitled "The Steam Whistle a Menace to Public Health."[7]

> "One city celebrating the opening of a subway permits, or rather does not enjoin, the blowing of steam boat and factory whistles for long spells of time, to the detriment and misery of thousands of invalids, of the sick and dying, of the nervous and overworked, an annoyance of such magnitude that all physicians agree it is a menace to health, and that nervous prostration, a disease of cities, finds in the incessant noise one of its causes . . .

> "The man of wealth has his suburban villa, the man of ordinary means is enabled to go to the country, but what shall we say of the poor laborer who is not only unable to take a vacation, but is compelled to live near this sleep-destroying nuisance, because the land is considered uninhabitable by those who can possibly afford to live out of the immediate vicinity of this modern scourge of cities. . .

> "Why should factories be permitted to make themselves a nuisance? Why should they not be compelled to make their surroundings less objectionable? What with piles of rubbish, stenches which might be suppressed, chimney stacks vomiting forth black clouds of soot, the useless shriek of steam whistles and sirens, their existence in any neighborhood is rendered a curse to comfort and self-respect. . . One [workman] told me of the sufferings of a daughter dying with typhoid fever, another confessed to me that the freight yard whistles hastened the death of his wife, whose last hours were those of agony from the hoodlum whistling."

And so on, for fourteen closely printed pages. The steam whistle has long since been replaced by the air horn on the nation's railroads, but similar complaints can be heard today. Defiant local municipalities continue to pass ordinances restricting the blowing of diesel horns at grade crossings, putting them in constant conflict with guardians of public safety such as the Federal Railroad Administration.

The sound of the steam whistle makes sporadic appearances in 19th century literature, usually in the service of Luddites protesting the incursion of the railroad. More favorable views of whistles and whistling can be found in the descriptions of train journeys. Beginning about 1840, such journeys appear here and there in memoirs and travelogues, and whistles often receive passing mention. One of the best of these travelogues is also one of the earliest. In 1842, as part of his American tour, Charles Dickens took a ride on the new Boston & Lowell Railroad, and found it both fascinating and appalling.

The imaginative fiction of the twentieth century contains two notable descriptions of epic train journeys, one Russian and one American. The Russian journey occurs in Boris Pasternak's 1958 novel *Doctor Zhivago* and takes 45 pages to describe. Surprisingly, the whistle of the locomotive is never mentioned. But there exists an American novel in which train whistles play a major role. The author is Thomas Wolfe (1900-1938), and the novel is *Of Time and the River*, the second volume of Wolfe's quasi-autobiographical tetralogy. Young Tom (called Eugene Gant in the novel) takes a train from Asheville, North Carolina (called Altamont in the novel) to attend college in Boston. (By coincidence, the year is nearly the same as the year of Zhivago's flight from Moscow.) Wolfe's extravagant and overheated prose defies description; it must be experienced first-hand. Here is the passage in which the train first arrives at the Altamont station:[8]

> "Then the locomotive drew in upon them, loomed enormously above them, and slowly swept by them with a terrific drive of eight-locked pistoned wheels, all higher than their heads, a savage furnace-flare of heat, a hard hose-thick hiss of steam, a moment's vision of a lean old head, an old gloved hand of cunning on the throttle, a glint of demon hawk-eyes fixed forever on the rails, a huge tangle of gauges, levers, valves, and throttles, and the goggled blackened face of the fireman, lit by an intermittent hell of flame, as he bent and swayed with rhythmic swing of laden shovel at his furnace doors."

Modern critics deplore Wolfe's prolixity and self-absorption, but almost all confess grudging admiration for his skills as a wordsmith. In another virtuoso piece of writing he mimics the hypnotic clickety-clack of wheels over the rail joints—"the four-footed thunder of phantasmal hooves"—in classical Latin verse!

> ". . . quadrupedante putrem putrem as with sonitu quatit ungula campum quadrupedante putrem . . . "

Throughout this long journey the train whistle plays the role of prophet and omen, marking major transitions in the boy's life in an almost formulaic manner. (This role had already been foreshadowed in *Look Homeward Angel*, the first volume of the tetralogy.) Eugene Gant's long journey ends with these words:

> "Down in the city's central web, the boy could distinguish faintly the line of the rails, and see the engine smoke above the railroad yards, and as he looked, he heard far off that haunting sound and prophecy of youth and of his life—the bell, the wheel, the wailing whistle—and the train.
> "Then he turned swiftly and went to meet it—and all the new lands, morning, and the shining city. Upon the porch his father had not moved or stirred. He knew that he should never see him again."

Years later, near the close of the first part of the novel, Wolfe returns once more to the metaphor of the train whistle, this time as harbinger of change:

> "And again he heard, as he had heard a thousand times in childhood, far, faint, and broken by the wind, the wailing whistle of a distant train. It brought to him, as it had brought to him so many times, the old immortal promises of flight and darkness, the golden promises of morning, new lands and a shining city. And to his sick and desperate soul, the cry of a great train now came with a sterner and more desperate hope than he had ever known as a boy. Suddenly he knew that there was one road, and only one before him—flight from this defeat and failure which his life had come to, redemption by stern labor and grim loneliness, the stern challenge, the sharp peril and the grand reward—the magic and undying image of the city. And suddenly he knew that he would go."

Thus the whistle is made to speak for the author's own formless yearnings and hungers. No American author has ever been more keenly attuned to the sights and sounds of American railroading, nor exploited the whistle metaphor more frequently or more effectively.

The Preface to this book asserts that no book has ever been written about steam whistles. That statement is not strictly true. There is at least one book in which the steam whistle serves as a central theme. It is a fifth grade schoolbook, a member of the "Alice and Jerry" series of readers, entitled *Engine Whistles*.[9] First published in 1942, it tells the story of the coming of age of a young man in a small midwestern town between 1879 and 1910. His growth parallels the growth of the railroad through town, for which the locomotive whistle is emblematic. Heavy with didactic purpose —there is even a companion Workbook—and borrowing shamelessly from the Tom Sawyer idiom, the book nevertheless manages to convey a vast amount of information about life in that era. The library card on the inside front cover of the author's copy shows that it was in regular use as late as 1969. One wonders what meaning the titular symbol could have had for children who had never heard an actual train whistle.

The alert reader with whistles in mind can of course find many additional citations in American literature. These range from Poe's "A Descent into the Maelstrom," in which the roar of the waters is compared to thousands of safety valves releasing steam at once, to Walt Whitman's "A Song of Joys":

> O the engineer's joys! To go with a
>   locomotive!
> To hear the hiss of steam, the merry shriek,
>   the steam whistle, the laughing locomo-
>   tive!
> To push with resistless way and speed off
>   into the distance.

Even today the steam whistle continues to exert its fascination. In a contemporary symbolist poem, Mekeel McBride's "Red Letters," the whistle of a passing freight train reminds the poet of a lost lover.

Whistles in the movies: from Edison to Disney

Hollywood has always loved trains, not merely for their own sake but as a locus for dramatic events of other kinds. Thus it is not surprising that steam trains—and of necessity steam whistles—figure in numerous American films. The list of railroad-related films is long, and extends backward to the earliest days of the American cinema. The film which created the genre, the very first "blockbuster" film, was *The Great Train Robbery,* shot by Edwin S. Porter in 1903 for Thomas Edison's studio. D. W. Griffith began his career with several short films on railroading themes, including *The Lonedale Operator* (1911) and *A Girl and her Trust.* (1912). In 1923 Hal Roach Studios made a short comedy, *The Noon Whistle*, starring Stan Laurel. In 1927 J. P. McGowen made *Red Signals* and Buster Keaton made *The General,* the latter regarded by many as the greatest railroading film of all time and certainly the funniest. Seven of its eight reels were devoted to a single locomotive chase, the longest ever filmed.

These were of course silent films, and whatever steam whistle sounds the audience may have heard were provided by the theater organist from the repertoire of his "toy box" or percussion department. With the arrival of synchronized sound in the late 1920's, theater audiences could hear the actual sound of locomotive whistles being blown. Perhaps the first film to exploit sound in this fashion was *Danger Lights* (1929), a compendium of high camp cinematic cliches, redeemed only by extraordinary footage of Milwaukee Road steam locomotives in action. Many others followed, including *Wild Boys of the Road* (Warner Bros., 1933), *Phantom Express* (Majestic Pictures, 1932), *Paradise Express* (1936), *The Broadway Limited* (United Artists, 1941), *Union Pacific* (Universal Pictures, 1939), *Denver & Rio Grande* (Paramount, 1952), *The Titfield Thunderbolt,* (Ealing Studios, 1952), *The Train* (1964), *Emperor of the North* (20th Century Fox, 1973), and *Runaway Train* (1985). By 1985, unfortunately, Hollywood had become dieselized, and a few seconds of the monotone eructations of a diesel locomotive air horn are more than sufficient for most whistle enthusiasts. Add to this list of rail-

The Steam Whistle In Popular Culture

THE ALICE AND JERRY BOOKS

READING FOUNDATION SERIES

ENGINE WHISTLES

MABEL O'DONNELL

Elementary Supervisor, Aurora, Illinois

Illustrated by

Florence and Margaret Hoopes

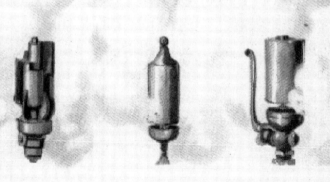

ROW, PETERSON AND COMPANY

NEW YORK CITY   EVANSTON, ILLINOIS   SAN FRANCISCO

From 1942 onward, hundreds of thousands of schoolchildren honed their reading skills on the Alice and Jerry series of readers. This is the title page of the fifth grade version. The small drawings of steam whistles are unusually realistic, especially the five-chime steptop.

road-centered films the innumerable films in which trains serve merely to provide a stage for events of another kind, two of the most memorable being David Lean's three-hanky weeper *Brief Encounter* (1945) and Alfred Hitchcock's spooky *Strangers on a Train* (1951).

Non-railroad films in which a steam whistle is featured are rare. One such is *Steamboat 'round the Bend*, a 1939 film by John Ford that concludes with a dramatic steamboat race, and of course, a great deal of collateral whistling. Another is the 1994 film *Maverick*, wherein much of the action takes place aboard the sternwheeler *Lauren Belle*, which is not, however, fitted with the traditional three-bell chime of Mississippi riverboats, but with what appears to be an 8" single-bell Lunkenheimer chime.

It must be admitted that in all of the foregoing films, the whistle plays at most a peripheral role, providing nothing more than an occasional sound effect. Surprisingly, there exists a film—perhaps the only such example—in which a steam whistle has a "speaking part," i.e., a role comparable in importance to that of a human bit player. The film is the fictionalized documentary *The Whistle at Eaton Falls* (Columbia Pictures, 1951), produced by Louis de Rochemont and directed by Robert Siodmak. It deals with troubled labor-management relations in a small New England town (actually Portsmouth, New Hampshire). A blue-collar labor leader suddenly finds himself in charge of a failing factory, and is compelled to close the plant in order to save it. The silent factory whistle—actually a rather splendid two-bell Fitts gong—symbolizes lost jobs to the townsfolk, and the plot revolves about their efforts to get it to blow again. You can be confident that it does.

When speaking of steam whistles and the cinema, a place of honor must be reserved for the animation art of Walt Disney. Disney was incomparably the greatest fan the reciprocating steam engine ever had. In his work the playful anthropomorphization of the steam whistle reaches its zenith; he was the first person to endow a steam whistle with an expressive face and a conical hat. This interest grew out of his boyhood experience. His first job was selling tobacco, candy, and newspapers on passenger trains of the Missouri Pacific, and for the rest of his life he retained his fascination with the railroads and everything associated with them.[10] He built (and lovingly operated) a one-eighth scale live steam railroad in his backyard, and named the locomotive *Lilly Belle* after his wife, perhaps as an indication of its rank in his affections. His chief animator Ward Kimball, not to be outdone, had a narrow-gauge railroad of prototype dimensions running around his home. Steam engines provided Disney with a rich source of comic inspiration and form a recurring motif in his output. This is especially evident in the early silent films, which are filled with the rhythmic pulsing, thrusting, and oscillation of machinery in motion.

Self-actuating anthropomorphic steam whistles in action, from Steamboat Willie, *Disney's first synchronized sound cartoon and Mickey Mouse's debut. © Disney Enterprises, Inc.*

The Steam Whistle In Popular Culture

The coming of sound in 1927 afforded Disney an opportunity to complement this visual music with the actual music of the steam whistle, the voice of the steam engine. In 1928 he and animator Ub Iwerks created the first cartoon with a fully synchronized sound track. It was called *Steamboat Willie*, a burlesque of Buster Keaton's earlier silent film *Steamboat Bill, Jr.*, and it marked the first appearance of Mickey Mouse in the form that became known throughout the world. In the film Mickey and Minnie transform the cargo of a riverboat, including livestock, into an impromptu band playing "Turkey in the Straw." Three whistles on the roof of the pilot house join in the general merriment. Animated whistles in the Disney tradition, self-actuated and speaking in convulsive yawps, live on today in the leader for Jay Leno's "Tonight" show.

Disney's comic image of a whistle was powerfully reinforced by the 1939 film *The Wizard of Oz*, in which the Tin Woodsman's head was capped by a funnel. Indeed, the notion of a whistle with a funnel-like top resonates strongly with the popular belief that whistles are made by tinkers or tinsmiths, and riveted together much like the Tin Woodsman himself. This belief is not without justification. The accompanying figure shows a rare and curious all-iron longbell whistle made by Lunkenheimer ca. 1912. The method of manufacture clearly derives from boiler fabrication, and the resemblance to the body of the Tin Woodsman could hardly be more apparent. In fact, as we have seen, the bells of many types of whistles were made from rolled sheet stock until roughly 1880, when seamless brass tubing at last became widely available. In no other case, however, was the seam so visible nor were the rivets so prominent.

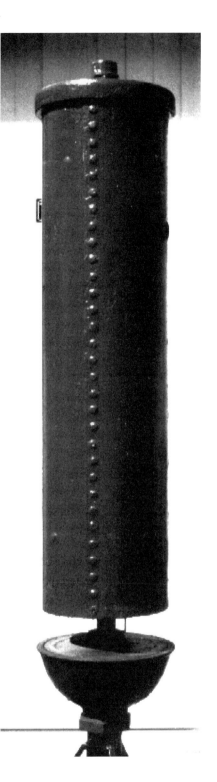

An all-iron long-bell Lunkenheimer plain whistle with riveted bell. Photo by Harry Barry.

Whistles in art and illustration: the road to kitsch

Graphic depictions of the steam whistle tend to fall into one of two principal categories: (a) nostalgic or sentimental portrayals of what might be called the Steam Age Milieu, in which the steam whistle appears only by inference, as it were, from its effects on the people depicted, or (b) illustrations from the world

The Tin Woodsman from The Wizard of Oz.

Popular calendar art of the 1960's: a sentimental reverie on boyhood in rural America.

of commercial or advertising art in which the image of the steam whistle performs one of the symbolic functions previously discussed.

Before there were steam whistles, however, there were steam trains, and whatever else a steam train may be, it is a compelling visual object. As a result, railroads and the railroading environment have captured the attention of artists ever since 1844, the year in which J. M. W. Turner painted his magnificent *Rain, Steam, and Speed: The Great Western Railway.*

Fittingly, the genre of railroad painting has flourished more vigorously in the U.S. than anywhere else, led by George Inness' seminal work *The Lackawanna Valley,* painted ca. 1854.[11] These great 19th century works set a standard of artistic merit within the genre which has never been exceeded, and it could be argued that the trend has been downhill ever since. Nevertheless there was at least one major

American artist of the 20th century sensitively attuned to the railroad environment, and that was Edward Hopper. His hundreds of works in the genre span his entire working life, from 1900 to 1965.

For explicit depictions of the steam whistle itself, however, or of whistle-related events in everyday life, one must turn to commercial artists and illustrators. By far the best of these portrayals is John Falter's painting, *The Noon Whistle* (see color insert). Falter was a well known illustrator of the 1950's and 1960's, renowned for his *Saturday Evening Post* covers, and second in popularity only to Norman Rockwell. In 1975 he was commissioned by the Minnesota Mining & Manufacturing Co. to create a series of six paintings commemorating the American Bicentennial. This one depicts with a wealth of detail the lunch hour scene in a typical American mill town around the turn of the century. The mill workers take advantage of their few minutes in the sun to loaf, to doze, to flirt, and to play games, while across

The Steam Whistle In Popular Culture

the street in their row houses other family members cook and clean. In the middle distance stretches the urban landscape of the industrial Northeast with its myriad factories and smokestacks, while in the background rise the timeless foothills of the Berkshires or the Adirondacks. It is a wonderfully warm and appealing portrait, a reverie about industrial America as we wish it had been. There is no hint of dissatisfaction, discord or exploitation, no poverty, crime, labor strife, or class struggle. The evocation of nostalgia doesn't get much better than this.

Many notches below Falter we encounter such works as *The Whistle* by David Mankin, one of numerous similar depictions (see previous page). This monochrome print was commissioned ca. 1960 by the Patrons State Bank & Trust Co. of Tennessee as one of a portfolio of ten called "Trailing the High Iron." We are now fully immersed in sentimental kitsch; almost no cliche has been overlooked. The barefoot lad with straw hat, fishing with bamboo pole beside the river bank, waves to the passing train, which responds with a friendly blast on the whistle. This vision of boyhood in rural America embodies some of our most enduring myths, and only the most cynical would say that it is altogether false. The fact that the engineer, who controls the whistle, sits on the right side of the cab and could not in reality see the boy, does nothing to diminish the popular appeal of this sort of image.

Surprisingly, a number of commercial artists have had considerable difficulty in rendering the implements of the Industrial Age with a degree of veracity which would satisfy the mechanically inclined. Consider for example the printmakers Nathaniel Currier and James Ives, who flourished from 1854 to 1880, and functioned as quasi-official portraitists of 19th century America. The color insert contains a reproduction of their well known print "The American Express Train." The most interesting thing about it from the standpoint of the engineer is that the locomotive is a mechanical absurdity. The artist seems not to have grasped that the width of the locomotive and cars is more than twice the separation of the rails on a standard gauge railroad. The driving wheels of a real locomotive sit under the boiler, not alongside it. Instead he has

placed the wheels and tracks at the outer extremities of the machine, as if it were a farm wagon. The result is a locomotive with running gear reduced to a thin plane of two-dimensional levers and cranks, and a track gauge which is apparently ten feet wide.

Depictions of steam whistles are often equally uninformed. A few of them, however, are not, such as those in the forementioned Coca-Cola advertisements (see color insert). Unlike most popular depictions of whistles, these are quite accurate, suggesting that the artist had either the original or an engraving of it at hand in his studio. The whistles are readily identifiable as American Steam Gauge & Valve Co. plain whistles of the long-bell variety, the first ca. 1930 and the second ca 1900. The only point on which the paintings can be faulted is that the whistles are apparently in operation even though their valve handles have not been pulled! Other depictions are substantially correct but inaccurate in minor details. And still others are entirely fanciful, and bear almost no relation to actual whistles, but only to the artist's intuitive notion of what a whistle should look like. Thus popular depictions of whistles run the gamut from the literally exact to the wildly imaginative, as we shall see.

Because of their association with factories in the public mind, steam whistles were frequently pictured on magazine covers during the years of the Great Depression. The color insert contains a rather fanciful depiction from the cover of the January, 1934 issue of the long-defunct *American Magazine*. The smiling lad with wings, although not a diapered infant, apparently represents the incoming year, which he joyfully welcomes with a blast of the whistle. The whistle itself, despite some improbable details, is clearly recognizable as a Lunkenheimer plain. Combined with the coveralls on the boy, the monkey wrench in his hand, and the NRA bug in the corner, it effectively suggests a nation about to be rescued from economic doldrums by the recovery of heavy industry.

A related but considerably more somber message is conveyed by the cover of *Fortune* magazine in March, 1937. Here the billowing steam from the factory whistle envelopes the smokestack and darkens the sky, suggesting (at least to captains of industry) that production has resumed in full force, and will once again become the economic engine of the nation. And once again the artist has neglected to pull the operating lever. (See color insert.)

Yet another picture in the color insert, taken from the shipping label of a popular brand of California produce, exemplifies illustrations that are largely but not entirely correct. The polished bell with its rounded top identifies the prototype as a Lunkenheimer plain whistle manufactured after 1898, although the acorn is somewhat abbreviated. The steam jet emerges from the bowl in a plausible manner, but the piping is somewhat ambiguous and the actuating valve is much too small. All in all, however, this is a fairly realistic depiction which almost everyone would recognize as a steam whistle in operation, although the connection to the peach harvest is obscure, to say the least.

Still further departure from reality is found in an advertisement for Quaker State Motor Oil from the early 1940's (facing page). Here artistic license has overwhelmed almost every vestige of mechanical accuracy. The result is not a whistle, but to the popular mind it nevertheless strongly suggests a whistle—more than strongly enough, one imagines, to support the somewhat far-fetched message.

As we descend still further into the realm of imaginative depictions, two characteristic trends emerge. The first is the replacement of conventional plain whistles (which in fact accounted for the majority of whistles in use) with whistles of the organ pipe type. The reason is not hard to discover. Organ pipe whistles have mouths which extend much less than the full circumference of the bell, typically only one-quarter to one-third of the way around. Thus they lend themselves well to anthropomorphization. The mouth is easily remolded into a semblance of a human mouth, which "speaks" in recognizable fashion when the whistle is blown. The other trend is the replacement of flat tops or round tops with conical tops. At one time whistles were in fact fabricated with conical tops. This was the prevailing style in the 1860's and 1870's, as shown here, a shop-built roundhouse whistle of 1873. But the apex angle of these conical-top whistles was much shallower than that in popular depictions. The latter are often so narrow that they resemble funnels more than whistle tops. The endpoint of this line of development, as we have seen, was the fully anthropomorphic whistle of Walt Disney's cartoons.

Whistles in music: the melody lingers

The association between music and railroads is almost as old as the railroads themselves, going back at least to 1828.[12] Throughout their century-long heyday, American railroads inspired literally thousands of popular songs. Some of these celebrate the life of the railroad worker or the hobo ("I've Been Working on the Railroad"), still others recall famous trains ("The Wabash Cannonball"), but the majority, sad to say, were inspired by disasters ("The Ballad of Casey Jones"). The main body of American railroad songs is an unremittingly morbid litany of fatal collisions, exploding boilers, failed brakes, death-dealing blizzards, catastrophic floods, washed-out bridges, collapsing trestles, split switches, and misread signals, all accompanied by tragic loss of

Shop-built whistle from the Lehigh Valley roundhouse near Nazareth, Pennsylvania, dated 1873 and representative of the designs of the era. Note the long base extension and the gracefully curved conical top. The massive top ornament is uncannily reminiscent of Kaiser Wilhelm's helmet.

I Keep Listening for the Whistles

Y OU see, this isn't my first war. I remember the last one and the day it really ended.

Well, if you thought they blew the whistles long and loud *then*, wait'll you hear 'em this time! That's the one thing I'm giving blood for and buying War Bonds and doing without a lot of the things I'd ordinarily buy.

I keep listening for the whistles. I want to hear them blow!

When they do, one of the first things *I* do is buy a new car—just as soon as they're in production. Meanwhile, I'm keeping my old car in shape—not just to keep it going, but to preserve my investment in it. I want it to be worth at least the down payment on a new car!

When I get that new car, I'm not going to forget the lessons I learned in caring for my old one.

For right now, I'm caring for my car for my country in the best way possible—with a strict diet of Quaker State. You see, Quaker State is a Pennsylvania motor oil, processed in Quaker State's four great modern refineries to make it the finest oil money can buy.

And not just Quaker State Motor Oil, but Quaker State Superfine Lubricants, too, are helping keep my car in top shape till the whistles blow. And then—they're going to help keep my new car *new* from the day I get it! Quaker State Oil Refining Corporation, Oil City, Pennsylvania.

Oil is ammunition

. . . Use it wisely

life, usually on the part of helpless women and children. These lugubrious ballads tend to be sentimental and formulaic. Nevertheless they have been widely anthologized, and have even been the subject of scholarly inquiry.[13]

A few of these songs incorporate attempts to imitate the sound of a locomotive whistle. In terms of fidelity to the original sound, these attempts are not very successful; at best they merely remind the listener of the prototype. This is partly because most of these songs were intended for guitar accompaniment, and the timbre of the guitar does not at all resemble the timbre of the steam whistle. On the other hand, the guitar has a major advantage over keyboard instruments. It permits a continuous *portamento* or "carrying" from note to note, mimicking the wailing of a train whistle. Below is an excerpt from "The Wedding of the Rails," one of many efforts to notate the sound of a steam whistle on a keyboard instrument.[14] The lyric is of the uninspired "woo-woo" variety, but at least the inverted major triad is a plausible chord for a chime whistle. The illustration serves primarily to demonstrate the inadequacy of conventional musical notation to convey the variety and subtlety of sounds which an expert whistle-blowing artist can produce.

It is a challenging exercise to collect references to the sound of railroad trains in "serious" or classical music. The primary example is of course Arthur Honegger's notorious *Pacific 231*, (i.e., Pacific 4-6-2; the French count axles rather than wheels.) This rambunctious orchestral piece created a sensation at its 1923 debut, and undeniably captures the relentless motoric impulse of a great passenger locomotive. Beyond this the list is rather short. It begins with an Elgar curiosity, *The Starlight Express*, an orchestral suite from 1915. It includes Villa Lobos' 1930 toccata "The Little Train of the Caipira," one of the four movements of *Bachiana Brasileira No. 2*, also Prokofiev's *Winter Bonfire* (1949), which opens and closes with a train ride to the skating pond. Additional train motifs can be found in the works of several American composers, including Aaron Copland, Charles Ives, George Gershwin, Percy Grainger, Samuel Barber, and Leroy Anderson. In our own time Steven Winteregg, Professor of Music at Wittenberg University, has contributed *TGV* (1991), a tribute to the "Train a Grande Vitesse" of the French National Railways. Although the train itself is electric, the piece embodies orchestral effects frankly imitative of railway stations, European train whistles and air horns, and the clickety-clack of wheels passing over rail joints and turnouts. For the rededication of Grand Central Terminal in October, 1998, Bruce Saylor of Queens College, New York, composed a concert march for wind orchestra, train whistles, sirens, and bells. In the same year Wynton Marsalis produced *Big Train*, an orchestral suite for big band, commissioned by Jazz at Lincoln Center. This twelve-part piece is filled with orchestral effects imitative of the sounds of mainline railroading, including horns and whistles of every description. Most recently Paul Winter and the Winter Consort premiered a piece for the 150th Anniversary celebration of the Pennsylvania Railroad, although details of this piece are still lacking.

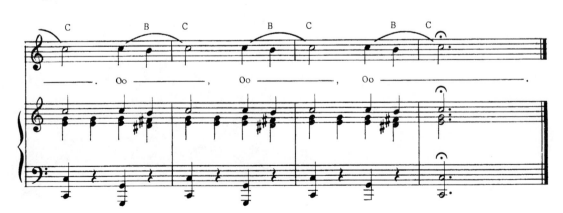

One of many efforts, partially successful at best, to represent the wail of a locomotive chime whistle on a keyboard instrument.
© 1990 by Lorraine S. Wilkinson.

Whistles in everyday speech

The reciprocating steam engine left an indelible impression on popular speech. More than two centuries after its ascendancy we still recognize and regularly employ such phrases as *getting up steam, running out of steam, letting off steam, moving under one's own steam*, and *full steam ahead*. *Building a fire under someone* still means to mobilize him (or her) for action. Even more recondite expressions survive, such as *stuck on dead center*, i.e., immobilized (e.g., by indecision) like a one-cylinder steam engine at the end of its stroke. These idioms are relics embedded in our language, their origins and derivations probably forgotten, but their meaning remembered. Railroading in particular, the principal American enterprise of the 19th century, has left us a rich legacy of idioms such as *railroaded, sidetracked, backtracking, on the right track, having the right of way, being in the clear, giving (someone) the green light, making the grade, spinning one's wheels, going off the rails*, and *reaching the end of the line*. Thus it is curious that the steam whistle, quite literally the "Voice of the Iron Horse" has left so small a legacy of vernacular speech. This legacy appears to consist of one gorgeous wittticism, a few authentic compounds, and a number of other compounds and phrases which on close scrutiny turn out to be spurious.

The gorgeous witticism is due to Mark Twain, who described a braggart or blowhard as "a four-foot whistle on a two-foot boiler." It would be hard to improve on this as a simile for the disparity between claim and performance. The only phrase worthy to stand alongside it is the Texas description of an impecunious rancher as "All hat and no cattle." The compounds authentically related to the steam whistle include *whistle punk*, a youth who signals the operation of a donkey engine in a logging operation, and *whistle stop*, a railway station of such slight importance that trains stop there only on signal. Almost all other idioms embodying the word *whistle*, such as *whistling down the wind* and *wet your whistle*, turn out on examination to refer to whistling by the human mouth. That leaves a small residue of compounds and phrases which at first glance appear to refer to steam whistles, but which in fact do not.

Typical of these spurious compounds is *whistle-blower*, one who exposes a secret or illicit activity. A moment's reflection, however, shows that this is unquestionably a sports metaphor and the whistle in question belongs to the referee. It is the referee, after all, who demands that participants in the game play by the rules. A somewhat subtler case is the expression *I don't give a hoot* (or *two hoots*). The authoritative Oxford English Dictionary (OED) recognizes *hoot* as the sound of a vehicle's horn or siren, and *hooter* as a factory siren or steam whistle, especially one which signals the hours of work. Thus it seems plausible that the expression refers to the sound of a steam whistle. Reading further, however, we discover that *hoot* also means "the smallest amount, a scrap or whit," and this is undoubtedly the intended sense.

That leaves the well known vernacular phrase *bells and whistles*. The OED attributes this phrase to computer programmers, who are inclined to adorn their programs with speciously attractive but superfluous features. This fails to explain where the computer programmers borrowed it, since computers contain neither bells nor whistles. In fact its use is far wider than the OED suggests, and almost certainly predates the computer era. Automobile salesmen have used it for decades to denote accessories of marginal or dubious utility, and lawyers use it to denote largely ornamental paragraphs in legal documents. At first glance it appears to derive from railroad practice, but this is unlikely to be the case. No steam locomotive in ordinary service ever carried more than (or less than) one bell and one whistle. Additional bells and whistles were not an option. The only place these are seen is on tourist locomotives restored to please an ignorant public rather than to adhere to historical authenticity, or on locomotives used on railfan trips, where the engineer may have installed his personal whistle in addition to the one regularly fitted. A much more plausible explanation has been offered by John Bowditch, Curator of Industry at the Ford Museum in Dearborn, Michigan. Bowditch suggests that the phrase comes from the language of the band organ or theater organ, such as those manufactured by Orchestrion and Wurlitzer. These instruments regularly included a department called the "toy box," which contained all the non-musical noisemakers and endeavored to simulate (among much else) bell and whistle sounds encountered in the everyday acoustic environment. The purchaser of the organ had license to specify how elaborate this department should be, i.e., which and how many of each type were to be included in its complement of noisemakers. Thus "all the bells and whistles" meant an instrument which incorporated as many as of these sound effects as the manufacturer could provide.

Toot! A roadside sign. Photo by Harry Barry

The Steam Whistle In Popular Culture

Contemporary whistle manufacturing at Cincinnati Valve Co.

2. Foundry work begins with the preparation of molds. Here patterns for the two halves of a whistle bowl and base are laid on molding boards before embedding in molding sand.

1. Foundry workers at Cincinnati Valve Co. charge the pouring ladle with molten bronze from the furnace, in preparation for casting a batch of whistle parts.

3. A worker carefully places sand cores in the mold. These cores produce the holes, hollows, and negative spaces within the finished casting.

4. The two halves of the mold are locked together, and the closed molds are filled from the pouring ladle.

5. A rough-cast whistle bell is machined on the lathe.

6. A batch of small whistles undergoes final assembly.

7. A finished six-inch whistle awaits packing and shipment. Photos by Larry Spreckelmeier.

5 Whistle Manufacturers and Their Products

The supreme law of the Republic of Technology is convergence, the tendency for everything to become more like everything else.

— Daniel Boorstin

Introduction

In the two previous chapters we have encountered many of the principal manufacturers of steam whistles, at least by name. Those chapters were addressed primarily to the industrial archeologist, the historian of science, and the sociologist. They focused on the uses of whistles, both real and symbolic. In this chapter and the three chapters that follow it, the focus shifts. Henceforth we address primarily the collector, the conservator, and the curator, and undertake a more systematic study of the whistles themselves and the firms which produced them. We enumerate the principal manufacturers of steam whistles, give brief summaries of their corporate histories, and depict and describe the whistles they manufactured, with particular emphasis on the time evolution of the product line. We hope this information will prove useful to the collector in acquisition, attribution, dating, and evaluation.

The problems of identification and dating are particularly vexing. It must be admitted that most steam whistles seem stupefyingly similar to the novice. For that matter, most red wines seem stupefyingly similar to the untrained palate. Yet the wine lover who has attained a high degree of connoisseurship can not only tell a Burgundy from a Bordeaux, he can unhesitatingly distinguish a 1985 Chateau l'Arrosee from a 1989 by its bouquet, acidity, finish, etc. In like manner, the experienced whistle enthusiast can not only tell a Lunkenheimer from a Powell, he can distinguish a 1901 Lunkenheimer from a 1905 Lunkenheimer by the shape of the acorn, the pattern of the lever, the style of the markings, etc. What is important about this example is that these skills can be acquired by patient study, observation and experience. We offer the reader as much of this experience as can be conveyed within the pages of a book. For the rest, he must learn in the same manner as those who preceded him: by attending auctions, by studying trade catalogs, by talking with fellow enthusiasts, by asking innumerable questions, and—let it be said—by making mistakes, quite possibly including some costly ones.

Our first task is to determine which firms sold whistles. For this we turn to that sturdy handmaiden of American industry, the *Thomas Register of American Manufacturers*. We choose the edition of 1905-6, which represents sufficiently well the peak years of whistle production in the U.S. Under the heading "WHISTLES" there are 56 entries. When this list is purged of entries that do not concern us, such as makers of toy whistles and teakettles, 45 entries remain. These are displayed in the table on the next page, arranged in alphabetical rather than the geographical order in which they originally appeared. Note that manufacturers are heavily clustered in the industrial Northeast, as might be expected. Note too the relatively small capitalization of those firms not manifestly associated with some larger industry. At its largest, the market for steam whistles was not very large.

The *Thomas Register* is a good place to start but a bad place to stop. It provides a representative cross-section of the whistle manufacturing industry just after the turn of the century, but not an exhaustive one. In the first place, inclusion in *Thomas* is discretionary not mandatory, and a number of manufacturers chose not to be listed, or to be listed under another heading. Some of these omitted firms had negligibly small output and may deservedly be ignored, but others were whistle manufacturers of

DOMESTIC MANUFACTURERS OF STEAM WHISTLES
Excerpted from Thomas' Register of American Manufacturers, 1905-1906

Name	Address	City	State	Size	Specialty
American Steam Gauge & Valve Mfg. Co.	-	Boston	MA	A	chime, steam
Ashcroft Mfg. Co.	85 Liberty St.	New York	NY	A	chime, steam
Ashton Valve Co.	271 Franklin	Boston	MA	A	steam
Belfield & Co., H.	435 No. Broad	Philadelphia	PA	AA	steam
Belknap Mfg. Co.	-	Bridgeport	CT	C	steam
Brightman Machine Co.	-	Cleveland	OH	D	steam
Buckeye Iron & Brass Works	-	Dayton	OH	AA	steam
Central Brass Works	322 W. Pearl	Cincinnati	OH	D	steam
Crane Co.	-	Chicago	IL	AAAA	steam, alarm
Crosby Steam Gage & Valve Co.	95 Oliver	Boston	MA	AA	chime, steam, locomotive, gong
Detroit Shipbuilding Co.	-	Detroit	MI	AAAA	steam
Eastwood Wire Mfg. Co.	-	Belleville	NJ	A	chime, steam
Eaton, Cole & Burnham	253 Broadway	New York	NY	AAAA	chime, steam
Fairbanks Co.	416 Broome	New York	NY	AAAA	steam
Farnan Brass Works, Mrs. M.A.	25 Center	Cleveland	OH	A	steam
Fewlass Leen Brass & Iron Co.	456 E. 2nd	Cincinnati	OH	D	chime
Fullmer & Co., A.J.	-	Camden	NJ	A	steam
Garratt & Co., W.T.	142 Fremont	San Francisco	CA	AA	steam
Hays Mfg. Co.	-	Erie	PA	A	steam
Jarecki Mfg Co.	-	Erie	PA	AAAA	steam
Kelly & Jones Co.	135 Water	Pittsburgh	PA	AA	steam
Kinsley Mfg. Co.	20 South Ave.	Bridgeport	CT	D	steam
Lonergan Co., J.E.	211 Race St.	Philadelphia	PA	AA	chime, steam
Lunkenheimer Co.	Beekman & Waverly	Cincinnati	OH	AA	chime, steam, alarm
Mansfield Mfg. Co.	57 First Ave.	Pittsburgh	PA	B	steam
McNab & Harlin Mfg. Co.	56 John St.	New York	NY	AAA	steam
Nelson, Charles	439 E. 10th	New York	NY	D	steam
Ohio Brass Co.	-	Mansfield	OH	AA	steam
Pittsburgh Brass Mfg. Co.	107 Wood	Pittsburgh	PA	D	steam
Powell Co., Wm.	-	Cincinnati	OH	A	chime, steam
Queen City Brass & Iron Works	-	Cincinnati	OH	B	chime, steam
Regester Sons, Inc.	43 West Holliday	Baltimore	MD	A	steam
Schaeffer & Budenberg Mfg. Co.	-	Brooklyn	NY	D	chime, steam
Scott Valve Co.	32 W. Randolph	Chicago	IL	D	steam
Sherwood Mfg. Co.	34 Washington	Buffalo	NY	B	steam
Springfield Brass Co.	82 So. Limestone	Springfield	OH	E	steam
Star Brass Mfg. Co.	108 E. Dedham St.	Boston	MA	A	chime
Swift Lubricator Co.	-	Elmira	NY	B	steam
Thomas Brass & Iron Co.	-	Waukegan	IL	A	chime, steam
Union Water Meter Co.	-	Worcester	MA	B	gong, steam
Vulcan Works	-	Chester	PA	B	chime, steam
Walworth Mfg. Co.	132 Federal	Boston	MA	AAAA	steam, alarm

importance and their omission is a serious limitation. Chief among these are the Hancock Inspirator Co., a division of Manning, Maxwell & Moore, Inc. of New York, and the Nathan Manufacturing Division of Wegner Machinery Co. of Long Island City, New York. These two firms were the principal 20th century manufacturers of locomotive whistles, and both elected not to register in this category. Furthermore, many whistles crossed our borders, but manufacturers outside the U.S. are not listed in *Thomas*. In particular, the northern tier of states saw a steady influx of whistles from Airchime in Vancouver, British Columbia, Morrison Brass in Toronto, Penberthy in St. Catherine's, Ontario, and McAvity & Sons in St. John, New Brunswick. Ships of U.K. registry brought to our shores whistles by Steven & Struthers of Glasgow, Smith-Hyson of Nottingham, Shipham of London, Willett Bruce of Liverpool, and P.T. John of Australia, among others. For these and other omitted firms one must seek information elsewhere.

Finally, a listing restricted to a single year—even though that year was probably the zenith of whistle manufacture—gives at best an instantaneous snapshot of the industry. It necessarily omits manufacturers who perished before publication, as well as whistle manufacturers not yet established. Those who came after 1906, e.g., Compressed Air Co. (CACO), Fulton, and Inter-State, manufactured primarily air whistles and automobile exhaust whistles, not steam whistles. But at least three firms of historical interest expired before 1906. The most important of these was the Miles Greenwood Co. of Cincinnati, perhaps the first domestic whistle manufacturer, but best remembered as the place where Frederick Lunkenheimer, progenitor of the vast Lunkenheimer clan, served his American apprenticeship. The Greenwood foundry was allegedly destroyed by Union forces early in the Civil War because it furnished rifles to the Confederacy. Hayden, Gere & Co. of New York City and Haydenville, Massachusetts, was also making whistles of unique design as early as 1866, but does not seem to have survived much past 1890. Needless to say, whistles by these two makers are exceedingly rare and much prized by collectors. Finally, the short-lived Ashley Engineering Co. of Hawthorne, New Jersey, was formed ca. 1892 to exploit the inventions of Frank Ashley. These included whistle bells which were spun or drawn rather than cast, affording great economies of construction. Apparently buyers preferred tradition to economy, because no Ashley whistles are known to have survived.

Even those listings which are included must be interpreted with caution. In particular, it is not possible to infer the importance of the corporation as a manufacturer of whistles from the amount of its capitalization. Obviously the Detroit Shipbuilding Co., one of the largest companies listed, did not derive the bulk of its revenues from whistle manufacture, and in fact whistles bearing its imprint are quite rare. The same is true of most other listings as well. Indeed, one would be hard put to name a firm that manufactured *only* whistles; the sole possibility that comes to mind is the highly idiosyncratic Kinsley Mfg. Co. of Bridgeport, Connecticut. In the

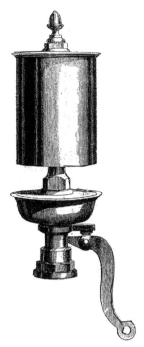

Hayden, Gere & Co. was one of several manufacturers that perished before publication of the 1905 Thomas Register. This classic post-Civil War design is from its 1866 catalog. For other examples of its wares, see figure on page 26.

THE ASHLEY DRAWN & SPUN BELL STEAM WHISTLES.

These whistles are shown below, have a clear tone and are finely finished in composition metal. The special feature is the bell which instead of being cast and turned is drawn from sheet metal and attached to the cup of the whistle in a very firm and substantial manner thus making a whistle equal in tone, design, and utility to any made, and for considerable less money.

The larger sizes such as 4 and 6 inches, are spun instead of drawn. These whistles are as fine in appearance as any made, much stronger, neater and cheaper.

MANUFACTURED BY
ASHLEY ENGINEERING CO.,
HAWTHORNE, N. J.

Ashley Engineering Co. was another whistle manufacturer that did not survive into the 20th century.

final analysis, a steam whistle is nothing more than a boiler accessory, and almost every firm that made whistles also offered a more or less complete line of boiler and engine fittings, not to mention other engineering specialties. The materials and methods of manufacture of a lubricator or a safety valve, for example, are essentially similar to those of a whistle, and potential customers are likely to be drawn from the same sector of industry.

As a further complication, it is often difficult to distinguish between firms that were primary or original manufacturers of whistles, and those that merely jobbed whistles made elsewhere. Outsourcing of whistles was almost never publicly acknowledged by the resellers, and identifying the true manufacturer is often a challenge to the scholar. These secondary sources fall into several classes. In the first class are large industrial supply houses such as Eaton, Cole & Burnham and the Fairbanks Co., both of New York, neither of which ever manufactured whistles at all or pretended to. Nevertheless they deserve mention because they occasionally imprinted their house brand on whistles made by others. Moreover, their catalogs provide valuable resource material. Fairbanks' massive 1906 catalog is perhaps the most complete and exhaustive record of whistle types commercially available in that year, including several whose manufacturers do not appear in *Thomas*.

Another class consists of purveyors of boiler fittings who found it unprofitable to maintain full product lines of their own, and filled the odd niche of demand by jobbing whistles of more specialized manufacturers. To name one example among many, American Steam Gauge & Valve offered its own line of plain and single-bell three-chime whistles, but simultaneously jobbed small four-chime whistles by Kinsley. Furthermore, as the demand for new whistles began to dwindle, certain firms that had previously manufactured their own whistles abandoned the effort as unprofitable and switched exclusively to jobbing. Chief among these was the Crane Co., possibly the nation's largest manufacturer of valves and pipe fittings, with a long and honorable history of independent whistle manufacturing going back at least to 1874. Yet from 1930 onward Crane jobbed only whistles made by Buckeye, although it marked them with its own name.

Finally, certain firms that were fully capable of making whistles, and that manufactured a wide variety of closely allied products, elected not to make whistles at all. The most notable of these was the giant Walworth Manufacturing Co. of Boston, a maker of brass and iron goods for the steamfitting and plumbing trades. Despite its size and prominence, it appears that Walworth never manufactured a steam whistle of its own. It carried a great variety of whistles in its catalogs for half a century or more, but the plain whistles were made by Star Brass, the chime whistles by Crosby or Kinsley, and the gong whistles by Union Water Meter. Some of these were even marked with the Walworth logo, but the discerning collector will not be deceived. All in all, the practice of jobbing was so widespread, and the web of commercial agreements so tangled, that the historian and industrial archeologist are often confronted with difficult problems in attribution. Merely to identify the true makers of jobbed whistles is often a test of scholarship and connoisseurship.

On the other hand, the identification of whistles sold directly by their manufacturers is usually not difficult. Most major manufacturers marked their whistles, and the experienced collector soon learns where to look for these markings. Most marks are in plain text, but a few are enigmatic, such as the interlocking C's of the Crane Company, the back-to-back W's of Westinghouse Air Brake, and the encircled S of the Cincinnati Brass Works. A certain minority of manufacturers, however, did not sign their products, or did so only erratically. Two Canadian manufacturers, McAvity and Morrison, were especially bashful in this regard, and a third, Penberthy, was highly inconsistent in its practices. In other cases, marks may have been deliberately omitted to conceal the origin of whistles resold through supply houses, and in still other cases marks may have been obliterated by wear or abuse, or effaced by well-intentioned but ignorant restorers. All in all, perhaps 40% of the whistles the collector encounters will not carry useful markings.

In the absence of marks, identification and attribution depend heavily on access to archival materials, and especially to trade catalogs. These are among the more reliable tools of industrial archeology, and the most valuable resource a collector can have is a voluminous file of trade catalogs, either originals or photocopies. Original catalogs tend to be rare and costly, and moreover they contain hundreds of pages of irrelevant material. Thus the collecting fraternity is bathed in a continual flux of photocopied catalog pages, circulating from collectors who have them to those who do not. This generous sharing of resource materials is one of the more admirable traits of whistle enthusiasts as a group. For many years this exchange was free and informal, but in recent years the demand for archival resource materials has grown so great that efforts arc currently being made to establish a centralized archive, with modest fees for reproduction.

A minor annoyance to historians and scholars, however, is that catalog numbers are not a reliable guide to date of issue. Some manufacturers seem to have issued a new catalog to accompany each major revision of prices. The most conscientious of these was the Lunkenheimer Co., which may have issued as many as 30 consecutively numbered catalogs prior to World War II. Even this frequent revision was insufficient for Lunkenheimer, which often inserted a footnote on each page warning customers that certain prices were now out of date and a current price list should be consulted. At the other extreme were manufacturers who maintained the same catalog number for decades, perhaps on the grounds that the goods described therein had not changed and therefore the catalog need not change either. Catalog No. 11 of the Powell Co. for example seems to have been in effect at least from 1936 to 1954, if not longer. Examples of Star Brass catalog No. 10 are dated as early as 1923 and as late as 1933. In such cases it is not sufficient to inspect merely photocopies of interior pages; one must have access to the flyleaf as well in order to search for indications of revision or edition number.

Given these sources of error and confusion, how is one to assess the relative importance of various whistle manufacturers? No authoritative census of whistles has ever been taken. Most production records have long since vanished, and in any case their interpretation has been forgotten. The author, however, can contribute some anecdotal evidence from his own experience. Of the first one hundred whistles I acquired, mostly during the 1970's and 80's when my collecting efforts were largely unselective, thirteen were made by Lunkenheimer or its predecessor, ten by Buckeye, seven by

Westinghouse Air Brake, six each by Crosby and Powell, four by Lonergan, three each by Crane, Fulton, Hancock, and Star Brass, two each by American, Kinsley, Nathan, and Reliance, and one each by Ashton, Bass Foundry, Buell, Greenwood, Interstate, Lorain, New York Air Brake, Penberthy, Schaeffer & Budenberg, Sinker-Davis, Steven & Struthers, and Western Brass. Thirteen more whistles were certainly or probably built by railroad shops; two more by private individuals; and seven have thus far defied attribution. The sample is far too small, and the author's experience far too individualized, to claim quantitative accuracy for this breakdown. Nevertheless I believe it is qualitatively correct, at least insofar as the half-dozen principal makers are concerned. There is no question that whistles made by Lunkenheimer and Buckeye are more commonly encountered than any others. It is noteworthy that neither of these firms was especially renowned for the manufacture of locomotive whistles, the application in which most collectors first became acquainted with the steam whistle, and that still evokes the most vivid memories. Thus we are reminded once again that the whistle belongs to the boiler, not the engine, and boilers were overwhelmingly more numerous than steam locomotives, and indeed more numerous than steam engines of any kind.

As we proceed, certain generic properties of whistle manufacturers will emerge, of which the most prevalent is inertia. One may view this as adherence to tradition or reluctance to change, but in either case there are few industries in which the product line evolved more slowly or innovation was more strongly resisted. Several manufacturers produced the same whistle essentially without alteration for half a century or more, and at least one manufacturer has maintained the same product numbering system for more than a century. This makes the task of dating such whistles a practical impossibility, but it also makes it irrelevant. Some slight justification for this inertia can be found on the production floor. Once the tracer or template lathes are set up to produce a certain piece in quantity, say an ornamental acorn, it is difficult to retool them. But the habit appears to owe more to an innate conservatism on the part of both buyers and sellers (the psychological roots of which we are not equipped

Drop-lever plain whistle from the American Steam Gauge Co. 1885 catalog. Was this the first commercially made round-top whistle?

Upright-lever plain whistle from American's 1885 catalog. Note that all the hexagonal portions stand on cylindrical or conical portions below them. This design detail was characteristic of the era.

American Steam Gauge & Valve plain whistle of 1901.

to explore) than to practical necessity. How else can we explain the vigor and finality with which certain innovations—some of them quite worthy or even necessary—were rejected? For example, plain whistles of conventional design have suffered since their invention from misalignment of the bell, causing them to overblow or underblow. The forces that hold the lower lip of the bell in proper alignment over the slit must travel up the central stem and down the bell again. The obvious remedy is to support the bell at its lower end by some form of open framework or "spider," and numerous patents to this effect were filed during the great flowering of whistle improvements in the 1890's. Yet very few of these spiders ever found their way into production models, the principal exception being the longbell (4X) designs of Lunkenheimer plain whistles. More radical innovations, such as the ingenious spherical bells and drawn bells of Frank M. Ashley ca. 1895—both ideas of considerable merit—simply failed to thrive, and perished in the marketplace after a few years' exposure.

Closely coupled with this innate conservatism was a sort of imitative timidity or "me-too"-ism. The product lines of the major makers were *very* much alike, and on those rare occasions when a new product was introduced by one maker, other makers hastened to add a similar version to their lines too. A case in point is the long-bell (3X or 4X) marine whistle, which seems to have been introduced by Star Brass ca. 1902 (and was probably taken in turn from an earlier English model). Within a few years every major manufacturer had a similar line of whistles in the catalog. It would be easier to name those whistle types specific to a given manufacturer than those it shared with others. Perhaps the best example of a unique product is the "mockingbird" variable-pitch whistle, always associated with Lunkenheimer. Others (e.g., Crane and Star Brass) made so-called mockingbird whistles, but these were in fact a rather different design, and never attained the market penetration of the Lunkenheimer version. Virtually the only manufacturers exempt from this collective mimicry were those small firms such as Kinsley, Barnes, Sinker-Davis, and Union Water Meter, all of which manufactured whistles of unique design to fill a specific niche of demand and made no effort to compete with the larger full-service manufacturers.

We turn at last to brief histories of some of the principal domestic manufacturers of whistles, and to descriptions of the whistles they produced. Our treatment is not exhaustive, nor could it possibly be so. Nevertheless we have endeavored to include those manufacturers whose products the collector is most likely to encounter, and to provide sufficient diagnostic clues so that the majority of whistles can be attributed to the proper maker. Needless to say, additions and corrections from readers will be welcomed. When reading the descriptions that follow, it is well to keep in mind the various items of whistle nomenclature contained in the sidebar in Chapter 3. In particular, recall that the nominal size of a whistle, the single number which best characterizes its dimensions, is the outside diameter of its bell. The next most important number is the length of the bell, because this establishes the scale of the resonator. The overall height of a whistle, so often offered as a descriptor by the inexperienced, is essentially meaningless because it varies with the length of the bell, the elaboration of the acorn, the presence or absence of a valve, and other factors.

American Steam Gauge & Valve Manufacturing Co.

The earliest known description of the company and its products is a brief advertisement in *Asher & Adams' Pictorial Album of American Industry*, issued in 1876 to commemorate the nation's centennial exhibition. Trade catalogs from the manufacturer itself are difficult to find, however, and the only dated examples known to have survived are from 1885, 1901, and 1908. There is also an undated catalog sheet from a much later date. The descriptions which follow are based entirely on this fragmentary evidence.

The company was established in 1851 and incorporated in 1854 as the American Steam Gauge Company, with headquarters at 46 Chardon Street, Boston. It billed itself as the "Original Steam Gauge Company," and from 1859 onward it enjoyed exclusive manufacturing rights to the Lane patent improvement on the original Bourdon steam gauge. In the fullness of time it also manufactured steam engine indicators, oilers and lubricators, polar planimeters, pantographs, speed indicators, and pop safety valves. No mention of steam whistles appeared in the 1876 advertisement, however. Two types of plain whistles were shown in the 1885 catalog, one with drop lever (i.e., a vertical valve) and one with upright lever (i.e., a horizontal valve). Curiously, they were not at all alike, and the drop lever version had a hemispherical top surmounted by a surprisingly modern acorn. This was probably the first dome-top whistle to be commercially manufactured, antedating (and perhaps inspiring) the similar designs by Lunkenheimer and Powell. The upright lever version is scarcely distinguishable from contemporaneous designs by Ashton and Crosby, except that the tip of the lever merely bears on the valve stem and is not held captive within it as in the competitive versions. Both whistles were available in sizes up to 6" diameter, and a valveless version up to 8" diameter. Bells were short, as was typical of the era, ranging in length from 1.50 to 1.67 times the bell diameter.

By 1901 the firm had become the American Steam Gauge & Valve Manufacturing Co. and had established branch offices in Chicago and New York. The line of whistles had been greatly enlarged and completely revised, and now included plain whistles with and without horizontal valves, marine service whistles with bells of length approximately three times their diameter, "original" single bell chime whistles in three versions, single bell chimes with compound valve, the obligatory three-bell chimes, variable-pitch piston whistles in both mockingbird and fire alarm versions, and a line of small organ pipe whistles. All of these whistles so closely resembled

American's long-bell plain whistle of 1901. The size and proportions of the bell strongly suggest that it was intended for marine use, although the catalog does not specify this application.

American's 1901 version of the "fire alarm" or "combination" whistle, a type also originated by Lunkenheimer.

American's 1901 version of the organ pipe whistle. Unlike their British counterparts, these were small whistles, no more than a few inches in diameter, and intended primarily for vessels such as steam launches.

American's 1901 version of the "mockingbird" whistle, a type first introduced by Lunkenheimer ca. 1895. Note the double "bowtie" fulcrum.

American Steam Gauge & Valve plain whistle of 1908, substantially redesigned since 1901. Note in particular the long, straight lever, and markings just below the top of the bell.

A single-bell chime whistle of very heavy and compact construction, intended for locomotive use. From the 1908 American catalog.

competitive versions by other manufacturers that even the specialist is challenged to find points of distinction. Nevertheless a few such points exist. The plain whistles strongly resemble those of the Crane Co. except that they lack the characteristic double "bowtie" lever fulcrum of Crane, and feature an unusually small nut on the valve access cover. They share the latter feature with Buckeye plain whistles, with which, however, they are unlikely to be confused. The long bell whistles, for some reason, have reverted to the older style of lever inserted within the valve stem. The single bell chimes, on the other hand, are identical with those of Crosby, suggesting either sincere flattery or interlocking business agreements. The mockingbird has a double lever fulcrum, a feature absent from the corresponding Lunkenheimer design, and the fire alarm has a unique tee-shaped base casting with the valve relegated to a side arm. This permits the use of a valve from the standard product line, rather than the elaborate specialized valve assembly employed by Crane, Lunkenheimer, and others. Finally, the organ pipe whistles have rectangular mouths, modeled on their British prototypes. All other U.S.-made organ pipe whistles, including those by Ashton, Crosby, and Star Brass, have semi-elliptical mouths, Morrison Brass organ pipes also have rectangular mouths, but they are manufactured in Canada. So do the organ pipes offered by McNab & Harlin, almost certainly British imports.

In 1903 the company reincorporated and relocated its general offices and factory to 208-220 Camden Street in Boston. It boasted that its plant was "the largest in the world devoted exclusively to the manufacture of gauges, valves, indicators, and kindred appliances." The boast might not withstand scrutiny, inasmuch as there were certainly nearby firms of larger capitalization engaged in very similar business, notably Crosby Steam Gage and Valve. By 1908 an additional branch office had been established in Atlanta, and the line of whistles had been extensively revised and consolidated. Only a single type of plain whistle was offered, distinguished by a rather flat bowl and a stout, squat acorn. The length of bell was standardized at twice the diameter, although longer bells were available on special order. The single bell chime whistles were still indistinguishable from the contemporaneous Crosby products, and the version with compound valve had exchanged its acorn for a starkly utilitarian cap nut. A somewhat beefier version of the latter, with a longer lever, was offered for locomotive use. The small organ pipe whistles had disappeared from the line, and in their place one found a line of single bell four-chime whistles manufactured by Kinsley, although not so identified. Finally, the three-bell chimes composed of individual plain whistles remained unchanged.

At some later date (historical evidence is lacking), American Steam Gauge & Valve Manufacturing merged with Schaeffer & Budenberg, becoming American Schaeffer & Budenberg Corporation. American whistle designs replaced those of Schaeffer & Budenberg, and only four distinct types survived the merger. Two of these were single-bell chime whistles, type 1579 with flanged inlet and without valve, and type 1583 with screwed inlet and compound valve. The other two were types 1575 and 1577 plain long-bell marine whistles, available with 3X and 4X bells. All of these retained the shallow bowl and straight lever which had characterized American whistles since 1908. All small whistles were discontinued, and only 5", 6", 8", and 10" diameters were offered.

Whistle Manufacturers and Their Products

Insofar as the available resource materials permit us to judge, American Steam Gauge & Valve seems to have functioned primarily in an imitative mode where whistles were concerned. They made competent, handsome whistles very similar to others on the market at the time, but they were responsible for no innovations that we are aware of, and never attained either the reputation or the market penetration of their better known competitors.

Ashton Valve Co.

The Ashton Valve Company of Boston was founded by Henry G. Ashton in 1871, incorporated in 1877, and reincorporated in 1916. Its main office and works were originally located at 271 Franklin Street, later at 161-179 First Street, Cambridge. Its principal products during the early years of its existence were pop safety and relief valves, on which it held certain basic patents. In 1892 or 1893 steam gauges were added to the product line, and shortly thereafter, steam whistles. By 1906 branches had been established in New York, Chicago, and San Francisco. The company quickly acquired, and maintained throughout the next three-quarters of a century, a reputation for goods of the highest quality. Ashton products were conspicuously well made, with heavy-walled castings, abundant reinforcements, and great attention to fit and finish. This made the firm a natural rival of its Boston neighbor, the larger and more diversified Crosby Steam Gage & Valve Company, *q.v.*, which also served the upper end of the market. The rivalry endured until 1946 when Crosby absorbed Ashton.

The oldest surviving Ashton trade catalog is dated 1896. It offered a line of common (i.e., plain) whistles from 1" to 10" in diameter, without valve and with side (i.e., horizontal) valve. Also offered was a line of single bell chime whistles from 2" to 12" in diameter, without valve, with upright (i.e., vertical) valve, and with side valve. As with several other manufacturers of the era, both lines of whistles are indistinguishable from the contemporaneous offerings of the Crosby Steam Gage & Valve Co. Crosby owned the fundamental patent on the single bell chime whistle, the Einig patent of 1877, but by 1896 that patent had presumably expired. Hence it is unclear whether this situation reflects a pre-existing jobbing agreement with Crosby or Ashton's position as a manufacturing licensee. On the frontispiece of the 1896 and subsequent catalogs Ashton tendered what might be construed as an apology for the arrangement: "By constant and careful attention we keep ourselves fully informed of all meritorious inventions of others, and do not hesitate to strengthen our position by purchasing such as are of value."

The 1906 catalog offered essentially the same goods, except for the introduction of a new numbering system. The plain whistles were now designated No. 90, the single bell-chimes were now designated No. 91, and a new line of organ pipe whistles with semi-elliptical mouths, also borrowed from Crosby, was designated No. 92. The only difference between the latter and Crosby's version was a very slight alteration in the shape of the domed top cover.

The 1914 catalog, however, broke completely with the past. Both plain and chime whistles were new and original designs, although the old numbering system was retained in order to maximize confusion. The valved whistles were fitted with very long straight levers, probably in response to ever-increasing boiler pressures. This also won them favor with the "whistle artists" among locomotive engineers, who welcomed

The American three-bell chime whistle, comprised of three plain whistles on a manifold of pipe fittings, and unchanged since the turn of the century. Note that the rims of the bells are aligned vertically, not the tops of the bowls, contrary to the practice of other manufacturers.

An Ashton plain whistle of 1896. The valveless plain whistle is identical except for the omission of the valve body from the base. These whistles, and all others in the Ashton line prior to 1914, were almost certainly made by Crosby, and merely jobbed by Ashton.

An Ashton No. 90 plain whistle of 1914. By this time the Ashton line has acquired some individuality. Note especially the 'cuff' or 'sleeve' on the top plate, within which slips the bell of drawn brass tubing. This is a characteristic feature of every Ashton plain whistle made subsequent to 1914.

An Ashton No. 91 single-bell chime whistle of 1914. Note the exceptionally long lever. The engraving also hints at the oversize outer diameter of the bowl.

The oversize bowl of Ashton chimes is particularly apparent in the smaller sizes. This is a 2" chime. Photo by Bruce Cynar.

the finer control these longer levers afforded. The highly ornate turn-of-the-century acorns were also supplanted by acorns of conventional design. A distinguishing feature of these whistles was that the maximum diameter of the bowl significantly exceeded the maximum diameter of the bell, even though the steam slot was correctly aligned with the lip of the bell. Usually these two diameters were made equal for esthetic reasons, giving a sort of balance or repetitive rhythm to the traditional design, but Ashton evidently thought it more important to strengthen the outer rim of the bowl. This gives Ashton whistles a characteristic and readily identifiable bottom-heavy appearance. The plain whistles, somewhat surprisingly, had bell walls of seamless drawn brass tubing rather than the traditional naval bronze or gun metal. The tubing had considerably greater wall thickness, however, than that employed in in the similarly constructed plain whistles manufactured by Buckeye.

The 1918 catalog was basically similar to its predecessor, except that Ashton now suggested that the plain whistle was better suited to freight service, whereas the chime whistle was better suited to passenger service. This was contrary to the distinction employed by most railroads at the time, which tended to assign high-pitched whistles to freight locomotives and lower-pitched whistles to passenger service. A variant of the No. 90 plain whistle was also introduced in 1918, the No. 90A with extra long bell, typically four times the bell diameter. This type quickly found application in marine service and on large factories. Finally, a line of three-bell chimes was added, designated No. 91A and composed of three individual No. 90 plain whistles. These three-bell chimes were distinguished by the use of a specially cast one-piece manifold. Ashton was one of only two domestic manufacturers (Lunkenheimer was the other) to erect its three-bell chimes on a dedicated manifold; all other manufacturers used a manifold constructed from ordinary pipe fittings. The 1928 catalog is essentially similar to the 1918 catalog, except that both plain and chime whistles have undergone some further differentiation in accord with the intended inlet pressures.

So far as is known, Ashton Valve never developed or employed a distinctive logo or hallmark. It has been suggested, however, that their initials appeared on whistles they made for the Westinghouse Air Brake Co. See the Westinghouse entry for further details.

Buckeye Iron & Brass Works

The Buckeye Iron & Brass Works was incorporated in Dayton, Ohio, on June 20, 1876. Its antecedents, however, can be traced back at least to 1838 when Horace Pease came to Dayton and built the H. & B. Pease mill, which reigned for the next thirty years as the largest distillery and milling business in Ohio. Horace Pease retired in 1854, and

An Ashton No. 90A plain whistle with extra long (4X) bell, introduced in 1918.

An Ashton No. 91 three-bell chime, ca. 1918. The manifold was specially cast, and marked just above the inlet.

Whistle Manufacturers and Their Products

the family business was taken over by his eldest son Walter. In 1861 Walter's younger brother Charles entered the business and assumed its management, relieving Walter, who promptly entered service in the Civil War. The following year, however, Charles himself entered military service and became associated with the quartermaster department in Nashville, Tennessee. Following the war he engaged in various enterprises in Kentucky and Tennessee with indifferent success, returning at last to Dayton in 1870. There he purchased the interest of S. D. Grafflin in the firm of Hoglen & Grafflin, makers of agricultural machinery, and renamed the firm Hoglen & Pease. Finally, in 1876, Pease bought out his partner and reconstituted the firm as the Buckeye Iron & Brass Works with himself as president, R. M. Anderson as vice-president and treasurer, and W. B. Anderson as secretary. In so doing he revived the name of the old Buckeye Foundry, founded in 1846 by Henry L. Shepherd and Jacob L. Shepherd. The choice of name was no accident, for the Buckeye Foundry subsequently became the firm of Shepherd & Pease, although it is not clear which member of the large and industrious Pease family is represented in the corporate name.

Initially, at least, the majority of Buckeye's revenue came from the manufacture of cottonseed, linseed oil, and castor oil processing machinery. A particular specialty was the celebrated Pease Tobacco Cutter, available in three sizes, the largest of which would cut five thousand pounds of smoking tobacco in a ten-hour shift. Also offered was the Tobacco Stem Crusher, whose purpose, forthrightly stated in Buckeye's advertising brochure, was to make stems look like leaves. But within less than a decade the manufacture of brass goods for engine builders and steamfitters surpassed the demand for agricultural machinery and became the principal component of Buckeye's trade. Near the end of the nineteenth century the firm employed almost 300 skilled workmen and occupied a large factory complex on East Third Street. The product line included iron valves, government valves, hydraulic valves, brass valves and cocks, water gauges and other specialties, and, of course, steam whistles.

Buckeye whistles were simple, serviceable, and relatively inexpensive. Their low cost may account for their ubiquity; the chances are good that the first whistle the novice collector acquires will be a Buckeye.

Buckeye's buck, with eye. This noble head adorned every page of the 1905 catalog. Unfortunately, the emblem of the state of Ohio (from which the firm took its name) is not a male deer but the fruit of the horse chestnut tree.

They were also quite attractive. Their narrow scale conformed well to the popular notion of what a whistle should look like, and the appearance of the plain whistles was further enhanced by the color contrast between the reddish bronze castings which formed the bowl and top cap and the yellow brass tubing which formed the cylindrical portion of the bell. The latter may have been a cost effective choice from the standpoint of ease of manufacture, but it was a less than ideal one from the standpoint of corrosion resistance, inasmuch as live steam will leach the minor constituents from yellow brass. Thus Buckeye plain whistles were more than usually subject to erosion and pitting at the lip of the bell, and were best confined to compressed air service.

There is much to be learned from the study of Buckeye trade catalogs. Its first illustrated catalog was issued in Dayton in September, 1883, and by good fortune a copy has survived. It showed plain whistles without valves, with both iron and brass bases, in sizes from 1-1/2" to 10" in diameter; also plain whistles with valves in two choices of lever fulcrum, stationary and adjustable. Although the catalog does not so state, it is probable that these early whistles had bells of rolled and soldered sheet stock, this being approximately the time of the general transition to seamless drawn brass tubing. The whistle section concluded with an offer to construct multiple-bell chimes with any number and size of plain whistles, all on a manifold of ordinary pipe fittings.

Buckeye valveless all-brass plain whistle of 1883. The appearance of the iron-based whistle was identical.

Buckeye plain whistle with valve, 1883. Note the slanting lever fulcrum cast integral with the valve body, a distinctive feature of all subsequent Buckeye whistles.

Buckeye plain whistle with valve and adjustable lever fulcrum, 1883. Although other manufacturers regarded the swiveling fulcrum as a valuable feature, Buckeye soon discontinued it in all but the iron-bodied whistle valves.

What is remarkable is the degree to which the plain whistles of 1883 resemble later Buckeye whistles. Apart from an extra curlicue in the base of the valveless whistles, these whistles are scarcely distinguishable from those sold 70 years later. The trademark features, such as the small valve access cover and the slanting support for the lever fulcrum, were already in place. There was, however, one curious feature. The upper part of the acorn did not have the usual straight sides, but was slightly bulbous or convex. This gave it a faintly mid-Eastern appearance, like an Islamic minaret or the dome of a Russian Orthodox church. If the engravings in the catalog can be relied upon, this swelling was especially pronounced in the constituents of the multiple-bell chime. In later years this anomaly was minimized, and eventually disappeared in all except the very largest whistles.

Buckeye's 1905 general catalog—a masterpiece of the engraver's art, by the way—introduced the Buckeye logotype, consisting of the initial letters of the firm name intertwined in an Art Nouveau design of Celtic intricacy (see facing page). This design appeared on the sides of iron-bodied valves of that era but not brass-bodied valves, a curious choice inasmuch as a pattern less well adapted to iron foundry practice could scarcely be imagined. Single-bell chime whistles made their first appearance, whereas the offer to construct multiple-bell chimes to order was withdrawn. This catalog also established the practice of identifying whistle types by means of the number of the engraving in the catalog, a practice followed by many other manufacturers as well. Thus Fig. 109 denoted a plain whistle with valve, Fig. 110 a chime whistle with valve, Fig. 111 a plain whistle without valve, and Fig. 112 a chime whistle without valve. Fig. 113 denoted a plain whistle similar to Fig. 111 but with an iron base, and Fig. 114 a separate whistle valve using the same internal parts as the valves integral to whistles. The Fig. 109 plain whistle with valve was offered in diameters from 1" to 8", whereas all other whistles were offered in diameters up to to 12". This numbering system was in effect at least from 1902 to 1949 and possibly longer. The plain whistle with a swiveling adjustable lever fulcrum, a genuinely useful innovation, seems to have been discontinued.

As previously remarked, the design of the whistles did not evolve at all during this period, and a whistle manufactured in 1949 is essentially indistinguishable from one manufactured in 1902. This would seem to make precise dating impossible, were it not for Buckeye's practice of stamping a two-digit number on one face of the pipe nut and/or the side of the iron lever. These numbers are widely believed to be the last two digits of the year of manufacture, although this interpretation is strongly contested by some specialists. These specialists point to Buckeye whistles of indisputable provenance and integrity which bear stamped numbers manifestly inconsistent with their era of manufacture. The author has one such whistle in his collection, a 2-inch plain with a seamed bell of rolled sheet stock (i.e., ca. 1880), but stamped "38". It is suggested instead that the stamped numbers are batch

Whistle Manufacturers and Their Products

numbers for internal use, intended merely to identify lots of mechanically compatible or interchangeable parts. This controversy has not been resolved.

The 1920 catalog shows only minor changes. The Fig. 113 iron-based whistle apparently did not meet with public favor and was dropped from the line. In its place appear Figs. 341 and 342, plain and chime whistles respectively, with integral valves and a new design of bell having a "waterfall" or rounded edge and a vestigial acorn. The bowls of these whistles, it is asserted, have been redesigned to permit easy cleanout. Apparently these new types did not meet with public favor either, because they did not appear in subsequent catalogs.

Buckeye whistles up to 4" in diameter can be found with relative ease by the collector. By contrast, those 5" in diameter or larger are rarely encountered. In most instances attribution is no problem, because Buckeyes are among the easiest of all whistles to identify. Even in the absence of markings, the relatively long bells (typically 2-1/2 times the bell diameter), the yellow brass sleeve on the plain whistles, the small nut on the valve access cover, and the diagonal slant of the integrally cast lever fulcrum are all diagnostic. So too is the swelling or bulbous acorn, on those rare occasions when it is encountered. Finally, Buckeye whistles are usually well marked, although seldom in the manner shown in their catalogs. The 1905 catalog shows the word BUCKEYE engraved on the pipe nut, and 1920 catalog shows it engraved on the side of the bowl or valve body. In fact, the engraving on Buckeye chimes usually appears on the rim of the top plate, and says BUCKEYE BRASS WORKS, DAYTON, O. Perhaps the only whistles which might be confused with Buckeyes of this era are the chime whistles of Schaeffer & Budenberg. But the latter are well marked on the side of the bowl, and in addition have a distinctive valve assembly in which the lever is held captive by the valve stem.

Attribution problems occasionally arise, however, because Buckeye seems to have made a variety of whistles that do not appear in its catalogs. A few large three-bell chimes were made for marine use, presumably as "one-off" specials. There appears to be a strong affinity between Buckeye whistles and traction engines. This was probably not the result of a formal business agreement, but it is certainly the case that many traction engines carried Buckeye whistles. Some Buckeye whistles were made in anomalous sizes. The author has in his collection a marked 1902 Buckeye chime which is ordinary in every respect except that it is 3-3/4" in diameter, a size not regularly offered by Buckeye nor by any other maker. Rarest and most curious of all was the Buckeye exhaust whistle, patented in 1924. This was an all-brass plain whistle of the organ-pipe variety with four mouths, 1-3/4" in diameter and 5-5/8" long overall. A whistle more remote from the main line of Buckeye products could scarcely be imagined. Contemporary advertisements tout its use as an alarm for fire engines, an application in which it was almost certainly inferior to an ordinary siren.

Whistle manufacturing at Buckeye seems to have died a lingering death, and pivotal events are difficult to identify. The last chime whistles were made sometime in the early 1960's. One of the few certain dates is

Buckeye's imposing three-bell chime of 1883. Note the curiously swollen acorns. Despite the abundance of nipples and couplings in the branches, the three whistles do not seem to have been aligned in accord with any discernible plan.

Art Nouveau invades the iron foundry, ca. 1905. The initial letters of the firm's name woven into an intricate monogram on the side of an iron-bodied whistle valve. Buckeye had the good sense not to apply this design to other products, and to discontinue its use in future years.

Buckeye Fig. 109 plain whistle with valve, ca. 1905. Note that the cast top plate has a small shoulder or step at its rim. Whistles were seldom if ever marked in the manner shown in this illustration.

Buckeye Fig. 110 chime whistle with valve, ca. 1905. Note that the top plate is perfectly flat. This whistle and the preceding one, Fig. 109, remained essentially unchanged for half a century or more.

Buckeye's short-lived Fig. 342 chime whistle, with 'waterfall' top plate and vestigial acorn, ca. 1920. The Fig. 341 plain whistle was essentially identical except for the partitioning of the bell.

An advertisement from the 1920's, a souvenir of Buckeye's unsuccessful excursion into the world of firefighting apparatus.

July, 1965, when Buckeye became a division of Emco-Wheaton Inc. of London, Ontario, a maker of fluid-handling products. A new consolidated manufacturing facility was established the following year at Conneaut, Ohio, 275 miles northeast of Dayton. Buckeye employees were invited to relocate there, but very few of them did. Under Emco-Wheaton leadership the line of whistles was gradually choked off, until by 1977 only the valveless plain whistle remained. Curiously, a new bare-bones utilitarian design of plain whistle appeared just as the traditional designs were phased out. The base casting and yellow brass bell were retained, but the top plate was radically simplified and the conventional cast acorn was replaced by a blind-tapped length of hexagonal bar stock, the simplest possible screw-machine product. The lever was bronze instead of steel and the name BUCKEYE appears intaglio on the valve body. Today the Buckeye Division no longer exists and Emco-Wheaton flourishes in Conneaut, its principal product being a line of automatic shutoff gasoline valves for filling stations.

Crane Co.

The Crane Bros. Manufacturing Co. of Chicago was established in 1855, probably as a bell foundry, and incorporated in 1865. The corporate trademark, not surprisingly, was a handsome engraving of a crane with a frog in its mouth. Ca. 1890 the corporate name was abbreviated to the Crane Co., and the corporation was well on its way to becoming one of the nation's largest manufacturers of valves, fittings, and plumbing supplies. By 1923 its Chicago works alone comprised 49 buildings on 151 acres, and allegedly shipped 40 carloads of products every day. The firm has never been absorbed nor taken over, and although it no longer manufactures whistles, it survives today under its own name as a member of the New York Stock Exchange. No other 19th century whistle manufacturer shares this distinction.

The earliest known Crane catalog carries the date September, 1874, and displayed a line of brass-bodied plain whistles ranging from 1" to 6" in diameter. The design was typical of the times, with slightly coned top caps, unusually small acorns, and vertical valves with downward-pointing levers. Curiously, the

Whistle Manufacturers and Their Products

Crane's crane, used as early as 1887. This device was sometimes cast in metal as a paperweight, and given by salesmen to favored customers.

The plain whistle with vertical lever from the 1874 Crane Bros. catalog.

The plain whistle with horizontal valve from the 1883 Crane Bros catalog. The plain whistles with vertical valves and without valves were essentially similar except for the bases.

whistles were offered in both "finished" and "painted" versions, the latter significantly less expensive, suggesting that the finished whistles may have been polished. Also offered was a 10" cast iron whistle and the usual line of separate whistle valves, similar to those furnished with the valved whistles.

By August, 1883 the whistle line had been substantially altered and enlarged. The brass whistles had acquired acorns of conventional appearance and horizontal valves with levers mounted on a separable fulcrum. The slightly coned top plate was retained. Since drawn brass tubing was not yet commercially available in large diameters, the bells were formed of rolled sheet stock, neatly soldered with a lap seam. With their gracefully curved levers, softly rounded contours, and elegant proportions, these whistles practically defined the classical ideal of whistle design. New to the catalog was a line of variable-pitch whistles of extremely robust construction, in sizes from 3" to 6". These were identified as mockingbird whistles, but in fact were rather different from the Lunkenheimer whistles of the same name. In the Crane version, the movable piston was actuated by a push rod protruding through a steam-tight gland at the bottom of the bowl, a type more usually called a fire alarm or combination whistle. Finally, there was the obligatory offer to build multiple-bell chime whistles with any number of whistles or size of bells. These were illustrated with acorns of an older and much more ornate style.

By 1887 Crane had built an enormous foundry between Jefferson and Desplaines Streets, just west of Chicago's Loop, and proclaimed that it was the nation's largest and most complete supplier of wrought iron pipe, steam and gas fittings, and engineers' supplies. The bells of the brass whistles were mostly unchanged except for the replacement of the conical top plate with a flat top plate, but the bowls were completely redesigned. Instead of a separable fulcrum they had a double or bowtie fulcrum cast integral with the valve body, permitting the lever to point either up or down. This double fulcrum was retained at least until 1941, and is one of the identifying marks of a

The Crane 'mocking bird' or piston whistle made its first appearance in the 1883 catalog and remained unchanged for many years thereafter. Note the crook in the piston rod which anchors the whistle lever in the closed position. In later years this whistle acquired a third external support rod, giving it a total of four ornamental acorns and an imposing appearance reminiscent of a Gothic church tower.

1883 version of the Crane Bros three-bell chime, actually quite handsome with its rimmed bells and bowls and large ornamental acorns. Note that these acorns differ from those of the plain whistle, and that the top plates are flat, not conical.

1887 version of the Crane plain whistle with valve. The valve body is unmarked, but the 'bowtie' lever fulcrum is diagnostic.

Crane's vertical two-bell chime, from the 1887 catalog. Note that it is not a true gong whistle, for the bells point in the same direction. This variant was quite short-lived, vanishing from the catalog before 1892.

Crane's rough-and-ready cast iron sawmill whistle of 1887. Although shown with a valve, the valve was sold separately.

In 1892 Crane replaced its usual piston whistle with this peculiar inverted or top-lever version. It was not a success, and appears for the last time in the 1893 catalog, after which Crane reverted to the earlier design.

Crane whistle. Among major manufacturers, Lonergan and Lunkenheimer also had double fulcrums, but these makes are easily distinguished by other means. The whistle line was further supplemented by a two-bell vertical chime in sizes from 2" through 6", and by a line of short-bodied iron sawmill whistles in sizes from 4" through 8". The line remained substantially unchanged in the 1892 and 1893 catalogs, except for the brief introduction of a bizarre variation of the piston whistle.

1897, however, saw major changes in the design of Crane whistles. Gone were the ornamental lips on the rim of the bowl and the top cap, replaced with simple rounded corners. This waterfall design persisted until the very end of whistle manufacture. It is another of the important identifying marks of Crane whistles, shared only with certain models by Powell. For the first time, Crane brass goods were marked with two interlocking C's ("Crane Company"), usually on the side of the valve body. Although the catalog does not mention it, some of the whistles of this era were furnished with copper-sided bells, giving them an extraordinarily handsome appearance when polished. Diameters up to 12" were available, with bell lengths typically twice the diameter or less in the larger sizes. The No. 607 single-bell chime whistle made its first appearance in late 1902, and although not so identified, it was clearly manufactured by Powell, not Crane. The iron sawmill whistles were terminated, but the fire alarm whistle remained, still called a mockingbird, and with a third external support rod added in the larger sizes. The whistle line in the 1914 catalog was virtually identical to that in 1902, as was the line in the 1923 catalog.

By 1941, however, nothing remained of the Crane whistle line except the No. 600 valved and No. 602 valveless whistles, in diameters up to 8". Single-bell chimes were offered without attribution, although by this time they were clearly made by Buckeye, not Powell. By 1949 the last of the Crane-built whistles had disappeared, and Crane offered only Buckeye plain and chime whistles, which it now explicitly identified as such.

Some questions remain. How were later Crane whistles marked? Ca. 1905 the interlocking C's on

The Crane plain whistle with valve, 1897 and later. Note the absence of rims on bowl and bell, the double 'bowtie' lever fulcrum, the slightly coned top plate, and the elaborate acorn. The valveless whistle is essentially similar.

Close-up of a brass-bodied Crane whistle valve, showing the characteristic marking of interlocking C's. This mark was introduced sometime between 1893 and 1897, and used at least until 1904.

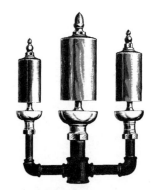

1902 version of the Crane three-bell chime. The individual whistles now resemble the corresponding plain whistles, except for the old-style acorns on the two outer ones. In contrast to the earlier version, Crane seems to have taken pains to align the tops of the bowls.

Whistle Manufacturers and Their Products

CHIME STEAM WHISTLES No. 606

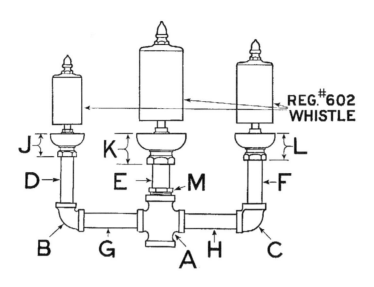

DATA FOR PIPE AND FITTINGS

Size of Bell......Inches	1½x2½x2	2x4x3	3x5x4	3½x5x4
A—Cross........Inches	1x½	1½x¾	2x1¼	2x1¼
B—Ell..........Inches	⅜x½	½x¾	¾x1¼	1x1¼
C—Ell..........Inches	½	¾	1¼	1¼
D—Nipple.......Inches	⅜x2½	½x4½	¾x5	1x5
E—Nipple.......Inches	¾x2	1¼x3½	1½x4	1½x4
F—Nipple.......Inches	½x2½	¾x4	1¼x4½	1¼x4½
G—Nipple.......Inches	½x2½	¾x5	1¼x6	1¼x6
H—Nipple.......Inches	½x3	¾x5	1¼x6	1¼x6
J—Dim.........Inches	1²⁵⁄₃₂	2⅛	2⁹⁄₁₆	3
K—Dim.........Inches	2¼	3³⁄₁₆	3⅝	3⅝
L—Dim.........Inches	2⅛	2⁹⁄₁₆	3³⁄₁₆	3³⁄₁₆
M—Bushing.....Inches	¾x1	1½x1¼	2x1½	2x1½
Size of Bell......Inches	4x6x5	5x8x6	6x10x8	8x12x10
A—Cross........Inches	2½x1½	3x2	3½x2½	4x3
B—Ell..........Inches	1¼x1½	2x1½	2½x2	3x2½
C—Ell..........Inches	1½	2	2½	3
D—Nipple.......Inches	1¼x5½	1½x7½	2x8	2½x5
E—Nipple.......Inches	2x5	2½x2½	3x6½	3x6
F—Nipple.......Inches	1½x5	2x7	2½x3	3x7
G—Nipple.......Inches	1½x8	2x10	2½x12	3x15
H—Nipple.......Inches	1½x8	2x10	2½x13	3x16
J—Dim.........Inches	3³⁄₁₆	3⅝	4¼	8½
K—Dim.........Inches	4¼	8½	4¾	7¼
L—Dim.........Inches	3⅝	4¼	8½	4¾
M—Bushing.....Inches	2½x2	3x2½	3½x3	4x3

Dimensional information for assembling a late-model (1923) Crane three-bell chime from standard plain whistles. The 8″ x 12″ x 10″ version is probably the largest "triple" offered by any American manufacturer. Curiously, the 10″ and 12″ whistles it contains are not listed as standard items under No. 602. The base height (J) specified for the 8″ whistle is probably an error.

the side of the valve body were replaced by the word CRANE and the pressure rating (generally 125 PSI) boldly embossed on the side of the bowl. (Crane seems to have had no interest in making whistles for service at pressures above 125 PSI, including railroad service.) This type of marking persisted up to the very end of whistle manufacture. Did Crane ever manufacture any single-bell chime whistles of its own? Apparently not, nor are any shown in trade catalogs. An alleged Crane chime in a private collection is actually a fake, a hybrid contrived from a Crane base and a B&O bell by an unscrupulous dealer in Virginia.

Crosby Steam Gage & Valve Co.

The Crosby Steam Gage (*sic*) & Valve Company was formed on September 1, 1874, by Joshua H. Millett, George H. Crosby and others, for the manufacture of valves and gauges under patents issued to Mr. Crosby. The company was incorporated in Massachusetts on August 6, 1875 with Millett as its president, an office he held until his death in 1914. The company began manufacturing in a small shop at Cambridgeport, Massachusetts, but soon afterward moved to the corner of Milk and Batterymarch Streets in Boston. About 1880 the plant and offices moved to 93-97 Oliver Street, Boston. In 1888, a factory was built on Roland Street in Charlestown, while the New England Sales Department remained at 93-95 Oliver Street. This factory was enlarged in 1894 and additional buildings were erected from time to time as the company grew. In 1946 Crosby merged with the Ashton Valve Company, an important producer of locomotive and power plant specialties founded in Cambridge, Massachusetts in 1871. In 1949 Ashton and Crosby combined their manufacturing operations in larger premises at 43 Kendrick Street, Wrentham, Massachusetts. Crosby still occupies these facilities which, after many expansions, now comprise 225,000 square feet on a 25 acre

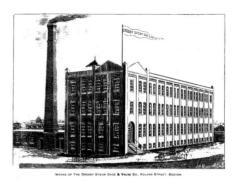

The Crosby works in Charlestown, Massachusetts, ca. 1888. No whistle is visible on the roof of the boiler house!

landholding. In 1973 Ashton Valve was officially terminated and Crosby became the successor corporation.

Although the product line was based on George Crosby's original patents concerning steam accessories, safety valves and pressure gages, many new patents were subsequently issued to Crosby and others. By 1907 the product line had expanded to include not merely safety and relief valves, gauges, gauge accessories, and whistles, but also steam engine indicators, reducing wheels, lubricators, feed water regulators, revolution counters, locomotive and marine clocks, mufflers, pyrometers, thermometers, planimeters, test pumps, dead weight testers, fluid pressure scales, wheel press recorders, water columns, blowoff, gate, globe and check valves, and "all instruments incidental to the use of Steam Engines, Boilers, Etc." The company quickly acquired a reputation as a manufacturer of engineering appliances of the highest quality. In particular, the Crosby steam engine indicator became the standard of the world, and turn-of-the-century training manuals for stationary steam engineers discuss indicator diagrams exclusively in terms of the Crosby design. The merit of Crosby products was recognized with medals and prizes at various trade and industrial expositions, including Philadelphia in 1876, Paris in 1889, Chicago in 1892, and St. Louis in 1904.

Owing to the rapid increase in domestic sales, Crosby soon found its store and general office in Boston inadequate. In 1889 a store was opened in Chicago, and in 1890, another store in New York. A regional sales office was opened in San Francisco in 1919, and subsequently moved to Los Angeles. At the same time, overseas sales were vigorously pursued. Demand for Crosby products in Europe led to the opening of a London office in 1884 and an office in Hamburg, Germany in 1888. In 1914, a British corporation was organized

Whistle Manufacturers and Their Products

under the name of Crosby Valve & Engineering Co. Ltd. to sell goods throughout Europe and the British Dominions. Today, although the character of its business has changed markedly from the heyday of the reciprocating steam engine, Crosby has subsidiaries, joint ventures, or licensees in England, Scotland, France, Canada, Japan, Singapore, Brazil, United Arab Emirates, and India, and maintains more than sixty international sales representatives and distributors in the industrialized nations of the world.

Crosby seems to have manufactured steam whistles from the first days of its founding. Initially, of course, these were plain whistles (Crosby called them "common" whistles), but the cornerstone of Crosby's fortunes as a whistle manufacturer was John Einig's patent of January 30, 1877 (US 186,718), the fundamental patent on the single-bell chime. Einig did not assign this patent to Crosby, but Crosby purchased exclusive manufacturing rights to the design. For the next seventeen years, the duration of the patent, it exploited these rights with great vigor and enterprise, engraving the date of the patent on every chime whistle it manufactured and cautioning buyers to beware of imitations.

The earliest surviving catalog dates from 1888, although this catalog refers to a still earlier release. The 1888 catalog offered "patent" single-bell chime whistles up to 12" in diameter, without valve (No. 1), with

"upright" (i.e., vertical) valve (No. 2), and with "side" (i.e., horizontal) valve (No. 3). Apart from the internally partitioned bells, these whistles were identical in every detail to the earlier plain whistles. The three flutes or chambers sounded the first, third and fifth of the musical scale, i.e., a major triad in root position, a harmonic formula which remained unchanged throughout the years of whistle manufacture. The 1888 catalog also offered plain whistles in the same three varieties, without valve, with vertical valve, and with horizontal valve, all in diameters up to 12". The acorns of these whistles were unusually ornate, and the levers of the valved whistles were short with a pronounced reverse curve. In typical 19th century fashion, the lever of the horizontal valve was secured by insertion in a slot in the valve stem. All three of these exceptionally graceful designs remained in the catalog until 1897, and collectors have long considered them among the handsomest of all whistles. The catalog also offered a selection of testimonials from users which are amusing to read today.

By 1897 the plain whistle with vertical valve had been dropped from the line and the horizontal valve version had been renumbered No. 2. An organ pipe whistle of conventional design was added to the line, in diameters up to 4". This whistle had two opposed semi-elliptical mouths embracing roughly

PATENT SINGLE BELL CHIME STEAM WHISTLE.

PATENTED JAN. 30, 1877, AND SEPT. 2, 1884.

No. 1.
Without Valve.

No. 2.
With Upright Valve.

No. 3.
With Side Valve.

STEAM WHISTLES.

No. 1.

No. 2.

No. 3.

Single-bell chime whistles made under the Einig patent, ca. 1888. These were the cornerstone of Crosby's fortunes as a whistle manufacturer. See Chap.3 for the patent itself.

Crosby's line of plain whistles, ca. 1888. In the author's judgment, the elegance of No. 3 has never been surpassed.

Whistle Manufacturers and Their Products

LETTERS IN REGARD TO

SINGLE BELL CHIME STEAM WHISTLE.

Office of THE NEW HOME SEWING MACHINE CO.

ORANGE, MASS., 14th April, 1883.

CROSBY STEAM GAGE AND VALVE CO., Boston, Mass.:

Gentlemen : The twelve-inch Single Bell Chime Steam Whistle you made for us is "immense," and gives PERFECT SATISFACTION. It has a deep, rich tone and can be heard a long distance. Have been told it was heard twenty miles away. I consider it superior to every whistle or gong I have ever heard. Thanking you for your efforts in furnishing us with so good a whistle, I am faithfully yours, W. L. GROUT,

N. H. S. M. Co.

ILLINOIS INSTITUTE FOR THE EDUCATION OF THE DEAF AND DUMB.

JACKSONVILLE, ILL., March 25, 1886.

CROSBY STEAM GAGE & VALVE CO., 95 & 97 Oliver Street, Boston, Mass.

Gentlemen : The No. 3, *twelve-inch,* Single Bell *Chime Whistle,* furnished by your people to this Institution, is *giving excellent satisfaction* both as a means of attracting the attention of our pupils, (of whom we have over five hundred), when they are awake, and of arousing them when asleep. Though its tones are musical and pleasant, yet they are powerful enough to produce a tremor of the ground and buildings, sufficient to be readily observable to the deaf, who, as is well known, are very quick in the perception of vibrations. I regard it as invaluable to such an institution as this, as it furnishes a ready and expeditious means of notifying them of fire, as well as signaling them for change of occupation as is done with other persons by means of a bell.

The tones of this instrument are so *far reaching* as to be heard, under favorable conditions of the atmosphere, *a distance of fifteen miles*, and we use it daily in communicating the weather probabilities to the dwellers in a large area of country, information appreciated by all classes of persons, but especially by farmers.

Respectfully yours,

PHILIP G. GILLETT, *Superintendent.*

J. S. DUNHAM'S TOWING & WRECKING CO.

CHICAGO, ILL., January 31, 1885.

CROSBY STEAM GAGE AND VALVE CO., Boston, Mass.:

Gentlemen : We have been using the Single Bell Chime Whistle on the tugs of our line for two years. We find it invaluable to us, in that we can hear it farther than any other whistle we know of, and distinguish it. We therefore consider it by all odds the best signal in the whistle line we ever saw. Its principal excellence consists in its far-reaching qualities, perfect, mellow tone, and freedom from the ear-splitting effects of common whistles when blown near at hand. Wishing you every success, we remain, yours truly,

J. S. DUNHAM'S TOWING & WRECKING CO.

PORTER MANUFACTURING COMPANY.
[LIMITED.]

SYRACUSE, N. Y., February 5, 1885.

CROSBY STEAM GAGE AND VALVE CO., Boston, Mass.:

Gents : We have had one of your Single Bell Chime Whistles on our shops for the past three years, and have sold several of them to our customers, in every instance giving good satisfaction. Ours is a six-inch whistle, and can be heard distinctly at a distance of three miles.

Yours truly, PORTER MANUFACTURING CO. [Limited.]

HATHAWAY, SOULE & HARRINGTON, Manufacturers of Fine Shoes.

NEW BEDFORD, MASS., February 5, 1885.

CROSBY STEAM GAGE AND VALVE CO., Boston, Mass.:

Gentlemen: Yours of the 3d received. We have had one of your Single Bell Chime Whistles for about two and one half years, and like it very much, for three reasons: 1st, Near at hand it does not deafen one. 2d, Can be heard readily at a long distance. 3d, The Chime is very pleasing, and can be distinguished from all other whistles in our part of the city. Has not been out of order since put on.

Very truly yours,   HATHAWAY, SOULE & HARRINGTON.

ELISHA T. JENKS, Monitor Museum Lock.

MIDDLEBORO, MASS., February 5, 1885.

CROSBY STEAM GAGE AND VALVE CO., Boston, Mass.:

Gentlemen: Your favor asking my opinion of the Single Bell Chime Whistle is at hand. I take pleasure in saying that I am very much pleased with it, and in fact it exceeds my expectation, both as to power and quality of tone. I am fully convinced that I should always use a whistle of this kind in preference to any others I have seen.

Very truly yours,   ELISHA T. JENKS.

MASTER MECHANIC'S OFFICE,

DETROIT, LANSING & NORTHERN RAILROAD CO.

IONIA, MICH., February 5, 1885.

CROSBY STEAM GAGE AND VALVE CO., Boston, Mass.:

Gentlemen: In reply to yours of January 30th in relation to the eight-inch Chime Whistle on our shops will say it is perfectly satisfactory. It has three perfect and distinct sounds, and in perfect harmony. It is heard several miles away. I consider it superior to any ordinary whistle. Our general officers are very much pleased with it.   Yours truly,   GEO. C. WATROUS,

Master Mechanic.

Office of COLUMBUS IRON WORKS COMPANY.

COLUMBUS, GA., January 29, 1885.

CROSBY STEAM GAGE AND VALVE CO., Boston, Mass.:

Dear Sirs: We placed several of your Single Bell Chime Whistles on cotton compresses, and one on the steamer Naiad, plying on the Chattahooche river. All unite in declaring their tone perfect, and while soft and musical can be heard a long distance.   Truly yours,   G. BUCHANAN WHITESIDE.

Sec'y and Treas.

"FRISCO LINE."

St. Louis & San Francisco Railway Company.

A. P. MAN, Jr., *Purchasing Agent.*

ST. LOUIS, January 6, 1885.

CROSBY STEAM GAGE AND VALVE CO., Boston, Mass.:

Gents: Your Chime Steam Whistles are giving all satisfaction so far as heard from. We have now applied them to all (or nearly all) of our passenger locomotives, and they are preferred as giving a more pleasing sound, and as a distinctive and more unmistakable signal, and for other reasons. They are heard a great distance and are convenient of attachment. The first one we tried was, I believe, about a year ago.

Yours very respectfully,   A. P. MAN, JR.,

Purchasing Agent.

NEW YORK, February 6, 1885.

CROSBY STEAM GAGE AND VALVE CO., 95 and 97 Oliver St., Boston, Mass.:

Gentlemen: After riding for several months behind No. 85 (The "Sam Sloan") equipped with the *five-inch* Single Bell *Chime Whistle* you furnished for us; we take pleasure in expressing the satisfaction we feel in *our* whistle, and think it the perfection of steam whistles, having the essential good qualities of clearness, penetration, and a mellow musical tone. We frequently hear its beautiful strains twenty-two minutes after leaving our station, certainly ten miles away.   Yours respectfully,

L. R. POMEROY,

THOS. G. JOHNSON.

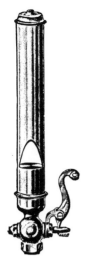

The Crosby organ pipe whistle, introduced in 1897,

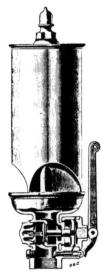

The Crosby single-bell chime, as modified in 1897 by the addition of a compound automatic valve.

This 1900 version of the single-bell chime has a conventional disc valve, but with renewable seats, and an extra-long lever for locomotive use.

two-thirds the circumference of the bell, and a horizontal valve substantially similar to the other plain whistles. The single-bell chime whistle, meanwhile, split into two distinct product lines, the "original" version with an unbalanced valve and an "improved" version with Crosby's newly patented compound automatic valve. The latter greatly facilitated the opening of the valve in large whistles operating at high pressures, and expedited the spread of Crosby chime whistles to marine applications.

1900 saw the introduction of the single-bell chime whistle with a renewable valve seat, covered by yet another Crosby patent. This whistle was offered only in 5" and 6" diameters with horizontal valve, a clear indication that it was intended for railroad service. In addition, all chime whistles with horizontal valves were fitted with a new style of operating lever, almost as long as the whistle was tall, and straight to the very end. This gave the operator much finer control of the valve opening, and permitted the wailing or "quilling" of whistle speech, an ability much prized by locomotive engineers. Finally, the exceedingly handsome and ornate 19th century acorn nut was replaced with an acorn of more conventional design on these railway whistles, but retained on all others. Within the next few years the new style of acorn spread throughout the entire product line.

In the 1907 catalog the organ pipe whistle made its last official appearance, although Crosby continued to manufacture it in small quantities for at least another decade. All other plain whistles apparently vanished from the line as well. Unlike other manufacturers of the era, Crosby never offered multiple-bell chime whistles compounded from two or more plain whistles; the only chimes Crosby ever listed were its patent single-bell chimes. Despite their disappearance from the general trade catalogs, however, Crosby continued to make plain whistles on contract for at least another three or four decades. In the 1920's and early 1930's hundreds of 3" plain whistles for compressed air service were furnished to the 8th Avenue Subway Line in New York City. These whistles had bells of drawn tubing rather than the elaborate cored castings of the chime whistles. Today, plain whistles of any type bearing the Crosby insignium are a rarity, much sought after by collectors.

At this point there is a long hiatus in the archival literature. Crosby seems to have fallen on hard times and did not issue a whistle catalog between 1907 and 1927, although its U.K. subsidiary did. Neverthless some significant changes occurred. From 1909 to roughly 1917 Crosby manufactured what it called a "petticoat" whistle, which was a chime whistle with an adjustable bell. The lower portion of the bell carried an external thread, onto which which threaded a sleeve or skirt to adjust the lip height. The sleeve was then fixed with a jam nut. The purpose of this modification was to permit optimum performance at a wide variety of inlet pressures. This whistle was manufactured in 1-1/2", 2", and 3" sizes, and is extremely rare today. In 1916 acorns of traditional shape were abandoned and replaced with a simple, slightly crowned hexagonal cap nut. By the time of the 1927 catalog Crosby had reduced the whistle product line to only two styles, both of which persisted until

Whistle Manufacturers and Their Products

the cessation of whistle manufacture. Style KA110 without valve and KC110 with horizontal valve were offered in diameters from 5" to 12", both with screwed inlets. Allegedly only the KA110 was available with a flanged inlet, but KC110's with flanged inlets are known to exist. The long lever acquired a slight reverse curvature. The Crosby insignium, a shield with two stars crossed by a banner bearing the word CROSBY, was cast into one side of the valve body, while an escutcheon with an ever-lengthening list of patent dates was cast into the other.

These numerous changes in details of the design have been painstakingly catalogued and codified by Larry Spreckelmeier of Cincinnati, Ohio, the nation's foremost whistle restorer. As depicted in the accompanying illustration (next page), he has identified five different styles of acorns, five different styles of actuating levers, at least three different styles of lever markings, ten different styles of inscriptions and patent markings, and four different styles of typeface on the pipe nut. What is lacking, regrettably, is the correlation between these various styles and the year of manufacture or the number stamped on the pipe nut.

In addition to the forementioned changes, sometime after about 1925 the arched mouths of chime whistles underwent a rather pronounced change of shape. Originally they were semi-elliptical when developed on a plane, a smoothly rounded shape probably chosen for its esthetic appeal. This choice was retroactively justified by the somewhat contrived argument that an arched mouth might be regarded as a mouth of continuously varying lip height, and therefore would prove adaptable to the widest possible range of inlet pressures. This dubious hypothesis proved false in practice, and internal memoranda reveal that early chime whistles were

An extremely rare Crosby "petticoat" whistle, a chime whistle with an adjustable bell. This whistle never appeared in any Crosby catalog, and only a few hundred were ever made.

Late-model Crosby single-bell chimes, style KA110 without valve and style KC110 with valve. From about 1920 onward, these two types were the only whistles offered by Crosby to the general public. Subsequent changes in the shape of the arches are not reflected in the catalog illustrations.

VARIATIONS IN DETAILS OF CROSBY SINGLE-BELL CHIME WHISTLES

Listed in approximate chronological order. Compiled and sketched by Larry Spreckelmeier.

ACORNS OR TOP NUTS

OLD STYLE   OLDER 10" DIA.   OLDER 12" DIA.   TRANSITIONAL   NEW STYLE

LEVERS

 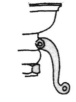   

OLD STYLE   VERTICAL VALVE   TRANSITIONAL   NEW STYLE   COMPOUND VALVE

MARKINGS AND INSIGNIA

(On rim of bowl or on side of bowl just below rim)

CROSBY STEAM GAGE & VALVE CO. BOSTON U.S. PAT. JAN. 30,1877

CROSBY STEAM GAGE & VALVE CO. BOSTON

　　　PAT. JAN 30,1877

CROSBY STEAM GAGE & VALVE CO. BOSTON U.S.A.

CROSBY STEAM GAGE & VALVE CO. BOSTON U.S.

CROSBY

(Usually on opposite sides of valve body, or on sides of bowl if without valve.)

PATENTS JAN. 30, 1877 FEB. 4,1896

(On hex flat)

NUMERALS ON HEX FLAT

87　　**59**　　**38**　　**92**

OLD STYLE　　FANCY　　TRADITIONAL　　PLAIN

frequently returned to Crosby for unsatisfactory performance at high pressures. Workmen then painstakingly filed or ground out the corners of the arches by hand, squaring off their tops until only a small radius remained in the corners, and reliable blowing was attained at the customer's specified inlet pressure. Eventually, after what may have been many years of such *ad hoc* remedies, the squared-off arches were incorporated in regular production. Thus Crosby was compelled to learn what organ pipe makers had known for centuries: when the blowing pressure is controlled within fairly narrow limits, a flat-topped mouth is best. (This lesson had already been learned by other makers of three-chime whistles, such as Lonergan, as well as by the makers of five- and six-chime steptops, such as Nathan.) Curiously, Crosby never acknowledged the design change to the newer flat-topped arches and they were never accurately depicted in any catalog, including those issued as late as 1939. Neverthless they can be seen in abundance on the most recently produced KA110 and KC110 whistles.

Crosby chimes were widely regarded as the most melodious and pleasing of all chime whistles. Commodore Vanderbilt ordered one for his private yacht. The Chicago, Burlington & Quincy Railroad purchased them in quantity. A measure of the esteem in which they were held in the United Kingdom is that in the mid-1930's 4" chimes (called "Tritones" by Crosby) were fitted, at the insistence of the designer, Sir Nigel Gresley, to the class A4 Pacifics, the most celebrated locomotives in all of England and holders of the world speed record for steam propulsion. They were frequently specified as original equipment by manufacturers. Following the success of the 3" plain whistles, hundreds of 2" chimes, styles KA 110 and KC 110, were installed on municipal subway systems throughout the nation. Their piercing tones are familiar to every New Yorker above the age of fifty. Many more Crosby whistles, usually 8" chimes, were installed on the tugs and ferries which plied New York rivers and harbors, and gave the waterfront some of its characteristic voices. Even today the sound of a large Crosby chime on high-pressure steam is one of the most thrilling experiences the hobby has to offer. Most desirable of all are the 12" chimes, the largest regularly manufactured. Fewer than twenty of these "Mother Crosbys" are

thought to have survived. Fifteen of them reside in museums or private collections, but a sixteenth is still in daily operation at the General Electric plant in Erie, Pennsylvania.

It is believed that every Crosby whistle larger than 2" in diameter bore an identifying number stamped on one of the flats of its pipe inlet or on the rim of its inlet flange. These are thought to be serial numbers, and range from less than 100 to more than 50,000 in known examples. Unfortunately the majority of the company's production records—some of which date back to the 1870's and were written with a crow quill pen—were inadvertently destroyed in the late 1970's. Recently, however, Craig Bliss of Crosby Valve, Inc. discovered a small cache of company files that had somehow escaped the mass destruction. These include production figures from September, 1914 through September, 1917, thousands of Crosby and Ashton engineering drawings, parts cards, foundry specifications for the composition of alloys, and catalogs from 1888 through 1939. He has made these available to Crosby fanciers through his Web site (www.crosby-steam.com), and issued a CD-ROM containing more than 1500 high resolution copies of the drawings.

These newly discovered production records reveal that approximately 3250 chime whistles were produced during the three-year period, which was probably close to the peak years of whistle production. This production rate is not inconsistent with a total output of 50,000 chime whistles or more over the entire lifetime of whistle manufacture at Crosby, suggesting in turn that the numbers stamped on chime whistles are indeed serial numbers. Regrettably, the correlation between serial number and year of manufacture has been lost. Amateur Crosby enthusiasts have recently mounted an effort to reconstruct this correlation by assembling data from whistles in private collections. The surviving production records also give useful information regarding the types of whistles produced by Crosby during these years. Insofar as these figures are representative of the entire history of whistle production, they may help the curator and collector to assess the relative rarity of the various types of Crosby whistles (see next page).

Nominal diameter in inches	Type as percentage of total production	Percentage of type without valve
1.5	10.9	16.7
2	15.9	51.4
3	18.2	55.0
4	4.1	11.1
5	5.5	66.7
6	19.1	38.1
8	17.7	82.1
10	7.7	70.6
12	0.9	100.0

One might have expected the smaller whistles to be in greater demand, so it is something of a surprise to learn that more valveless 8" chimes were produced than any other type. It is no surprise, however, that the 12" chime is the rarest of all Crosby chime whistles. Neverthelesss if one can extrapolate reliably from these figures to the whole of production, it appears that Crosby made at least several hundred 12" chimes. If so, it is regrettable that so few of these majestic whistles survive. During these years the production of all other types of whistles was negligible in comparison to chime whistles: a few dozen organ pipe whistles, and a handful each of petticoat whistles and common (i.e., plain) whistles, all of which types had long since ceased to be carried in the catalog.

Crosby officially ceased to manufacture whistles in 1939. An internal company memorandum dated November, 1945 states that all whistles, whistle valves, and parts were permanently discontinued in the period July, 1939 to September, 1941. All remaining foundry patterns were allegedly destroyed between 1950 and 1955. It is also known, however, that a whistle repair service was maintained at least until 1951, at which time it was turned over to the Clark-Cooper Co. of Palmyra, New Jersey. During World War II Crosby, like every other American manufacturing company, fell under the jurisdiction of the War Production Board. During this period of wartime exigency it seems to have manufactured a variety of whistles for naval and marine use, including long-bell plain whistles in sizes 6" x 30", 6" x 36", 8" x 30", and 10" x 40". Few if any of these large whistles were new designs; most were merely adaptations of whistles originally designed in the period between world wars.

With the demise of the reciprocating steam engine as a prime mover, and a decline in the number of industrial plants generating process steam, Crosby was compelled to alter the nature of its product line in order to survive. Full nozzle safety, safety relief, and relief valves became the mainstay of its business, and the "Crosby safety valve" was recognized throughout the world as a generic term for this type of valve. In 1956 the word "Steam" was dropped from the corporate name, signifying its new emphasis on pneumatic and hydraulic applications. Crosby pioneered in the development of valves for nuclear applications, including the first nuclear submarines and the first commercial power reactors. Finally in 1995 the word "Gage" was dropped from the corporate name, recognizing that no gauges had been manufactured since 1988, and Crosby became simply Crosby Valve, Inc.

These changes in product mix were accompanied by rapid and somewhat bewildering changes in corporate ownership. From 1976 to 1981 Crosby was employee-owned. It was then acquired by Geosource, Inc. of Houston, Texas, which was acquired in turn by Aetna Life & Casualty of Hartford, Connecticut. In 1984 Crosby became part of Moorco International under a leveraged buyout. Moorco in turn was acquired by FMC Corporation in 1995, and in 1998 Crosby was acquired from FMC by Tyco International Ltd. Today Crosby operates as Anderson Greenwood Crosby, Tyco's Flow Control division. Crosby products are sold to the hydrocarbon processing (petroleum, chemical and petrochemical refining), power (fossil-fueled and nuclear), shipbuilding (marine and Navy), original equipment manufacturing, and other industries worldwide. Thanks to its ability to adapt to changing times, the little valve and gauge company which once made the world's most widely admired chime whistles still flourishes more than 125 years after its founding, an achievement almost without parallel among 19th century manufacturers of steam specialties.

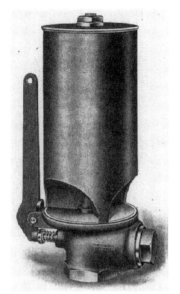

The Hancock Fig. 248 three-chime locomotive whistle with horizontal valve, ca. 1928.

Fig. 48
Upward Lever

Fig. 47
Downward Lever

Variations of the Hancock Fig. 248 whistle with vertical valves, ca. 1928.

Fig. 49

The Hancock short-bell plain whistle of 1928, a real "screamer."

Hancock Inspirator Co.

The Hancock Inspirator Co. and the Nathan Manufacturing Co. (*q.v.*) were the two principal suppliers of steam whistles for locomotives in the twentieth century. It is their products which gave the American steam train its characteristic voice. Thus it is all the more regrettable that archival material relating to them has proved extraordinarily elusive, and virtually nothing is known about their corporate histories.

Nevertheless a minimal inference can be drawn from the corporate name itself. An inspirator is a boiler accessory which forces additional water into the boiler to replace that lost through discharge as steam. An alternative name for this device is "injector." To the layman its operation seems almost magical. Unlike a conventional force pump, it has no moving parts, and it (necessarily) develops a pressure greater than that of the steam which operates the device itself. The injector was invented in France ca. 1857 by Henri Jacques Giffard, and its manufacture in the U.S. was begun in 1860 by Wm. Sellers & Co. of Philadelphia. Presumably Sellers enjoyed exclusive manufacturing rights for the usual 17-year period, whence Hancock is unlikely to have been founded earlier than 1877.

It is but a short step from the manufacture of injectors to the manufacture of other boiler accessories such as steam whistles. By 1928 Hancock had become a division of Manning, Maxwell & Moore, Inc., with general offices in the Pershing Square Building at 100 East 42nd Street in New York City. This was succeeded in turn by the Consolidated Ashcroft Hancock Co., Inc., Ashcroft being a

A Hancock three-chime steptop, successor to the flat-top chime whistle of the 1920's and '30's. This is the short-bell version.

The long-bell or "steamboat" version of the Hancock three-chime steptop. Note the alternative fulcrum below the valve stem, to accommodate a downward-hanging lever. Not all production models had this feature.

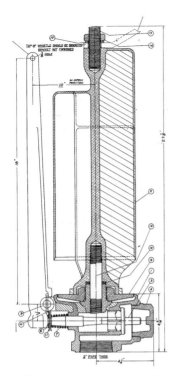

A 1938 engineering drawing of the long-bell three-chime steptop, from Hancock's own files. This sonorous device was regarded by many as the acme of American steam locomotive whistle design, rivaled only by the five- and six-chime Nathans.

highly regarded old-line maker of steam gauges.

The only surviving catalog literature from this era is Bulletin No. 360, dated 1928 and entitled "The Hancock Locomotive Whistle." In fact this bulletin described four different whistles. The first of these was depicted in Fig. 248, a 6" three-chime whistle of no-frills design, distinguished by an extremely shallow bowl, a horizontal valve with long straight lever, and a simple hex nut on the top plate instead of an acorn. Although the accompanying description asserted that all major parts were made of bronze, versions with a cast iron bell are known. Still other versions had a second lever fulcrum below the valve stem so that the lever might be inverted. Heavy embossed lettering on the side of the valve body identified the maker. Bulletin 360 also exhibited Figs. 47 and 48 chime whistles, no longer in production. The bells of these whistles appeared to be identical to that of Fig. 248, but the bowls were adapted to vertical valves, the former to a downturned and the latter to an upturned lever. Finally, Fig. 49 was a plain whistle with very short bell, of the type known as a "screamer" or "banshee." This whistle had a vertical valve and was intended for freight service.

Almost everything that is known about Hancock products in later years comes from its contributions to the Simmons-Boardman *Locomotive Cyclopedia*, a standard reference work of the industry. Here may be found engineering drawings of the celebrated "steamboat" Hancocks, long-bell three-chime whistles of exceptionally low pitch. These were available in models for both saturated and superheated steam, at pressure ratings up to 300 PSI, and were the only commercially manufactured whistles so rated. As such they were much favored by the Norfolk & Western and Illinois Central railroads among others, as well as by the countless trackside hearers who thrilled to their sound. In later years Hancock appears to have formed an alliance with the Viloco Railway Equipment Co., for Viloco pneumatic actuators were frequently pictured with Hancock whistles and conversely. Hancock also undertook to manufacture an unusual air-operated whistle based on the audibility experiments of Prof. A. L. Foley, as previously described in Chapter 3.

Jarecki Mfg. Co.

Jarecki was established in 1852 in Erie, Pennsylvania. Seven years later, in nearby Titusville, Edwin Drake drilled the world's first oil well. The company was formally incorporated in 1897 and soon earned a reputation as a supplier of specialties to the burgeoning petroleum extraction industry, with branch stores in all principal oil fields. Its line of goods included malleable iron, cast iron and brass pipe fittings, bronze and iron valves and cocks, pipe threading machines, governors and unloaders, and of course all manner of boiler fittings, including whistles. The company still flourishes today in the city of its founding, although it has not manufactured whistles for more than six decades.

The Jarecki emblem is an initial "J" inscribed in a vertically oriented rhombus. Marked Jarecki whistles are extremely rare, and most collectors have never seen one. Those that are marked carry also the legend JARECKI, ERIE PA. Owing to the scarcity of authentic examples, it is unusually difficult to trace the evolution of the Jarecki line of whistles. The earliest surviving catalog is dated 1894 and was issued

by Jarecki Mfg. Co. Ltd., a Canadian subsidiary. It showed a line of plain and chime whistles substantially indistinguishable from those made by Penberthy, another Canadian firm, although these whistles bore the Jarecki emblem on the side of the bowl or valve body. The presumption is that Jarecki was merely jobbing whistles made by Penberthy. The elaborate acorn is distinctive. The valveless whistles were available up to 12" in diameter, with brass or iron bases, in both short-bell (length less than twice the diameter) and long-bell (length twice the diameter or greater) versions. The valved versions were similar and feature a double lever fulcrum which could be adjusted to pull up or down. Single-bell chimes were offered up to 12" in diameter, with or without valves. Finally, multiple-bell chimes were furnished with any number of whistles or size of bells. The manifolds of these chimes were composed of ordinary pipe fittings, with the center cross bearing the Jarecki emblem.

Curiously, a domestic catalog from early in the 20th century showed plain whistles of a different and highly individual design. The bell, of length roughly twice the diameter, had a "waterfall" or rounded top edge, and was surmounted by a large and handsome acorn. The rimmed bowl had a long lower extension to contain a vertical valve. The most unusual feature was the lever, which was pivoted at the far edge of the rim and extended across the top of the languid plate, bisecting the center stud and actuating the valve by means of a concentric push rod. The lever was bronze and stamped JARECKI, ERIE. In later years Jarecki seems to have abandoned this distinctive line of plain whistles. Catalog No. 34, issued in 1936, reverted again to plain and chime whistles indistinguishable from those made by Penberthy, and in fact unchanged since the 1894 catalog.

Although marked for Jarecki, this plain whistle was clearly made by Penberthy.

The Jarecki/Penberthy single-bell chime, ca. 1910.

Kelly & Jones Co.

Very little is known about the Kelly & Jones Co., "manufacturers of brass, iron and steel goods and specialties for steam, gas, water, and oil." Their headquarters were at 135 Water Street in Pittsburgh and their works in Greensburg, Pennsylvania, with branch offices in New York, Chicago, St. Louis, Cincinnati, and San Francisco. Although a relatively large firm, with capitalization comparable to that of Crosby or Lunkenheimer, they seem to have manufactured very few steam whistles. Today Kelly & Jones whistles are among the rarest of all 20th century steam whistles.

Only catalogs from the years 1912 through 1923 survive, and no evolution of the design is apparent during these years. Plain whistles with and without horizontal valves were offered in diameters from to 1" to 8", in both short bell (ca. 1.5X) and long bell (ca. 2X) versions. The acorn and reverse-curved lever were conventional, and in general these whistles were devoid of innovative or distinctive features, except that the bells have rounded or "waterfall" tops, in the manner of contemporaneous whistles by Crane, Jarecki, and Powell. Unlike these other whistles, however, the

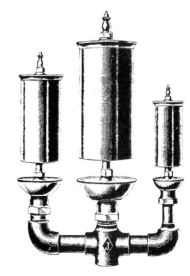

The Jarecki/Penberthy multiple-bell chime, ca. 1910.. Note that the tops of the bowls are aligned.

The Kelly & Jones Fig. 310 valved plain whistle. Note the rimmed bowl, the rimless bell, the separable and rotatable lever fulcrum, and the large square nut on the valve access cover. The company logo can barely be discerned on the side of the valve body. The Fig. 309 valveless whistle is very similar.

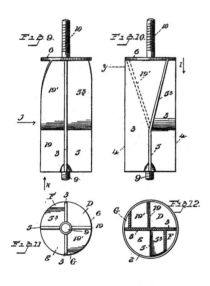

Selected drawings from the ingenious Frisbie patent of 1894, No. 520,418, showing the use of slanted and curved internal partitions to produce four different pitches from resonant chambers of the same overall height. The patent also describes a similar three-chime version.

bowls have flared rims. All known examples are marked on the side of the bowl or the valve body with the Kelly & Jones logo, consisting of the letter "K" superimposed on the letter "J". Also offered was the usual three-bell chime assembled from plain whistles on a manifold of pipe fittings, but no single-bell chime.

Kinsley Mfg. Co.

No widely known manufacturer of whistles is more difficult to document than the Kinsley Mfg. Co. of Bridgeport, Connecticut. It is doubtful that the company ever issued a trade catalog, and the little that is known must be inferred from advertisements and the patent literature. This is unfortunate because Kinsley whistles were unique in concept and execution, owing little or nothing to more conventional designs.

The company seems to have been formed in 1892 or shortly before as Kinsley & Frisbie, an alliance between Frank Kinsley and the prolific inventor Henry R. Frisbie of Newark, New Jersey, who holds more patents on steam whistles than any other individual. In that year Frisbie assigned one-half of his first two whistle patents (US 466,403 and 466,404) to Kinsley. In the next two years he was to assign three more, of which the seminal one was US 520,418. This is the fundamental patent on the use of tapered and twisted internal partitions to produce a musical chord from a single-bell chime whistle with resonant chambers all of the same length, the distinguishing characteristic of every Kinsley whistle ever manufactured. The shapes of the chambers defy conventional acoustical analysis, and it is clear that they were determined by a lengthy trial-and-error procedure. As early as January, 1894 Kinsley was advertising a three-chime version of this whistle to the trade as the "Frisbie Single Bell Chime Whistle," in a form substantially unchanged throughout the lifetime of the corporation.

Kinsley whistles are distinctive not merely in their internal arrangements but in many other details of construction. The complex internal partitions were a bronze casting, and the outer surface of the bell was a removable sleeve of seamless yellow brass tubing. The axial position of this sleeve could be adjusted, permitting tuning of the whistle for optimum performance on various inlet pressures. The length of the bell was twice its diameter in small whistles,

An 1894 advertisement for the three-chime Kinsley. Frank Kinsley's name may have been on the factory, but Henry Frisbie's name was on the whistle. Eventually Kinsley took over, but the design of these little whistles never changed during the lifetime of the company, nor did Kinsley ever make any other type of product.

Whistle Manufacturers and Their Products

less in larger whistles. The acorn was utterly unlike any other, with a four-sided body and a pointed tip. The languid or top plate was unfastened, held in place by the bell, and had a pronounced taper on its edge, thus forming a converging nozzle. The rim of the bowl was marked with the maker's name and address in upper case letters. If an integral horizontal valve was supplied, the valve body was cubical, echoing the shape of the acorn. In whistles of later manufacture, one face of the inlet hex carried a stamped number. Numbers in excess of 50,000 have been seen, but in the absence of corporate records it is unclear whether this is a serial number or some sort of production code.

Three- and four-chime whistles of this description in 2" diameter were supplied by the hundreds to municipal subway and elevated systems, and can still be found with relative ease. (See also the entry under Ohio Brass Co.) On the other hand, Kinsley whistles of larger diameter are quite rare. The four-chime whistles were sometimes known as "quartets," and were the only domestically manufactured four-note chimes; all other chime whistles produced two, three, five, or six notes. Kinsley was unique among manufacturers in offering whistles up to 20" in diameter, the largest whistle ever to appear in a trade catalog. At least one 20" Kinsley is rumored to have survived, although its existence has proved to be as elusive as that of the Great White Whale.

Occasionally one encounters small four-chime whistles which resemble Kinsleys in every respect, including even the 1892 patent date, but which are marked for the Yankee Co. of Utica, New York. Production numbers as high as 83,000 are known, suggesting that Utica may have been Kinsley's corporate successor, or may have purchased manufacturing rights from them in later years. In any event, whistles with Yankee marking are quite rare, and command a premium even over Kinsley whistles themselves. In recent years, Boothman & Johnson Specialty Products of Texas have produced a highly finished replica of a rare 5" four-chime Kinsley without valve, ca. 1894. This is clearly marked as a reproduction, and intended for the hobbyist/collector market, not as original equipment.

J. E. Lonergan & Co.

John Lonergan, a machinist, inventor, and former locomotive engineer, had already patented an improved form of spring-feed oil cup when he established his own company at Philadelphia in 1872. He remained its president for at least the next 38 years. From its origins, Lonergan was a vertically integrated manufacturing operation, with a foundry on Florist St. and executive offices and machine shops on nearby Race St. As brass founders and finishers they undertook to supply every form of steam appliance, including sight-feed self-oilers and lubricators, power oil pumps, water relief and snifter valves, steam traps, low water alarm injectors, ejectors, and other safety equipment. A particular specialty was the Lynde pop safety valve, the manufacturing rights to which were purchased from the inventor.

Lonergan Catalog 900-W, dated 1955, claims that the firm had been making whistles for 75 years, i.e., since 1880. This may be true with respect to plain whistles, but the single-bell chime whistles offered during those early years were unmistakably made by Crosby, reflecting Crosby's iron-fisted hold on the Einig patent. The practice of jobbing Crosby chime whistles continued through the 1901 and 1907 catalogs. The 1910 catalog, however, proclaimed "Everything Illustrated In This Catalog Is Of Our Own Manufacture." By this time Crosby's exclusive manufacturing rights to the single-bell chime had expired, and henceforth Lonergan was scrupulous about maintaining the integrity of its product line. The chime whistles were utterly transformed in appearance, acquiring bells with high rounded arches, and shallow bowls. The larger whistles had long-bodied acorns of conventional design, but for some unknown reason those 4" in diameter or less had a distinctive little button-like acorn which quickly earned the popular name "baby's prick." The Lonergan name, surrounded by a six-sided outline, was impressed in the mid-side of the bell according to the catalog, but in fact was more usually found on the rim of the bowl. The plain whistles had contrasting bells of drawn yellow brass tubing, in the manner of

The Lonergan adjustable bell chime whistle, ca. 1910, "for use on motor boats, launches, subway and interurban trolley cars." Both external design and market are obviously borrowed from Kinsley.

The Lonergan plain whistle, ca. 1910. Note the hefty jam nut and pipe nut.

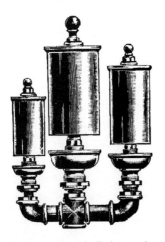

The Lonergan three-bell chime of 1910. These spherical acorns were not used anywhere else.

A trio of single-bell chime whistles from Lonergan's 1910 catalog. These are the first Lonergan single-bell chimes not made by Crosby nor sold under license from them.

Extra-heavy short-bell locomotive whistle for freight service, ca. 1910.

Extra-heavy long-bell locomotive whistle for passenger service, ca. 1910.

Lonergan types 3E and 4E (formerly type LBW) extra-long-bell plain whistles, an outgrowth of the ordinary plain whistle of 1910. First offered in 1918, these whistles found widespread application on ships.

Ashton, Buckeye, and Kinsley. An adjustable bell chime whistle, also with bell of yellow brass tubing, was offered in small diameters for compressed air service. Also available were plain whistles up to 8" in diameter with side valves, and short-bell (freight) and long-bell (passenger) locomotive whistles with vertical valves to Erie Railroad specifications. Three sizes of the three-bell chime whistle completed the whistle line. These were assembled on a rather coarse and clumsy manifold of ordinary pipe fittings, and the individual whistles were capped with distinctive acorns terminating in spheres.

In succeeding years the ampersand was dropped from the corporate name, and it became simply the J. E. Lonergan Co. The product line remained substantially unchanged in scope and appearance, except for the abandonment of locomotive whistles and the introduction of the 3E and 4E series of long-bell plain whistles. The former had bells three times their diameter and the latter four times. They shared the long-bodied acorn of all other large Lonergan whistles, and were generally marked on the side of

Whistle Manufacturers and Their Products

the bowl. They were made in sizes up to 12" x 36" and 12" x 48" respectively, and found widespread application in factory and marine settings, where they offered long projection distances with relatively tolerable local sound levels. In particular the 10" x 30" model was widely used on Great Lakes freighters, as was the 8" x 32" model on Liberty and Victory ships during World War II. Production of these whistles was continued at least until 1955. Sometime before 1977 Lonergan ceased whistle production altogether, and henceforth represented itself only as a manufacturer of safety relief valves.

The Lunkenheimer Co. *

The Lunkenheimer Co. is unique in several respects. First, it has probably produced more whistles than any other manufacturer. By the turn of the century it plausibly claimed to be the nation's largest maker of engineering specialties, and its catalogs were approaching 500 pages in length. Second, Lunkenheimer was quick to position itself as the Rolls-Royce of valve manufacturers, a reputation which was in fact merited by the quality of its products. This self-proclaimed supremacy was reflected in the prices it charged for its steam whistles. In 1907, for example, a 4" Buckeye single-bell chime with valve cost $18, the comparable Crosby chime cost $20, but the comparable Lunkenheimer chime cost $28. Third, an offshoot of the original firm continues to manufacture whistles on a production basis even today, and is probably the only firm in the nation to do so. Fourth and last, it is the only maker of whistles to have claimed the attention of a professional historian, Prof. James M. Laux of the University of Cincinnati. His scholarly article has provided much of the material for the brief review which follows.[2] Readers who seek further information are directed to the original article.

The patriarch of the Lunkenheimer family was Frederick Lunkenheimer, who was born in the Rhineland in 1825 and entered the metalworking trade at the age of fourteen. In 1845 he saw opportunities in America and emigrated to New York. He had no trouble finding work there, but decided to head west, spending two years in St. Louis. He then worked briefly in New Orleans, surviving the great yellow fever epidemic of 1853, in which 7,800 persons died in the Crescent City

alone. In 1854 he journeyed up the Ohio River to Evansville, Indiana, where he worked briefly at the Heilman machine shop to recoup his finances. He then continued up the Ohio to Cincinnati and obtained a job in the brass goods section of the Miles Greenwood metal works, which at that time employed about 500 men. He was soon promoted to foreman and acquired a wife and family. In 1862 he struck out on his own and founded the Cincinnati Brass Works, makers of brass bearings and lubricating devices for machinery. In this he may well have been encouraged by Miles Greenwood himself, whose manufacturing facilities were swamped with Civil War orders for bronze cannon and gun carriages and had no room to manufacture such specialty items.

Frederick Lunkenheimer, 1825- 1889, patriarch of the Lunkenheimer family.

At that time Cincinnati, with about 161,000 inhabitants, was the largest city in the west and a major manufacturing center. In addition to the Greenwood works it contained eleven brass founders and finishers and two bell founders. One of the oldest and largest of these firms was the Union Brass Works, founded by the English immigrant William Powell in 1846. Union Brass eventually became the Powell Co., a major manufacturer of whistles in direct competition with Lunkenheimer. Lunkenheimer's Cincinnati Brass Works began to manufacture whistles in 1865, in addition to globe valves, angle valves, gauge cocks, steam and water gauges, check valves, safety valves, and lubricators. The globe valves in particular embodied the first of several Lunkenheimer patents relating to *in situ* regrinding of the valve seats. Business prospered, and Lunkenheimer soon found himself in need of larger manufacturing facilities. In 1867 he moved his brass foundry into the improbable surroundings of a former synagogue, the walls of which contained embedded Hebrew tablets. There he remained for the next thirteen years.

* In collaboration with Lin Chapman

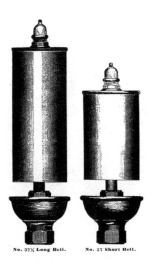

Cincinnati Brass Works plain whistles without valve, from the 1874 catalog.

No. 43.

Cincinnati Brass Works plain whistle with horizontal valve, from the 1874 catalog.

No. 82.

Lunkenheimer's first excursion into variable pitch whistles: the curious 'telescoping whistle' from the 1874 Cincinnati Brass Works catalog. The left margin is partially obscured in reproduction.

The Cincinnati Brass Works issued its first catalog, now a rarity, in 1870. The 1874 catalog showed two styles of valveless plain whistles, the No. 37 short bell and the No. 37-1/2 long bell, both available in diameters up to 8". They were conventional in every respect. The No. 43 whistle, on the other hand, was distinguished by a rimless bell, a horizontal valve with an invertible lever of alarming fragility, and some rather attractive (and entirely superfluous) ornamental turnings of the base. The whistle line was rounded out with a genuine curiosity, the No. 82 "patent telescopic whistle," another Lunkenheimer invention, in which the upper half of the bell slid over the lower in order to vary the length of the resonant gas column and hence the pitch. Insofar as the catalog engravings can be trusted, none of these whistles carried the marking which was to become the insignium of the Cincinnati Brass Works, consisting of the letter "S" (for Standard) inscribed within an oval on the side of the body.

The 1887 catalog offered essentially the same whistles, except that No. 43 had now become Fig. 45, and acquired a double fulcrum and a much more robust lever. The Cincinnati Brass Works insignium still was not depicted, although whistles of the era were known to carry it. Nor was any mention made of the availability of copper bells, another characteristic feature of Cincinnati Brass Works whistles. The telescopic whistle was dropped from the line, but Lunkenheimer's fascination with tunable whistles continued. The 1887 catalog marked the first appearance of the Fig. 49 piston whistle, in which a movable

Detail of an angle valve, showing the celebrated 'Circle-S' emblem of the Cincinnati Brass Works on the side of the valve body. This emblem was also applied to whistle valves, although for some reason this feature is not depicted in the catalog.

Cincinnati Brass Works Fig. 45 plain whistle with adjustable lever, from the 1887 catalog. Note the I-beam cross-section of the new lever.

Cincinnati Brass Works Fig. 49 piston whistle, the first of a long line of variable-pitch whistles offered by Lunkenheimer.

Whistle Manufacturers and Their Products

piston within the bell was actuated by a central rod protruding through a steam-tight gland at the bottom of the base casting. Finally Fig. 50 introduced three sizes of three-bell chimes, a type for which Lunkenheimer would subsequently become famous.

In the late 1880's Frederick decided to incorporate, and on February 4, 1889 the Cincinnati Brass Works became the Lunkenheimer Brass Manufacturing Co. Less than ten weeks later Frederick died at the age of 63, and the firm was taken over by his elder son Edmund. In 1893 the corporation adopted the name by which it is still known today, The Lunkenheimer Company. Edmund shortened his name to Lunken in 1892, but the family would not permit him to do the same with the corporate name, although the shortened version does appear in contemporary catalogs and on certain of Edmund's patents.

The newly incorporated firm issued catalogs prolifically, and these constitute an invaluable resource for the historian and collector. Catalogs known to survive include the years 1890, 1892, 1895, 1896, 1898, 1901, 1902, 1906, 1908, 1912, 1919, 1920, 1933, 1939, 1948, 1950, 1960, 1966, 1971, 1976, 1981, and 1987. They can be obtained with relative ease on the used book market, although the earlier ones are inclined to be expensive. Up through 1920 at least, these were produced primarily or exclusively in an octavo or pocket-sized version; from 1939 onward only in a quarto or full-sized version. The catalog numbering system is confused and confusing. Catalogs from 1906 or earlier were identified only by the year of issue. Catalogs issued from 1908 until World War II were numbered in accord with the years elapsed since 1862, the date which the firm regarded as the year of its founding. Thus, for example, catalog No. 50 was issued in 1912 and No. 58 in 1920. Sometime after World War II, possibly when Lunkenheimer became a division of Conval, catalogs were denoted by the last two digits of the year of issue. Thus No. 76, issued in 1976, follows by many years No. 78, issued in 1939 or 1940.

Although high quality valves remained Lunkenheimer's core business, the firm made some surprising excursions into other fields during its early years. In 1901, incredible as it seems, it fielded a gasoline-powered race car of its own manufacture. At that time the supremacy of the internal combustion engine for automotive use had not yet been established, and in fact steam cars and electric cars outnumbered gasoline-powered cars on the road. The 10 HP Lunkenheimer defeated a 9 HP Winton in a one-mile race around a harness track, but was itself defeated by a steam-powered Locomobile in a subsequent heat. There followed a five-mile race which was convincingly won by the Lunkenheimer machine in the record time of 10.5 minutes. This success initiated a long tradition of manufacturing accessories for motor cars, motor boats, and airplanes. The valves in Lindbergh's "Spirit of St. Louis" were made by Lunkenheimer, a distinction which the company did not fail to exploit. In another excursion far afield, in 1903 Edmund Lunken developed a steel frame window for residential and commercial use, and began to manufacture it at the Cincinnati plant. But the market for these windows collapsed when the union tradesmen who

The 1887 Cincinnati Brass Works catalog also brought the first appearance of the three-bell chime, which was to undergo numerous alterations and refinements in succeeding years.

Beginning around the turn of the century, Lunkenheimer frequently used this image of a hand upholding a valve in support of its slogan, "The One Great Name in Valves."

In 1890, now under the Lunkenheimer name, the three-bell chime acquired an elegant manifold made especially for it.

Lunkenheimer suffered massive confusion while attempting to notate the sounds produced by its three different sizes of three-bell chimes. The smallest whistle should be at the top, and several notes appear in the wrong octave.

The Lunkenheimer Fig. 441 plain whistle with valve, from the 1895 catalog. Note the acornless round top and the double fulcrum. As can be seen from the cutaway, the lower end of the bell was supported and aligned by a spider. This highly effective design feature was unaccountably replaced with a center stud the following year.

The Lunkenheimer Fig. 445 variable-pitch whistle of 1895, christened a "Mocking Bird" whistle. The guide rod N protrudes from the top of the whistle and travels up and down with the piston. In a later version, shown in Chap.3, a stationary guide rod is incorporated within the whistle bell.

installed them learned that Lunkenheimer was a non-union shop, and refused to work on their products.

Let us return to the steam whistle product line. In 1890, the first year under the Lunkenheimer name, the three-bell chimes acquired an elegantly curved cast manifold or "branch." Ashton Valve was the only other American manufacturer to cast a manifold specifically for its three-bell chimes; all other manufacturers contrived their manifolds from ordinary pipe fittings. Musically adept readers will observe that Lunkenheimer's efforts to notate the simple G major and D major triads produced by these whistles are hopelessly confused. The top and bottom examples have been transposed by the typesetter. The two upper notes of the largest whistle are written an octave too high, and the lowest note of the smallest whistle is written an octave too low. Pitch ambiguity is notoriously greatest when judging octaves, and especially when the sound is rich in overtones.[3] Nevertheless it is hard to believe that Lunkenheimer did not know the pitch of the whistles it manufactured. One can only guess that the musical notation was intended to depict what was heard rather than what was generated.

In addition, for a brief period around 1890, Cincinnati Brass Works seems to have jobbed plain whistles made by the Crane Co. of Chicago (Catalog figs. 237, 238). The reason for this curious departure from its usual policy is not known, although one may speculate that they were experiencing delays in bringing their own newly patented designs into production.

By 1895, under Edmund's leadership, the whistle line had been completely redesigned and expanded significantly in size and scope. Furthermore (as with Buckeye *q.v.*) the various types of whistles were henceforth identified by a numbering system which endured without change for nearly a century. Thus Fig. 441 denoted an all-brass plain whistle with horizontal valve, Fig. 442 the same whistle without valve, Fig. 443 a plain whistle with iron base and no

The Lunkenheimer Fig. 446 "Fire Alarm" or "Combination" whistle of 1895, completely redesigned from the earlier version shown p.114 bottom right. The 1912 version is substantially identical except for the style of lever.

The Lunkenheimer Fig. 450 three-bell chime takes on quite a handsome and distinctive appearance with the new round-top bells. This is the 1896 version with center studs supporting the bells; the 1895 version still employed spiders.

valve, Fig. 444 a whistle valve with adjustable lever, Fig. 445 a variable-pitch whistle of the mockingbird type, Fig. 446 a variable-pitch whistle of the combination or fire-alarm type, Fig. 447 a single-bell chime whistle with horizontal valve (Crosby's exclusive rights to the Einig patent had presumably expired by this time), Fig. 448 a single-bell chime without valve, Fig. 449 the same whistle with vertical valve, "locomotive style," and Fig. 450 a three-bell chime. In a stroke of marketing genius, the new whistles were given hemispherical rather than flat tops, distinguishing them on sight from all other whistles then available and from the flat tops of the former Cincinnati Brass Works offerings. Moreover the new line of whistles had no acorns, and their shiny polished domes soon earned them the nickname "baldies." Because of their rarity and exceptionally handsome appearance, Lunkenheimer baldies are much prized by collectors.

Lunkenheimer's single-bell chimes deserve special discussion. Unlike many other manufacturers, Lunkenheimer did not at any time in its history sell single-bell chimes made by Crosby under the Einig patent. Sometime in the late 19th century, possibly as early as 1888, Lunkenheimer developed its own design of single-bell chime. This was the so-called flat-top chime, the predecessor of the round-top chimes listed above. Lunkenheimer seems to have introduced this whistle with uncharacteristic timidity. It did not appear in any known catalog and today it is exceedingly rare. (Regrettably, a few spurious flat-tops have come to market; these are hybrids comprised of marked Lunkenheimer bowls with unmarked flat-topped bells from other makers.) Despite the name, the top was not quite flat; rather it was slightly convex with rounded edges, and might best be called lenticular. The bells were cast in one piece, with no acorn. The holes necessary to support the internal cores during casting were closed with yellow brass plugs during finishing operations. The bases of these whistles were the same as those of their single-note counterparts in the product line. The flat-tops were produced only until 1895, when they were superseded by the acornless round-tops, Figs 447 and 448, described above. A peculiarity of both flat-top and round-top acornless chimes was that the longest chamber had no internal top plate or closure, but opened directly into the dome. This increased the resonant volume of the chamber and deepened its pitch, giving the resulting three-note chord a unique (and not particularly melodious) sound. (The same practise was followed by Powell in its chime whistles.)

The round-top baldies also turned out to be rather short-lived, possibly because of a patent dispute with Powell. Ca. 1898, acorns reappeared on all plain whistles, including those incorporated in three-bell chimes. The return of the acorn greatly simplified production, for the protruding end of the center stud afforded a means of chucking the whistle body between centers on a lathe. It also solved a field maintenance problem, because it permitted the lip height to be adjusted to suit various inlet pressures merely by rotating the bell, rather than by screwing the center stud and bell assembly into or out of the base.

A very rare Lunkenheimer 'flat-top' single-bell chime, ca. 1890. Photo by Bruce Cynar.

Fig. 441.

In 1898 an acorn of traditional shape was restored to the top of the Fig. 441 plain whistle with valve.

Fig. 450. Three-Whistle Chime.

The whistles that comprise the Fig. 450 three-bell chime also acquired acorns in 1898. This is arguably the most handsome form taken by this famous whistle in its long history.

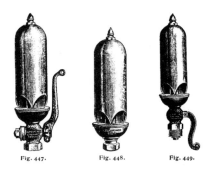

Fig. 447.   *Fig. 448.*   *Fig. 449.*

Only in 1902 did the single-bell chimes acquire acorns again. 1902 was also very nearly the last year for the double "bowtie" fulcrum on whistles with horizontal valves.

By 1906 all whistle valves, including those integral to whistles, had been fitted with the new style of separable lever fulcrum, rotatable to any angle and fixed by a jam nut. The lever itself remained unchanged.

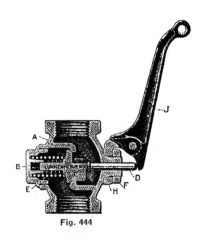

Fig. 444

In 1918 the actuating lever on all whistle valves became straight except for a slight crook at the far end. It has remained straight ever since.

Curiously, the single-bell chimes remained bald for another four years. They did not recover their acorns until 1902. At the same time the internal top plate was restored to the longest chamber, resulting in a more melodious chord. Numerous other small changes in design occurred over the years, many of them so minute that they can be appreciated only by specialists. For example, various schemes for aligning and supporting the lower end of the bell were applied to plain whistles in the 1890's. Eventually these were all abandoned as too costly to manufacture, except on the longest (3X) members of the three-bell chimes and on the mockingbird and fire alarm types, where the variable-pitch mechanism interfered with the usual means of support and made "spiders" a necessity.

Two design changes, however, are immediately apparent, and form one of the truly reliable means of dating Lunkenheimer whistles. Prior to 1903, whistles with built-in valves employed a double bowtie fulcrum cast integral with the valve body. This permitted the valve lever to stand upright or hang downward. After 1903 the double fulcrum was replaced by a single separable fulcrum which rotated freely around an externally threaded boss, and was fixed in angular orientation by a jam nut. Curiously, this separable and orientable fulcrum had already been applied to the Fig. 444 whistle valves as early as 1896. In 1918 the actuating lever itself, which had hitherto been given a gentle S-curve, was replaced with a more robust lever straight throughout except for a slight angle at its tip. Granted that levers are often replaced because of loss or breakage, if there is some assurance that the lever is original, then its shape is an infallible means of distinguishing pre-1918 from post-1918 production. Finally in 1920, the Jones patent (US 1,260,775) permitted the lever to respond either to an outward (radial) or a downward (vertical) pull. This completed the evolution of the valve assembly.

Changes took place among the more exotic whistles too. In 1908 the protruding center rod which guided the movable piston of the mockingbird whistles gave way to a fixed rod entirely contained within the bell. The manifold or branch on which the three-bell chime was erected underwent several changes. Sometime between 1902 and 1908 the side arms lost their graceful curves, and in 1920 the Lunkenheimer name was moved from the stiffening rib to the body of the casting. Meanwhile the line proliferated with a variety of new whistle types. In 1908 a line of small

The three-bell chime took its final form in the 1920 catalog. The straight-line manifold, although doubtless easier for the foundry to cast, is decidedly less attractive than the former curved manifold. Prior to 1920 the Lunkenheimer name, shown here on the body of the manifold, was cast on the stiffening rib above it.

Whistle Manufacturers and Their Products

low-pressure whistles was introduced, Fig. 160 being a single, Fig. 161 a double, and Fig. 162 a triple whistle. These had flat tops and very shallow bowls, much like calliope whistles. They were restricted to pressures less than 20 PSI, and intended for use on motor boats and trolley cars, where of course they were operated by compressed air rather than steam. The 1912 catalog introduced the line of long-bell steam whistles, Figs. 802 and 803 (without and with valve respectively) having bells of length three times the diameter, and Figs. 165 and 166 having bells of length four times the diameter. These were available on special order in up to 12" in diameter, and obviously intended for marine and fire alarm service. They could be had with polished copper bells and were extraordinarily handsome. Around 1919 the Fig. 951 "Tritone" single-bell chime was introduced. This was an aggressively ugly, all-iron top-lever whistle of simple and ingenious design, available up to 4" in diameter and evidently intended as a bottom-of-the-line economy model. Finally, numerous variants of existing designs appeared. Whistles formerly available only in brass could now be had with iron bases, albeit at lower pressure ratings. Those with threaded inlets spawned versions with flanged inlets, etc. It was, in Darwinian terms, an epoch of rapid species differentiation.

By 1939, owing to dwindling demand, the whistle line had contracted significantly. There remained only those stalwarts with which production had begun almost half a century earlier: Figs. 441, 442, 444, 446, 447, 448, 450, and their variants with bowls of different materials. Even the Fig. 445 mockingbird, much favored by locomotive engineers with a flair for showmanship, had vanished. Magnificence could still be purchased for $780, however, in the form of the No. 3-1/2 Fig. 1182 three-whistle chime with bronze branch and bases, and bells 5" x 15", 6" x 18", and 8" x 24". Fortunate is the collector who has one of these beauties in his collection, even though he may lack the boiler of minimum 500 HP rating and the 3" supply line necessary to blow it. By the 1970's there were only four survivors from the original line: the Fig. 441 plain whistle with valve, Fig. 442 plain whistle without valve, Fig. 447 single-bell chime with valve, and Fig. 444 plain whistle valve, plus two newer varieties of balanced valve. In emulation of Kinsley, Lunkenheimer began to stamp a production code or serial number on the hex nut or on the side of the fulcrum of these recently manufactured whistles. Numbers in excess of 92,000 are known. Valves and valved whistles produced in later years were also stamped on the side of the valve body with their nominal diameter in inches and their pressure rating in PSI, the latter usually 200 PSI. There was scarcely room on the bowls of the smallest whistles to engrave the lengthy corporate name, and in these cases it was often abbreviated merely to "L CO."

Incredibly, Lunkenheimer is still manufacturing whistles today. Always a small, profitable, but not particularly dynamic producer of industrial valves, in the late 1960's Lunkenheimer found itself the target of a hostile takeover by the Condec Corporation, a conglomerate of machinery firms from the Chicago area. A prolonged court battle ensued, which Condec eventually won, and in June, 1968, 105 years after its founding,

A gentleman of the Edwardian age was expected to own a fast motor launch, and Lunkenheimer stood ready to equip it with whistles.

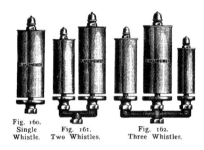

Fig. 160.
Single
Whistle.

Fig. 161.
Two Whistles.

Fig. 162.
Three Whistles.

The Lunkenheimer line of low pressure whistles for motorboat use. These were blown on air compressed by an "accumulator," powered in turn by spent gases from the engine.

The Lunkenheimer Fig. 803 long-bell (3X) plain whistle made its first appearance in the 1912 catalog. At this time whistle valves still had the old S-shaped lever.

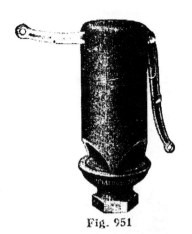

Fig. 951

The short-lived Lunkenheimer Fig. 951 'Tritone' whistle made its first appearance in 1919. An alternative mounting position for the top lever, suited to a vertical pull, is shown in phantom on the left side of the whistle.

No. 2.

The McNab & Harlin No. 2 plain whistle with valve, 1907 to 1920, and possibly later. Note the unusually short bell and generally robust construction.

No. 3.

The McNab & Harlin No. 3 plain whistle, ca. 1907. Note the crowned top plate and the heavily engraved lever, holdovers from an earlier era.

Lunkenheimer was merged into Condec and ceased to be an independent corporation. Tales of its imminent demise circulated for many years thereafter, reflecting uncertainties within the parent company. But in recent years a small firm named Cincinnati Valve has licensed a portion of the former Lunkenheimer facilities, as well as tooling, patterns, drawings, and the Lunkenheimer name, in order to produce bronze specialty goods. At this writing, Figs. 441 and 442 plain whistles in sizes up to 6" in diameter are being produced in the old foundry and machine shops at the rate of approximately 100 pieces per month. It is surprising that a market of such magnitude still exists. Even more surprising are the uses to which these whistles are put. The most popular item appears to be the 2" plain whistle, apparently because of its use on amusement park trains. The larger whistles are sold to prisons as backup alarm systems, presumably on the grounds that convicts bent on escape would find it more difficult to disable a steam line than to snip the wires of an electric signal system. Others are sold to the U.S. Navy for use on submarines, because the air horns and sirens usually employed on Navy vessels cannot withstand prolonged immersion in salt water.

McNab & Harlin Manufacturing Co.

This firm was one of the oldest of whistle manufacturers, originating in New York City in 1854 as a co-partnership under the name of the McNab-Carr Co. John Harlin was a member of this original partnership. In 1856 McNab-Carr outgrew its headquarters at the corner of Hester and Elizabeth Streets, and moved to larger headquarters on Mercer Street. In 1859 manufacturing operations were moved to Ward Street in Paterson, New Jersey, while sales were handled from an office at 16 John Street in New York. In 1862 Carr retired, ending the original partnership, and a new partnership was formed by McNab and Harlin. The firm moved back to New York and resumed manufacturing at 86 John Street. Two years later manufacture and sales were consolidated at 56 John Street.

In 1871 the McNab-Harlin partnership was officially terminated and replaced by a New York corporation under the present name. The following year manufacturing was again moved to Paterson, New Jersey, at Straight Street and Ramapo Ave. In 1911 the company discontinued the practice of jobbing goods from other manufacturers at its John Street office, and henceforth catalogued only goods of its own manufacture. These were shipped directly to customers from the factory in Paterson. Executive and sales offices, however, moved next door to 55 John Street.

Whistles were never more than a sideline for McNab & Harlin, which regarded itself as a general manufacturer of brass and iron goods for steam, water, and gas. The product line included valves and cocks of every description, as well as cast iron and malleable iron pipe and fittings. Only plain whistles were manufactured; there are no McNab & Harlin single-bell chimes. The 1907 catalog listed plain whistles of conventional design up to 8" in diameter, No. 1 without a valve and No. 2 with an integral horizontal valve. Curiously, these plain whistles were rated for no more than 125 PSI on steam despite their apparently heavy construction. Also listed were the No. 3 type of plain whistle with bell length twice the bell diameter and an elaborate conical top, three-bell chimes to the customer's specification, composed of three No. 1 whistles mounted on a manifold of ordinary pipe fittings, and a variable-pitch fire alarm whistle of narrow scale. The whistle portion of the 1907 catalog concluded with two curiosities: single and double organ pipe whistles, in all probability imported from an English manufacturer. The single organ pipe was offered in sizes up to 8" x 30". The fire alarm and the organ-pipe whistles remained in the catalog at least until 1920, but by that time the bell of the No. 3 plain whistle had undergone considerable simplification, losing its elaborate flanged top plate. It is not known when whistle production ceased altogether.

McNab & Harlin whistles are moderately rare. Whistles marked with the large "MH" monogram in the manner depicted in the catalogs are unknown, although valves so marked are known. The markings on whistles, if any, usually take the form of a single line of small type running circumferentially around the bell just below the top cover, and saying McNAB & HARLIN MFG. CO., followed in some instances by BROOKLYN, NY, USA and in other instances merely by NY. Whistles with valves were sometimes similarly marked on the valve body. In the absence of markings, McNab & Harlin whistles can be recognized by their unusually short bells (only 1.25 times the bell diameter in larger sizes), relatively large pipe inlets, absence of chamfer on the lip of the bell, and generally sturdy construction. The short bells contribute to the unusually high efficiency of the design. McNab & Harlin whistles with vertical valves can be recognized by the distinctive bracket arm extending from the base, supporting the lever fulcrum on a yoke with a short threaded tail. The levers of horizontal valves are cast of brass with deeply incised intaglio ornamentation.

WHISTLE CHIME.

The McNab & Harlin three-bell chime, ca. 1907.

The McNab & Harlin fire alarm or combination whistle, ca. 1907. The short engraved lever was shared with the No. 3 plain whistle, the organ pipe whistles, and the separate whistle valve.

Closeup of the peculiar lever fulcrum on McNab & Harlin whistles with vertical valves. The lever pivots on a clevis threaded into a bracket extending from the base. Photo by Bruce Cynar.

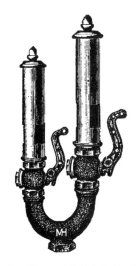

The rather bizarre McNab & Harlin double organ pipe whistle, ca. 1907, almost certainly of English origin. The single organ pipe whistle of 8" diameter was the largest offered by any American manufacturer.

The Morrison short-bell plain whistle with valve, ca. 1907. Note the ornate acorn and the shield on a stippled background on the side of the valve body. Long-bell and valveless versions were essentially similar.

Larger sizes of the Morrison plain whistle could be furnished with compound automatic valves, longer levers, and flanged bases. Again, the long-bell versions were essentially similar except for the 3X bell.

The Morrison single-bell chime owes very little to competitive designs by Crosby and others. This whistle was also available with compound automatic valve and flanged base, in both short-bell and long-bell versions. The 12" x 36" model must have made a wondrous sound.

James Morrison Brass Manufacturing Co.

Morrison Brass was a large and important Canadian manufacturer of engineers' and steamfitters' brass goods. Although its headquarters were in Toronto, its whistles frequently crossed over to the northern tier of the United States, and a whistle acquired in Michigan, Ohio, or northern New England not infrequently turns out to be a Morrison product. Like Hancock, Kinsley, and Nathan, trade catalogs of Morrison Brass are hard to find. Moreover Morrison numbered its catalogs rather than dating them, so a coherent history of the firm must be pieced together from ancillary clues. Nevertheless the effort is well repaid because Morrison made a large variety of whistles, including two models which are quite unlike those of any other maker.

The 1907 catalog showed a comprehensive line of plain whistles up to 10" in diameter, available with and without horizontal valves, and in both short bell (2X) and long bell (3X) versions. The valved whistles had ornate acorns in the style of the time, and slender, highly curved levers mounted on double fulcrums. Their distinctive feature, however, is the Morrison logo on the side of the valve body, a shield on a stippled background, crossed by a bar sinister. The Morrison name did not appear anywhere. This line of plain whistles with conventional disc valves was augmented by a parallel line of plain whistles with compound automatic valves for use on high pressure sources. The Morrison compound valve was unique. The auxiliary disc was not coaxial with the main disc,

A two-chime whistle in the guise of an ordinary organ pipe whistle. A central fin divided the interior of the bell into two independent chambers.

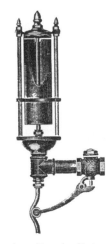

The Morrison 'Standard' piston whistle, from the 1907 catalog. Very similar to the combination or fire alarm whistles offered by American Steam Gauge & Valve and Crane, although called a "Mocking Bird" by Morrison.

The Morrison "Improved" piston whistle, ca. 1907.

but contained in a separate chamber below the main disc, which in turn had a large cylindrical protuberance surrounding the near end of the valve stem. Single bell chime whistles were also offered in diameters up to 12" with conventional valves and compound automatic valves of the same type used on the larger plain whistles. A curiosity was the two-chamber organ whistle with twin rectangular mouths, the bell split by an internal fin along its diameter.

Variable-pitch piston whistles of the fire alarm type were also offered, although they were called mocking birds, contrary to the name established by Lunkenheimer. As with similar whistles from American Steam Gauge & Valve, the base casting was a simple tee, permitting the use of a stock valve on the side arm. In the improved version of this whistle, the piston could be operated by a bicycle chain running over a pulley as well as by a central rod, thus effecting a sort of amalgam of the mockingbird and fire alarm designs. Extra-heavy long bell plain whistles in diameters up to 12" were offered for marine service, but no mention was made of railroad service. There followed a pair of truly extraordinary whistles available nowhere else, the double-bell "Harmonium" gong and the double-bell vertical chime, allegedly made in diameters up to 14" and intended for the largest factories and industrial applications. (See Chapter 3.) The whistle portion of the 1907 catalog concluded with a line of steam sirens (or "syrens") frankly imitative of Star Brass models, and an offer to build "combination whistle chimes" with any number and size of bells. The latter were based on British prototypes and bore an eerie resemblance to baroque candelabra.

Catalog No. 70, undated but probably issued between 1920 and 1930, essentially repeated the whistle line of 1907. In addition there was a fairly extensive line of locomotive whistles, including short bell and long bell plain whistles, a three-chime flat-top, a five-chime short bell steptop, and a six-chime long bell steptop. All had drop levers (vertical valves) and all were nominally 6" in diameter. These so closely resembled their counterparts in the Nathan line that one is tempted to believe they were of Nathan manufacture. If so, however, this would be the only known instance in which Nathan permitted its products to be jobbed by another maker. Finally there was a so-called wild cat pattern whistle which appears to be an exact copy of the Lunkenheimer mockingbird, except for the presence of the Morrison shield on the side of the valve body.

With the exception of the huge double-bell chimes, Morrison seems never to have made an original whistle. A few collectors believe that Morrison made no whistles at all. Its plain whistles, they assert, were in fact manufactured by Penberthy of St. Catherines, Ontario, and its single bell chime whistles by Crosby. Although Morrison's product lines bore a strong family resemblance to their counterparts elsewhere, this assertion is uncorroborated. It does seem to be true, however, that Canadian buyers favored long bell plain whistles to a greater extent than U.S. buyers. In any event a much larger proportion of the Morrison plain whistles which come to market are long bell versions than in the case of domestically manufactured whistles.

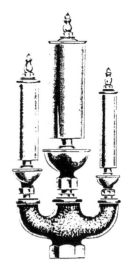

Who could resist a three-bell chime that seems to have been borrowed directly from the church altar? From the 1907 Morrison catalog.

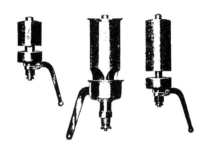

A trio of locomotive whistles from the 1920 Morrison catalog. Left to right: short-bell plain, single-bell three-chime, long-bell plain.

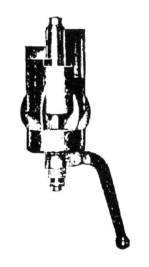

A five-chime short-bell steptop from the 1920 Morrison catalog, as regularly furnished to the Canadian Pacific and Canadian Northern railroads.

The Nathan type 963-A-1050 long-bell plain whistle for passenger engines.

The Nathan type 963-A-1030 six-chime long-bell steptop whistle, one of the world's most admired locomotive whistles, and certainly one of the most widely imitated. The lever (not shown) hung vertically downward.

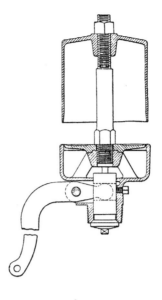

The Nathan type 963-A-1060 short-bell plain whistle for freight and switch engines.

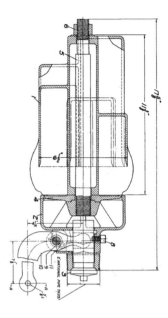

The Nathan type 963-A-1070 five-chime short-bell steptop whistle, from a 1943 company blueprint. Note that all Nathans in the 963-A series utilized the same bowl.

The Nathan type 63 plain whistle. This and the type 848 three-chime whistle were the only Nathans regularly offered with horizontal valves.

The Nathan type 848 three-chime flat-top whistle.

Nathan Mfg. Co.

Together with the Hancock Inspirator Co. and the Kinsley Mfg. Co., Nathan is one of the several whistle manufacturers whose corporate history is almost impossible to trace. Generally speaking, current management has not been responsive to inquiries from historians and industrial archeologists. This is

unfortunate because Nathan steptop chime whistles were the *de facto* standard for use on American locomotives throughout the second through fifth decades of the twentieth century, and are highly prized by collectors in consequence.

The earliest extant catalog dates from May, 1880, at which time the company was known as Nathan & Dreyfus, 108 Liberty Street, New York. Its specialty was the manufacture of ejectors, water elevators, and Friedmann's patent injectors for locomotives and marine boilers, although it also made a line of self-acting lubricators, oilers, and grease cups. By 1893 Dreyfus had been dropped from the company name, which now became the Nathan Manufacturing Co., new headquarters had been established at 92-94 Liberty Street, and Max Nathan was firmly installed as

Whistle Manufacturers and Their Products

president. The 1893 catalog and price list showed essentially the same product line as the 1880 catalog, and does not contain any steam whistles.

At this point, regrettably, there is a long hiatus in the archival record, and the next available catalog dates from 1907. By this time Nathan had become a major manufacturer of boiler appliances and accessories. Under the heading "miscellaneous appliances for use on locomotives," the 1907 catalog included many familiar types of whistles, notably the type 963-A-1030 six-chime long bell whistle with vertical valve for use on passenger engines. This is the earliest known appearance of the steptop in modern form. Also available were the 963-A-1050 long bell plain whistle for passenger engines, the 963-A-1060 short bell plain whistle for freight and switch engines, and the 963-A-1070 five-chime short bell whistle for freight and passenger engines. Nathan boasted that these four types were standard equipment on products of the American Locomotive Co. Finally the catalog listed the type 63 short bell plain whistle with horizontal valve and the type 848 three-chime flat-top whistle with horizontal valve. These last two bore no resemblance to each other or to other whistles in the line, and may be holdovers from an earlier era of manufacturing.

Bulletin No. 27, first issued in 1927 and in effect as late as 1959, showed types 963-A-1030, 1060, and 1070 still carried in the line and essentially unchanged, a tribute to the soundness of the original design more than five decades earlier. Meanwhile, Nathan had become a division of the Wegner Machinery Corp. in Long Island City.

In the absence of catalogs, some information about Nathan products can be found in the various editions of the Simmons-Boardman's *Locomotive Cyclopedia*, an annual industry handbook. Because of its dominance in the area of locomotive whistles, Nathan regularly contributed engineering drawings of its principal products to the chapter on boiler accessories. In addition, Nathan produced a variety of "one-off" whistles which are known only through their preservation in the hands of collectors. An example of the latter is the magnificent three-chime flat-top long bell whistles fitted to the J-1 class Northerns of the Western Maryland. It is not known whether these were a regular catalog item or made on special order. In general the company seems to have been quite accommodating to its customers, fitting whistles with top supports, reflectors, special levers, etc. as requested. So far as is known, Nathan never made a whistle that was not intended for railroad use.

Nathan steptops were widely imitated, and it is not always evident whether a given whistle was made by Nathan or in a railroad's own shops. In later years Nathan made a practice of embossing its trademark in bold upper case letters on the side of the bowl; in such cases the provenance cannot be doubted. In all other instances, however, the collector is advised to view the alleged attribution with appropriate scepticism.

Nathan no longer makes steam whistles, but it still exists today as a manufacturing division of the Windham Machinery Co. of South Windham, Connecticut. For more than four decades it has produced an extremely popular line of multiple-bell air horns, used by virtually every major U.S. railroad. Perhaps the most widely recognized of these is the type K-5LA air horn, the distinctive voice of every Amtrak locomotive, which it produces through an alliance with Airchime Mfg. of Vancouver, Canada.

Ohio Brass Co.

The Ohio Brass Co. of Mansfield, Ohio was a purveyor of accessories to light-rail and interurban railroads, including such items as insulators, trolley lines, rail bonds and tools, brass valves, and car equipment specialties. Within this last  category, it furnished throughout the 1920's and 1930's a valveless three-chime compressed air whistle of 2" diameter. The whistle was available in either of two bell lengths, 4" or 10". The shorter of the two whistles was identical in all respects to the corresponding offering from Kinsley, *q.v.* The Ohio Brass version was marked with its trademark logo, an upper-case "O" enclosing an upper-case "B", on the lower rim of the bell. It is unclear whether these whistles were manufactured by Ohio Brass under license from Kinsley, or merely resold by them under their own rubric.

The 10" long chime whistle, although overtly similar to the Kinsley, was conventional in design and lacked the tapered and twisted internal partitions which were the essence of Kinsley products. Like its predecessors, this whistle is intended for compressed air service only. Surprisingly, this whistle, somewhat simplified with respect to earlier versions, is still manufactured and sold today. Ohio Brass is now a subsdiary of Hubbell Inc., and its whistles are jobbed by the Passenger Transit Division of the Westinghouse Air Brake company

A two-inch three-chime Kinsley with Ohio Brass markings, intended for interurban use.

The 10" long Ohio Brass three-chime whistle, as manufactured today. Since the takeover by Hubbell, the traditional embossed logo has been replaced by a cheap foil sticker with a new logo.

The Penberthy logo ca. 1907. The shadowing of the letters appeared only in printed matter, not in the actual engraving on products. Despite several changes in detail, the basic bowtie shape was retained over the years.

Penberthy Injector Ltd.

Penberthy Injector was a Canadian firm, but its whistles were frequently seen in the northern tier of the United States. The firm was established in 1886 in Windsor, Ontario, later moving to St. Catherines, Ontario, with branch offices in Montreal, Toronto, Winnipeg, and Vancouver. In later years an additional manufacturing facility was established at Prophetstown, Illinois. Its principal product was its eponymous line of automatic feedwater injectors, on which it held fundamental patents. These were well regarded in their time and are still well regarded today, for Penberthy and Sellers injectors are more commonly encountered than any other brands. The product line was quickly supplemented with other boiler accessories, however, including gauge cocks, steam and water gauges, oil and grease cups, lubricators, and steam whistles.

Penberthy began to manufacture steam whistles at its Canadian facility in 1902. The oldest surviving catalog dates from 1907 and is identified as No. 22. This

was probably not preceded by 21 earlier catalogs. It is more likely that Penberthy, following the custom of Lunkenheimer and certain other manufacturers, numbered its catalogs in accord with the years elapsed since the founding of the company. This is consistent

The Penberthy No. 409 plain whistle with valve. The design remained essentially unchanged for half a century or more. See also the other Penberthy models under Jarecki.

Penberthy, like most other manufacturers, did not scale its whistles linearly, with the result that levers and acorns appeared disproportionately large on smaller models. When viewing this 1-1/2" Penberthy, the word "cute" springs irresistibly to mind. Photo by Bruce Cynar.

with the 1907 issue date. This catalog showed a line of plain whistles 1-1/2" to 4" in diameter, available with horizontal valve (No. 409) or without (No. 410), in both short bell (2X or less) and long bell (3X) versions. The distinctive features were a rather shallow bowl, an unusually ornate acorn with a spherical body topped by a blunt cone, a double or bowtie lever fulcrum cast integral with the valve body, a short lever with a pronounced "swan neck" reverse curve at its end, and a valve access cover capped with a large four-sided nut. The design closely resembled that of the corresponding Morrison Brass plain whistles, the principal difference being that the Morrison valve access cover is capped with a small hex nut. The smaller whistles are particularly attractive because the ornamental details are large compared to the bell. Long-bell whistles of 3" or 3-1/2" diameter were much favored for use on traction engines.

Penberthy customers must have been well satisfied with this design, for it remained essentially unchanged for the next 45 years, retaining even the same part numbers. The only discernible alterations in that period are that the length of the short bell was eventually standardized at twice its diameter, and 5" and 6" versions were added to the line. Apparently these larger whistles did not sell well, for sometime after 1952 they were dropped again, as were all the longbell versions. Later versions of the Penberthy plain whistle had a lighter top plate and jam nut with tapered sides. In 1960 the nut was replaced with a simple length of hex

bar stock. The last Penberthy whistle was shipped on April 7, 1974, allegedly to the International Nickel Co. at Copper Cliffs, Ontario.

The marking of Penberthy whistles is a vexing topic. Penberthy itself contributed to the confusion by insisting in its catalogs that "Our name is stamped on all our goods." This is simply not true, at least not in later years. The catalogs show a large bowtie logo on the side of the bell. No whistles marked in this fashion are known. When the Penberthy name does appear, it usually takes the form of a much smaller version of the bowtie logo on the side of the valve body. Plain whistles manufactured at the Prophetstown facility do not carry the Penberthy name, but do have the whistle diameter cast into the lever. Nominally identical whistles manufactured in Canada do carry the Penberthy name but do not have the whistle diameter cast into the lever. On the other hand, chime whistles manufactured in Canada are unmarked except for the diameter cast into the lever. Despite these inconsistencies, there is little risk of confusion with Morrison Brass whistles, inasmuch as the latter invariably carry the stippled Morrison shield on the side of the valve body.

Powell Co.

Lunkenheimer's chief rival was the Union Brass Works of Cincinnati, not to be confused with the United Brass Co. of New York or the United Brass Works of Randleman, North Carolina. Union Brass Works later became the Wm. Powell Co., and still later, Powell Valves. In fact Union could claim priority over Lunkenheimer, having been established in 1846, although not incorporated until 1886. Union Brass Works catalogs as early as 1884 have survived. They carry the legend "Wm. Powell & Co. Proprietors" just below the firm name, foreshadowing their corporate future. A complete line of shortbell (2X) and longbell (3X) plain whistles was offered, with or without horizontal valves, in diameters up to 8". The distinctive feature of these whistles was a peculiar acorn, sharply necked in just above the internally threaded portion. This would seem to offer very little latitude for adjustment of the lip height. There was also the obligatory three-bell chime composed of

A plain whistle with valve from the 1884 catalog of the Union Brass Works, predecessor of Powell. Note the distinctive narrow-necked acorn. The short-bell and long-bell plain whistles are similar except for the absence of a valve.

Union Brass's 1884 version of a three-bell chime. A different acorn was often used on these composite whistles, for no discoverable reason. These acorns look like Penberthys, although the whistles themselves do not.

Powell's plain whistle with valve in 1898. Acorn and base are the same as before, but the bell is transformed.

plain whistles on an in-line manifold of pipe fittings. Powell issued catalogs almost as prolifically as Lunkenheimer—fortunately for the collector, because the whistle line underwent numerous changes over the years. In addition to the forementioned 1884 catalog, surviving catalogs include the years 1898, 1903, 1907, 1915, 1936, 1940, 1943, 1951, 1952, 1954, and 1964. One version of the 1898 catalog quoted prices in shillings and pence, indicating that Powell had already established a branch office in the U.K. by this time. In that year the product line was augmented by the addition of iron-based plain whistles and a single-bell chime, perhaps under license from Crosby. The rimmed bells of all whistles were replaced with a rimless waterfall design; Powell never again made a whistle with a rimmed top plate. All other features of these whistles were carried over from the prior Union Brass Works designs, including the peculiar acorn, now applied to the single bell chimes as well. The valved whistles had an extremely large and distinctive valve access cover or bonnet with internal threads and a concave nose. There was also a threaded joint between the bowl and the valve body, permitting the manufacturer to offer the whistle with or without valve by a simple interchange of parts. This joint is diagnostic; no other manufacturer's whistles ever had this feature. All the valved whistles and the separate whistle valve carried the Powell emblem, consisting of a five-pointed star in outline surrounded by the words POWELL'S VALVE, or in some cases POWELL'S IMPROVED WHISTLE. (The star insignium has led some novice collectors to confuse Powell whistles with Star Brass products.) Curiously, the star and the lettering on the separate whistle valve were oriented so that they read correctly only if the lever is on the underside, and indeed this is the way the valve is pictured in the catalog. Perhaps Powell expected all whistle valves to be installed in overhead lines! At least two whistles in the author's collection also have this odd feature, although it contradicts the depictions in the catalog. Another curious feature was that some of the valve levers from the ca. 1900 era were heavily engraved with curlicues, stars, and other superfluous ornaments, the richness of which is scarcely apparent in the catalogs.

Between 1898 and 1907 the line of Powell whistles underwent major design changes. Unfortunately the catalogs needed to document these changes precisely have not yet been recovered. The 1907 catalog—which incidentally still titled itself a catalog of the "Union Brass Works, Wm. Powell Co., Proprietors"—showed the plain whistles substantially unchanged except for a somewhat straighter lever and an acorn of more conventional proportions. But the line of single-bell chimes was utterly transformed. Perhaps in imitation of the Lunkenheimer line, they were now pictured as round-top baldies without acorns, a configuration they retained until the final days of production. The transition from conventional flat-top design to acornless round-top design did not take place overnight, however. During a brief transition period around 1903, Powell chimes had a vestigial and non-functional acorn cast directly onto the round top of the bell. This short-lived

Whistle Manufacturers and Their Products

variation appeared only in the 1903 catalog. The button-like adornment gave whistles of that era the nickname "baby's prick," not to be confused with the button-like acorns on the smaller Lonergan chimes. As remarked previously in connection with Lunkenheimer baldies, a whistle without an acorn is more difficult to manufacture because there is no way to chuck it between centers on a lathe. Hence every bald Powell chime had an inserted plug at its very top to conceal the stub used for centering. As with contemporary acornless designs from Lunkenheimer, the longest chamber had no internal closure at its top, but opened directly into the dome. Furthermore, the emblem on valved whistles was substantially altered. The Powell star was now inscribed in a circle and overlaid with the word POWELL, and the emblem reads correctly when the whistle is upright. Finally, the valve access cover was now externally threaded and of much more modest proportions. Plain whistles without valves were depicted with the brand name engraved on the side of the bowl below the rim, but in the author's experience were more likely to be marked on one flat of the pipe nut, the words WM. POWELL CO. appearing in an arc over CIN. O. Another face of the pipe nut carried a stamped number indicating the nominal diameter of the whistle in inches.

But the truly novel item in the 1907 catalog was Fig. 704, the three-bell chime "with improved base fixture." On the dubious premise that a conventional in-line manifold delivered more steam to the central whistle than to those on either side, Powell spaced three plain whistles evenly around the rim of an enormous cast iron tub or urn, a massive structure having many times the necessary volume. Why a simple three-armed spider would not have achieved the same end was never made clear. In any event, these Powell triples are authentic curiosities of great rarity. Less than a handful survive, all in private collections so far as is known.

By World War II, the Wm. Powell Co. had grown considerably. In its 1940 catalog it characterized itself as a valve manufacturer, and boasted general offices and two large plants in Cincinnati, an engineering and export department in New York, branch offices in Chicago, Cleveland, and St. Louis, and stocking distributors in 45 U.S. cities. The line of plain whistles remained substantially unchanged, except that iron bases were no longer available. There remained just six varieties: with and without valves, each in three different bell lengths, 1.5X, 3X, and 4X. The single-bell chimes numbered just three varieties: without valve or with plain valve in diameters up to 10", and with balanced valve in 5", 6", and 8" diameters. The valve access cover on the plain valve models was essentially unchanged from the 1907 version, but in 1936 and later versions the balanced valve models reverted to the enormous internally threaded covers used in the 19th century. Thus a whistle with an enlarged valve access cover is either quite old or rather new with a balanced valve. Unlike most other large manufacturers, Powell seems never to have made a 12" diameter whistle of any type, and even the 10" diameter whistles were made sparingly. In fact the large Powell whistle most often encountered is the 8" diameter chime, and deservedly so, for its tone is powerful and pleasing.

Powell's single-bell chime of 1898. The principle may be due to Crosby, but certainly not the design.

Powell's separate whistle valve of the 1890's. The emblem reads correctly only when the valve is overhead! Note the large internally threaded valve access cover, which was to reappear decades later on balanced valves.

Closeup of the curious engraving on the levers of Powell whistle valves, ca. 1900.

Whistle Manufacturers and Their Products

129

By 1907 Powells had begun to look like Powells. This is the single-bell chime with horizontal valve. Valveless and vertical valve versions were also offered. The round top was used only on chime whistles. Powell never made a plain whistle with a round top.

The utterly original Powell three-bell chime, ca. 1907. Incredibly, it remained in the product line until 1956.

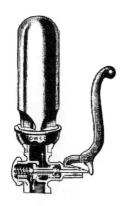

From 1936 onward the single-bell chime was offered with an optional balanced valve. To accommodate the mechanism of this valve, Powell reverted to the old style large valve access cover with internal threads.

The 1954 catalog showed no changes of consequence. The introduction did however contain the curious assertion that "whistle bells are made of a special bronze for withstanding vibratory action during operation." This claim appears to have been confected by the marketing department rather than the engineering department, for no whistle ever failed due to "vibratory action," unless it be the constant pounding endured by locomotive whistles. Powell's claim may be contrasted with the assertions of other manufacturers that their whistles were composed of alloys specially chosen to *promote* resonance, i.e., vibratory action. Taken together, the two statements indicate how poorly whistle manufacturers understood the mode of operation of their products, even as late as the mid-twentieth century. The 1956 catalog contained the final appearance of the bizarre three-bell chime. 1964 appears to be the final year in which Powell independently manufactured and sold whistles. The catalog offered the usual six varieties of plain whistle and three varieties of chime whistle, all essentially unchanged for almost six decades. These whistles continued to be produced for a few more years, and were sold under the name "Dart" through major industrial supply houses such as McMaster-Carr of Chicago.

Schaeffer & Budenberg Mfg. Co.

Schaeffer & Budenberg is one of the older manufacturers of boiler appliances, having been founded in 1850. Manufacturing facilities and general offices were located in Brooklyn, New York, with sales offices at 66 John Street in New York and 22 West Lake Street in Chicago. The 1893 catalog showed a very extensive line of pressure gauges, both bourdon and spring type, together with time clocks, calorimeters, tachometers, thermometers, engine indicators, injectors, ejectors, and numerous other steam accessories. For use in breweries and engine rooms, the gauges and clocks could be mounted in clusters on tall columns so richly ornamented with curlicues that they seemed more appropriate to the High Baroque than to the Victorian age. Only one steam whistle was listed, and that was an incidental accessory to a low water alarm.

The most interesting products in the 1893 catalog, however, were not steam whistles but a line of steam "syrens" (so spelled), available in four different types and six different sizes. Sirens are not true aerodynamic whistles, of course, because they contain a revolving rotor, but they appeal to many whistle collectors nevertheless. The characteristic

"Whoop! Whoop! Whoop!" of a U. S. Navy destroyer, heard in innumerable Hollywood war films, is the sound of a steam siren. Schaeffer & Budenberg syrens were identical in every respect to the line of steam syrens offered contemporaneously by the Star Brass Mfg. Co. *q.v.* The use of the archaic English spelling, however, suggests that neither product was indigenous to the U.S. It appears instead that both products were derived from the original patent by the brassfounders Steven & Burt of Glasgow.

No 20th century catalogs from Schaeffer & Budenberg are known. Nevertheless whistles of their manufacture are not particularly rare, and come to market with some frequency. Those available for study appear to be entirely unexceptional in appearance and construction, following the well known designs of Crosby and others. Levers tended to be short and curly, and were held captive by the valve stem in earlier models. Stamped markings are typically found just below the rim of the bowl, saying SCHAEFFER & BUDENBERG / NEW YORK in two lines. A model number is frequently stamped on one flat of the inlet hex nut. At some later date—the exact date is not known—Schaeffer & Budenberg merged with American Steam Gauge & Valve Manufacturing, becoming American Schaeffer & Budenberg Corp. At that time whistles of its own manufacture were discontinued in favor of existing American designs.

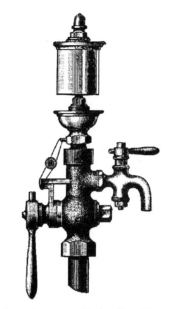

The only steam whistle offered by Schaeffer & Budenberg in 1893 was this small component of a low water alarm.

Star Brass Mfg. Co.

The Star Brass Manufacturing Co. was a well known and prolific maker of pressure and vacuum gauges, safety valves, steam engine indicators, globe and angle valves, lubricators, test pumps, and all manner of engine and boiler appliances, including of course steam whistles. Its main office and works were originally located at 33 Lancaster Street in Boston, Massachusetts, with branch offices in New York and San Francisco. Sometime before 1900 its office and works relocated to 108-114 East Dedham Street in Boston, and an additional branch office was opened in London. Beyond this, very little is known about its corporate history.

Star Brass trade catalogs are a bit peculiar. Until about 1904 they were dated, but for the next three decades they were merely numbered. Dating resumed with Catalog No. 10 in 1933. Collectors are warned that the engravings in these catalogs were numbered consecutively regardless of what they depict. Hence, unlike the catalogs of Lunkenheimer and other makers, there is no unique model or pattern number attached to a whistle throughout the years. The earliest surviving catalog is dated 1892, and was probably preceded by several others which have not survived. It offered "The FRISBIE Improved Single Bell Chime Whistle with Adjustable Bell," with or without horizontal valve, in diameters up to 12". These were identical to the contemporaneous offerings from Kinsley, and the dates of two of Henry Frisbie's many patents were cited below the engravings. It is not clear whether Star Brass was merely jobbing whistles made by Kinsley, or had reached its own licensing agreement with Henry Frisbie, or was

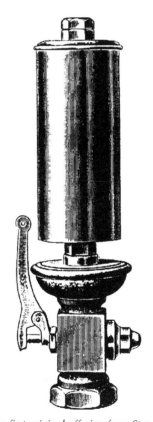

The first original offering from Star Brass: the strictly utilitarian extra-heavy Lauder whistle for locomotive and marine use, 1894. Regardless of its merits, it remained in the product line only six years.

1904 saw a burst of innovation in the Star Brass product line. This is the "Locomotive Style Improved Single Bell Chime Whistle" of reduced height.

The Star Brass "Extra Heavy Long Bell Whistle," ca. 1910. These rugged whistles with their balanced valves set the standard for marine whistles for a generation to come.

cloaking an act of piracy under the Frisbie name. In any event a Kinsley-like whistle with Star Brass or Frisbie markings would be an extraordinary rarity, and none are known to have survived. Also included in the 1892 catalog was a line of plain whistles, with or without horizontal valve, in diameters up to 10". These were indistinguishable from contemporaneous offerings by Crosby although they are not so credited, and as with several other firms, one may presume that Star Brass was merely jobbing them on Crosby's behalf.

The 1894 catalog essentially recapitulated the 1892 product line with one significant addition, the Star Locomotive or Marine Whistle, designed by James N. Lauder, superintendent of motive power on the Old Colony divison of the New Haven Railroad. This no-nonsense plain whistle was very heavily constructed, with a 5" x 13" bell, a horizontal valve with a short lever, a double end nut on the top plate instead of an acorn, and a curious cubical valve body resembling that of the Kinsley line. No surviving examples are known.

The 1900 catalog continued to list the Crosby plain whistles, but the Lauder-designed plain whistle had vanished. Furthermore, the Kinsley chimes were replaced by "extra heavy pattern" single-bell chime whistles in sizes from 1-1/2" through 12". Models without valve, with vertical valve, and with side valve were pictured. These single-bell chimes appear to be identical in every respect to those offered by Crosby as early as 1888. Even the accompanying text was identical, suggesting once again that Star Brass was merely jobbing whistles manufactured by Crosby, following expiration of the latter's monopoly on the Einig patent.

In 1904 the larger sizes of single-bell chimes were made available with compound automatic valves, facilitating operation at higher boiler pressures. Also offered in 1904 was a 5" "locomotive style" version of the single bell chime, with shallow bowl and a simple hex nut replacing the acorn. This lowered the overall height of the whistle to meet limited clearance situations. "Extra heavy" plain whistles with horizontal valves—Star Brass does not seem to have made any whistles of ordinary weight—could be had in diameters from 2" to 12", and again a locomotive version of reduced height was available in 4" through 6" diameters. Two more types of locomotive plain whistles of extremely massive and robust construction were offered, one with a moderately short bell of 5-1/2" diameter and vertical valve, intended for freight service, and the other with an extremely short bell, no taller than it was wide, and a horizontal valve, intended for freight engines or switchers. (See figure on p. 30 for these whistles.) Finally there was a line of plain whistles intended for marine use, with extra long bells and horizontal valves. This model was to become Star Brass's best known and most durable product, seeing service on innumerable ships and remaining essentially unchanged through the end of World War II. The balance of the whistle section was filled out with organ pipe whistles, obviously made by Crosby, and a line of common (i.e., plain) whistles for low pressure service, possibly made by Buckeye. Unlike Buckeye whistles, however, these plain

Whistle Manufacturers and Their Products

Work
refreshed

A pair of Coca-Cola ads (on this page and the next) that cleverly reinforce the association between the soft drink and breaks in the rhythm of the work day.

Where you work

*The pause that refreshes
with ice-cold Coca-Cola*

Coca-Cola 5¢

A whiskey ad, featuring a Lunkenheimer three-bell chime in action.

"The Noon Whistle" by John Falter, an idyllic evocation of life in an American mill town near the beginning of the 20th century. Copyright 3M Corp. Reprinted by permission.

Currier and Ives' "The American Express Train": long on atmosphere, short on mechanical accuracy.

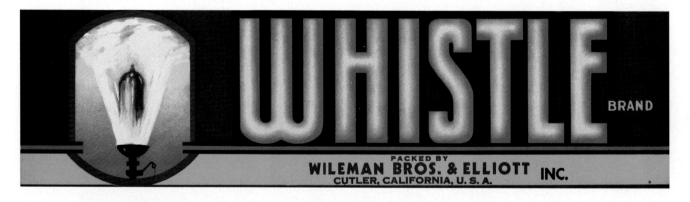

The steam whistle used to sell fruit. The connection is obscure, to say the least.

Whistling in the New Year during the depths of the Great Depression.

Fortune

One Dollar a Copy   MARCH 1937   Ten Dollars a Year

The steam whistle is the central figure in a rather somber image of the revival of heavy industry. Obviously the concept of industrial pollution had not yet been invented. The celebrated graphic designer A.M. Cassandre was the artist.

whistles were distinguished by a square (four-sided) nut on the valve access cover, a feature which they retained for at least another three decades. As previously remarked, Star Brass also manufactured from its earliest days a complete line of steam sirens. Although it was not the only manufacturer to do so (cf. Schaeffer & Budenberg, above), Star Brass came to dominate this market utterly, so that a steam siren was universally called a "Star Brass siren," regardless of its actual manufacturer, just as facial tissue is universally called "Kleenex."

In catalog No. 10 (1923?) the single bell chime whistles and long bell marine whistles were essentially unchanged. The two low-clearance locomotive whistles have been clearly differentiated in function: the single-bell chime intended for passenger service and the considerably lower pitched plain whistle intended for freight service. This is the reverse of the usual practice of assigning lower pitches to passenger engines and higher pitches to freight engines. The massive and squatty plain locomotive whistles were gone altogether, and a novel type of whistle appeared in their place: the "Star Improved Five Tone Locomotive Chime Whistle," a steptop design with a horizontal valve and protruding ears between the chambers. Because of uncertainty in the date of issue of this catalog, it is not clear whether Star's offering preceded or followed the very similar Nathan design of 1907. Nevertheless this type of whistle is indelibly associated with Nathan, and in the absence of a credible conflicting claim from Star, Nathan may be presumed to have originated it. Regrettably, there does not seem to be a patent to support either claim. Whatever its origin, it quickly swept all other types of locomotive whistle before it, and became the characteristic sound of the American steam locomotive. Also new in this catalog was the "Star Improved Variable Tone or Mocking Bird Whistle", available in 5", 6", and 8" diameters and intended primarily for use as a fire alarm. Despite the name, this was properly a combination whistle, because the piston was actuated by a push-rod protruding through a steam-tight gland in the bottom of the bowl, rather than by a chain-and-pulley arrangement. It was frankly imitative of similar designs by Lunkenheimer and Crane, and followed them by many years. Finally, Star no longer jobbed Crosby or Buckeye whistles, and they have vanished from the catalog. The distinguishing and unmistakeable feature of these and all other flat-topped Star Brass whistles was the manufacturer's name and address cast into the top plate in a bold circumferential intaglio. The only other form of manufacturer's marking known to have been employed were the words STAR BRASS embossed on the top of steptop whistles.

The 1933 edition of catalog No. 10 appears to be identical to the 1923 edition in every respect, including even the prices. It is not known when Star Brass ceased to manufacture whistles, although whistles bearing their imprint were fitted to countless Liberty ships and Victory ships during World War II. In 1944 or 1945 the assets of Star Brass were sold to the Kunkle Valve Co. of Fort Wayne, Indiana, which promptly discontinued almost the entire product line except for safety and relief valves. All parts, materials, and inventory were scrapped and all production records were

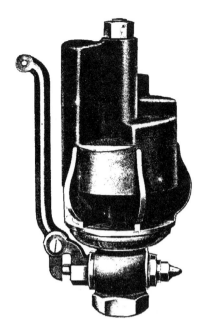

The Star Brass "Improved Five Tone Locomotive Chime Whistle," ca. 1910. Was this the first steptop? The historical record leaves room for doubt.

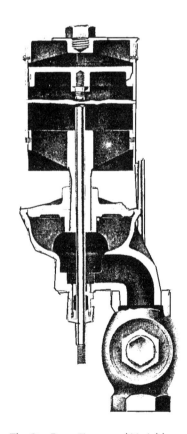

The Star Brass "Improved Variable Tone or Mocking Bird Whistle," ca. 1910.

lost or destroyed. Star Brass whistles are valued by collectors today because of their distinctive markings, sturdy construction, and reliable operation.

Steven & Struthers

Steven & Struthers was not a North American manufacturer, but its products were so widely dispersed in maritime applications that it has become relatively well known in this country. A Scottish firm of engineers and brassfounders, with headquarters in Kelvinhaugh, Glasgow, it specialized in marine hardware and enjoyed an enviable reputation as purveyor of high quality fittings of all kinds to the British Admiralty and War Office. Its steam whistles adorn countless vessels of foreign as well as British registry. In the 1880's Steven & Struthers either absorbed, or more likely succeeded, Steven & Burt, brassfounder of Glasgow and inventor of the steam siren.

The overwhelming majority of Steven & Struthers whistles were of the organ pipe variety, with bells having speaking lengths at least five times their diameter, and two opposed rectangular mouths, slightly taller than they are wide, each embracing one-quarter of the circumference of the bell. Top caps were slightly domed, and soft-soldered or riveted in place. Whistles were usually supplied with an integral valve of the vertical type, with downward-hanging lever. Only the "Admiralty No. 6" whistle had a horizontal valve with upright lever. Bases were usually flanged rather than threaded, and invariably so on whistles 6" to 10" in diameter. A peculiarity of the Steven & Struthers line was the availability of combined signaling devices, comprising two or three organ pipe whistles, one whistle and a siren, or two whistles and a siren. The various constituents of these combination signals were usually fitted with individual valves. It also offered a short bell plain whistle of conventional design, allegedly in diameters up to 18", but none of these are known to exist in private collections.

Steven & Struthers whistles are not marked, but their style is so distinctive as to make identification virtually certain. The only possibility of confusion is with whistles manufactured by Shipham & Co. Ltd. of Hull, U.K., and the latter are readily identified by the threaded joint between bowl and bell.

Westinghouse Air Brake Co.

Those who associate the name Westinghouse with toasters, turbogenerators, and other products of the great Westinghouse Electric Co. may not be aware of the full range of George Westinghouse's inventive genius, represented by more than a hundred patents in virtually every field of engineering. In 1868, at the age of 22, he invented the air brake system that bears his name. The following year he organized the Westinghouse Air Brake Co. to exploit this invention. This was not the first attempt to employ compressed air for braking trains, but in all previous efforts the air pressure was used to *apply* the brakes. If a coupler failed and the train parted—a fairly common occurrence in the 1860's—the air escaped from of the system and train braking ability was lost. Westinghouse had the revolutionary notion of using air pressure to hold the brakes *off.* Thus if air pressure were lost, the train automatically came to a halt. The importance of this invention far transcends that of the air brake itself; it was the first application of the fail-safe principle. The obvious advantages of this design were resisted by the greedy railroad magnates of the day, and it took an act of Congress (The Railroad Safety Appliance Act of 1893) to compel them to install air brakes and automatic couplers on both freight and passenger trains.

The Traction Brake Division of Westinghouse made brake gear for interurbans and other light-rail vehicles, but it also made a variety of peripheral accessories, such as the well-known "Pneuphonic" series of air horns, an extensive line of quick-acting valves, and two distinctive types of whistles. These were the "Clarion" whistle, a two-bell horizontal gong also known as a caboose whistle, and the "Trombone" whistle, a plain whistle of unusually narrow scale and nasal timbre. The origins of these fanciful names are obscure,

A representative large organ pipe whistle by Steven & Struthers, as furnished to the British Admiralty. Note the slightly crowned top, the two opposed square mouths, and the flanged base.

Whistle Manufacturers and Their Products

inasmuch as neither whistle resembles its namesake—a shrill medieval trumpet and an orchestral trombone respectively—in either appearance or sound. Like all Westinghouse pneumatic products, these whistles were not intended to operate on steam, but on compressed air from the brake line at a pressure of about 135 PSI. Nevertheless they are so commonly encountered, and so frequently confused with steam whistles, that they merit inclusion in this chapter. An anomalous 3" three-chime whistle with Westinghouse markings and the word MASTER engraved on the hex nut exists in a private collection. This whistle does not appear in any catalog and nothing more is known about it. In addition Westinghouse jobbed three-chime and four-chime whistles of 2" diameter, manufactured by Kinsley and also intended for light-rail vehicles.

The Clarion whistle presented an unusually handsome appearance owing to the use of contrasting metals: a central bronze casting flanked by bells of yellow brass. The Trombone whistle had three separate arched mouths and a three-lobed inner divider, occasionally leading novices to mistake it for a three-chime whistle. In fact it had only one resonant chamber, and functioned quite well without the divider. Early versions of this whistle had a cast brass top bearing the Westinghouse insignium; later versions had a similarly marked brown Bakelite top. Although not shown in its catalogs, Westinghouse also sold a shorter version of this whistle, only 6-1/4" tall and an octave higher in pitch, used by the Chicago Transit Authority (CTA).

In the mid-1970's Westinghouse Air Brake became a subsidiary of American Standard, a maker of plumbing and heating supplies, and was henceforth known by the acronym WABCO. The 1978 catalog still carried both Clarion and Trombone whistles, and in addition, a line of three small cab signal whistles, known as bell type, willow type, and "H" type respectively. These were intended to relay signals from conductor or brakeman to engineer or fireman. The so-called bell whistles were manufactured in high, medium, and low pitch versions, and were universally called "peanut" whistles, either because of their appearance or because of their aural resemblance to the whistles of the carts of peanut vendors.

Westinghouse whistles are easily recognized by their unique appearance and by the embossed logo shown on the next page. This rather enigmatic design has provoked much speculation regarding its meaning. Novices frequently interpret it as two "X"s side by side, but offer no hint of its significance. Others describe it as two "W"s back to back, one upright and one inverted, mirrored in the horizontal line which joins them. This interpretation has at least the merit of employing the initial letter of Westinghouse. A third school holds that the logo is actually an "A" superimposed on a "V" and stands for Ashton Valve. It must be admitted that this interpretation fits the design better than any other, and it carries with it the implication that Ashton manufactured these whistles for Westinghouse under a subcontract. If so, this would not be the first instance in which Westinghouse had some of its catalog items manufactured by others. It is known for example that some Westinghouse gauges were manufactured by

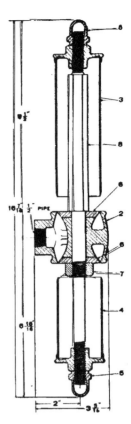

Outline drawing of the Westinghouse "Clarion" air whistle, ca. 1942.

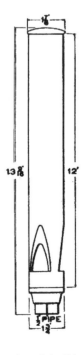

Outline drawing of the Westinghouse "Trombone" air whistle, ca. 1942.

Ashcroft or Star Brass. On the other hand, although the logo appears frequently in Westinghouse literature, it was apparently never used by Ashton Valve itself. Moreover, as we have seen, Ashton Valve was absorbed by Crosby in 1946 and ceased to have an independent existence. A competitive firm, the New York Air Brake Co., made a whistle superficially identical to the Westinghouse "Clarion," but its logo was quite different, consisting of an upper-case "N" with the vertical strokes adorned with swashes. This logo is often misinterpreted by novices as "JNJ" with the second "J" inverted.

After Westinghouse was absorbed by American Standard, the so-called XX logo was replaced by a new logo consisting of the acronym WABCO surmounting a stylized letter "W". Although Westinghouse Air Brake products are often referred to generically as Wabco products, it is important to note that the XX logo and the Wabco name belong to different eras, and were never employed simultaneously.

A handful of "peanuts": the three sizes of WABCO bell type cab signal whistles, ca. 1978. Photo by Barbara Sherwood.

The Westinghouse logo, ca. 1942.

The Westinghouse logo, ca. 1978.

Whistle Manufacturers and Their Products

Rowland Humble of Bodmin, Cornwall, U.K., surrounded by a portion of his collection of steam whistles, including the immense three-bell Smith-Hyson chime from the Mauretania. Photo by Bill Williamson.

6 *Collecting Whistles* *

> Ownership is the most intimate relationship that one can have to objects. Not that they come alive in him; it is he who lives in them.
>
> —Walter Benjamin

> Lives based on doing or being are freer than lives based on having.
>
> —William James

Introduction

The contrasting quotations that head this chapter reflect the mixed feelings with which the world regards collectors and their activities. A similar ambivalence is apparent in the titles of two recent books about collectors and collecting: *Collecting: An Unruly Passion*[1] and *Magnificent Obsessions*.[2] To call collecting a "passion" is to acknowledge that it springs fundamentally from the realm of the emotions, as we shall have further occasion to observe. To characterize that passion as "unruly" is to emphasize that it sometimes borders on abnormality. "Obsession" too is the stuff of psychopathology, a clinically identifiable disorder of the personality. Yet as the author recognizes, some obsessions can be magnificent in their scope and intensity.

Certainly history furnishes many examples of the collecting urge carried to pathological extremes. Consider for example the tulip mania that swept Holland in 1635. At its peak a single bulb of the variety 'Viceroy' was exchanged for two lasts of wheat, four lasts of rye, four oxen, eight swine, twelve sheep, two hogsheads of wine, four tuns of beer, two tuns of butter, one thousand pounds of cheese, a bed, a suit of clothes, and a silver cup, the whole valued at 2500 florins.[3] Great fortunes were bartered away and great houses brought to ruin before the madness subsided. In another celebrated example, around 1820 the English bibliophile Sir Thomas Phillips began his quest to obtain "one copy of every book in the world," and to that end he sacrificed his wife, his family, his comfort, and his fortune. By all accounts Sir Thomas was a mean-spirited, bigoted, egotistical old wretch, but at his death in 1872 he left a library of at least sixty thousand manuscripts and fifty thousand books, probably the largest and most important collection ever assembled by a single individual. 160 men, 230 horses, and 103 wagons were needed to transport it from one manor house to another.[4]

Certainly no collector in modern times has exceeded these heights—or depths. Moreover it is misleading to focus on the sensational excesses of the few while ignoring the vast majority of collectors who lead ordinary lives. People who collect steam whistles come from every walk of life, and are alike only in their fondness for these "voices of the Industrial Revolution." In this respect they resemble most other collectors, including stamp and coin collectors, tool collectors, and the collectors of such quotidian objects as beer cans, matchbook covers, and lunch buckets. And like these other collectors, some of them have amassed collections of extraordinary size. A whistle is not intrinsically inexpensive, in the manner of a bottle cap or a matchbook cover. Every whistle in a collection represents a substantial investment of the collector's time, energy, and treasure. Yet there are a dozen or more collections in the U.S. that contain more than 200 whistles, and at least two that exceed 500 whistles. A private museum in Cornwall, U.K. contains more than 600. So whistle collectors need not defer to collectors of other kinds in terms of single-minded dedication to their hobby.

Rarity is an important consideration in many areas of collecting. This is especially true in areas

* In collaboration with David Fultz

where the item is manifestly unique, as in the more elevated reaches of the fine arts. There was only one van Gogh and he painted only one "Irises," and it sold in 1987 for $53.9 million. Many other collectable[5] items, such as etchings and commemorative medals, were produced only in limited editions. But with exceptions to be noted later, whistles are (or were) neither rare nor unique. More than 60,000 steam locomotives were built in the United States and every one of them had its own whistle. Furthermore, there were probably three or more whistles on ships and factories and firehouses for every one on a locomotive, making a grand total of several hundred thousand whistles. Thus we are dealing with objects that, if not exactly commonplace, were at least made in considerable quantity. Regrettably, no manufacturer's complete production records have survived, so the exact number will never be known.[6] Hence "rarity" in a whistle is an ill-defined quality, derived mostly from the anecdotal reports of experienced collectors. This gives a rather different and less imperative flavor to the tasks of acquiring and preserving them.

Finally, at the risk of underscoring the obvious, it must be remembered that private ownership is central to collecting. This is an important difference between the collector and the connoisseur. The connoisseur may cherish or admire an object but the ownership of it is not essential to his emotional life; he can live without possessing it. The dedicated collector, on the other hand, draws security and satisfaction from possessing the object, and exhibits great reluctance to part with it. It must be admitted that this profound difference in attitude has led to some ill will between the two groups, the collectors regarding the connoisseurs as snobs, and the connoisseurs viewing the collectors as mere magpies, accumulating whatever shiny objects strike their fancy.

Motives for collecting

Collecting has been defined as "the selecting, gathering, and keeping of objects of subjective value."[7] Note the word "subjective," signifying that the collector attaches a value to the object that is not necessarily commensurate with, and usually

exceeds, its intrinsic worth. No one (except perhaps Harry Winston) collects cut diamonds, in the same sense as true collectors use the word, because diamonds are primarily commodities, not objects of affection. Thus the discussion of collecting is immediately and inescapably thrust into the realm of the emotions, and it is in this spirit that we examine some of the principal reasons why collectors collect steam whistles. It scarcely needs to be pointed out that the classification scheme proposed below merely identifies pure strains within the complex mixture of motivations which drive most collectors, and that the collector who falls exclusively within a single class is a rarity.

Sentiment or nostalgia

Many—perhaps even most—whistle collections have at their root a lingering fondness for the events of childhood. The boy who grew up in a house alongside the tracks will forever associate the sound of locomotive whistles with occasions both happy and sad in his young life. Or perhaps his father or his uncle was a railroad man, presented on retirement with a cherished whistle that now sits on the mantelpiece. Similarly the lad who grew up in a coastal town or seaport may long to hear again the far-off braying of ships entering and leaving the harbor on foggy nights. These early recollections run very deep, and when given expression in adulthood have resulted in some of the nation's largest and most comprehensive whistle collections.

There is little more to be said about nostalgia as a motivating force except that it is both potent and exceedingly long-lived. It can endure throughout an entire lifetime, because it has no self-evident termination. The collector who collects in order to recapture the past is never wholly satisfied, because recapturing the past is an undertaking that can never be completed. Nevertheless those with the wisdom to value the process more than the result can derive great pleasure from it.

Preservation

When one enters the trophy room or game lodge of a hunter, one cannot escape the melancholy realization that the creatures which once bore these magnificent tusks and antlers are now necessarily dead.

Collecting Whistles

Similarly a whistle on the mantelpiece signifies that the machine whose boiler it once adorned is dead, or at least out of service, perhaps rusted away to nothingness, perhaps foundered at the bottom of the sea, perhaps re-melted in the open hearth into washing machines and Fords. But unlike the mounted head in the game lodge, the whistle can be reborn. Although silent now, it retains the possibility of life. It can be blown again; it can sing once more the song it sang during its years of service.

Thoughts like these animate the collector whose principal interest is industrial archaeology, i.e., the preservation of artifacts for the benefit of future generations. In this sense they are true protectors of our industrial heritage, saving whistles that would otherwise be lost to the scrapper. It must not be thought, however, that such collectors are wholly disinterested in the present. They take just as much joy in the pursuit, acquisition, restoration, and operation of whistles as collectors motivated by other considerations, but their activities have an additional component of concern for the future.

To collectors of preservationist bent, a steam whistle does not exist merely as a metal artifact. It consists instead of the object *plus its history*. It is just as important to preserve—or at least to investigate—the record of its use as to preserve the whistle itself. Furthermore, learning that history may demand more field effort and more research than acquiring the whistle in the first place. One could almost define the preservationist strain among whistle collectors as those who exhibit comparable concern for the whistle and its provenance. It follows, unfortunately, that collectors who do so scorn collectors indifferent to history, and tend to look with contempt on those who lose, ignore, or worse still, falsify a portion of the historical record.

Demonstration

Some collectors just like to blow whistles. These same collectors also tend to collect fire and air raid sirens, foghorns, trip gongs, carbide cannons, and other noisemakers. Taken together they constitute the audile segment of the whistle-collecting fraternity, the lovers of sound. Moreover, it is usually the case that the louder the sound, the better they like it. The pure examples of this type can sometimes be found with portable sound-level meters strapped to their belts,

much as engineers were once identified by the slide rules carried at their waists.

Regrettably, the love of sound is often coupled with indifference to qualities that other collectors value. The sound-lovers tend not to polish their whistles or even clean them. They make repairs in the most expeditious manner possible, without regard for appearance or authenticity. They show scant concern for the preservation of a whistle's provenance or historical record. Above all, from the point of view of those differently motivated, they show a shocking disregard of sentiment. Whistles tend to be ranked in accord with the decibel level they produce, rather than the fond remembrances they elicit.

Investment

There was a time in the late 1940's and early 1950's when a steam locomotive whistle (or virtually any other railroad artifact) could be had for $5 or $10. This was the cost of a box of cigars or a bottle of Scotch whiskey. The whistle-seeker, bearing a gift under his arm, wandered down to one of those melancholy graveyards where steam locomotives were being cut up for scrap. He then hollered up to the workman sitting astride the boiler with a cutting torch in his hand, "Cut off that whistle for me and I'll give you this bottle of Scotch!" It almost always worked. Whistles acquired in this fashion have increased roughly a hundredfold in value since that time, a rate of increase which far exceeds the rate of inflation or return on fixed income securities, and compares favorably with the return on equities.

It is no longer possible to play this game. Except for "stuffed and mounted" specimens, the extinction of the steam locomotive is substantially complete, and whistles are widely recognized as objects of value. Viewed as a commodity, they are moderately valuable now and in general are becoming more valuable as time passes. At the moment, steptop locomotive whistles are caught up in an unprecedented inflationary spiral. Suddenly everyone wants one, and prices for desirable examples are now firmly established in the four-figure range. This has led a few dealers to buy whistles "on spec" in the hope of reselling them at a profit, but they constitute a minority. Surprisingly few collectors collect whistles exclusively, or even primarily, as an investment.

There are sound reasons for this. In the first place, whistles constitute an almost wholly unregulated market. As with most collectable objects, there are no powerful "market-makers" with the power to manipulate prices; no monopolies comparable to deBeers in the diamond trade. No value books or price guides exist that report prices on a nationwide basis. In the second place, the whistle market is swept by largely unpredictable fads and vogues. The sudden spurt of appreciation in locomotive whistles follows on years, or even decades, in which the prices of all whistles rose very slowly indeed. Thus the collector who expects his collection to appreciate at a steady 7% per year like gilt-edged bonds is certain to be disappointed. On the other hand, it must be admitted that whistle prices have not declined since the Great Depression, so the possibility of appreciation is always present. Collecting whistles as an investment is not a certain road to wealth, but it is not utter foolishness either.

It might be thought that as whistles become increasingly difficult to obtain, and prices rise still further in consequence, that whistle collecting would become the exclusive province of the rich. British experience suggests strongly that this will not be the case. The market for steam era artifacts in the United Kingdom is more mature and better regulated than in the U.S. It is also astonishingly high. The sale prices of locomotive nameplates at auction now sometimes exceed the original cost of the entire locomotive, and the prices of whistles are variously two to five times the American average. Yet the directors of the principal British auctions report that it is not wealthy industrialists nor landed gentry who are paying these record prices; it is middle class working people. Moreover it appears that purchases are not made with intent to resell at a profit, but primarily out of affection for the artifact itself. According to Ian Wright, director of the Sheffield auction, England's largest, "Most people who have collections will die still owning them."

This completes our quick survey of the principal motives for collecting whistles. A few minutes conversation with a collector will often reveal where his primary interests lie. The key is the language he uses to describe the whistles in his care. If he refers to a particular whistle as "the whistle from Neely's sawmill over in Richmond," he is evidently driven by the memory of familiar surroundings. Consider too the difference between describing a whistle as "a five-chime steptop" and "the whistle from Santa Fe No. 3751," the former generic and the latter indicative of a keen interest in the historical record. Keep your ears open and your mouth shut in order to learn why collectors do what they do.

Giving the collection a focus

In the early stages of his career, a whistle collector often behaves like a magpie, eagerly and indiscriminately snatching up whatever whistles he encounters. He suffers a frenzy of acquisitiveness (a disorder often seen in bibliophiles as well), which aims to acquire as many whistles as possible, as quickly as possible. He pays scant attention to such matters as provenance, condition, or type. His purchases are constrained only by the depth of his purse, and sometimes not even by that.

A few collectors remain in the magpie mode throughout their careers. This behavior tends to earn them the scorn of more sophisticated collectors, but the scorn is undeserved. Even the magpie performs a useful function, for he is saving whistles from the scrap pile. A whistle safely sequestered in a den or study is much more valuable than one on its way to the re-melting furnace.

Sooner or later, however, most collectors attempt to impose some sort of organizing principle on their collection, in order to guide future acquisitions. This typically happens when the collection exceeds what can conveniently be displayed on the mantelpiece, say at the tenth or twelfth accession. This organizing principle or focus commonly takes one of several forms:

Emphasis on type or application

It is probable that more Americans are familiar with the sound of the steam locomotive whistle than with any other whistle sound. It is a soul-stirring sound, as we have already remarked, and its powers of evocation are unequalled. Hence many collectors make railroad whistles the primary focus of their collections, and this is the case with several of the largest American collections. The enduring popularity of these whistles, nearly half a century after the death of mainline steam, is attested by their relatively high market prices.

Perhaps the second most popular type of whistle is the marine whistle. Marine whistles are the focus of what is arguably the largest private collection in the U.K., displayed in the Whistle Museum of Rowland Humble at Bodmin, Cornwall. Mr. Humble served many years in the Royal Navy, and amassed his collection by scouring scrap yards and antique shops whenever he put into port. Several American collections have this focus also, although they tend to emphasize vessels on inland lakes and waterways rather than ocean-going vessels. Marine whistles are by nature large and expensive, and private collections of more than a few dozen examples are rare.

If there is a third type of whistle favored by collectors, it is probably municipal and institutional whistles, especially fire and disaster alarms. Many of these are variable-pitch whistles, which constitute a unique and readily identifiable genre. They are also sufficiently rare so that acquiring them presents a significant challenge.

Note that all three classes of application lend themselves to elaboration. The collector of steam locomotive whistles frequently acquires a few air horns as well, so that the sound of the diesel locomotive will be represented in his collection. From there it is just a short step to the collection of other forms of railroadiana, such as number and builder's plates, headlamps, marker and switchstand lights, lanterns, padlocks, dining car china, etc. in unending proliferation. Similarly, the collector of marine whistles often supplements his collection with steam horns, foghorns, sirens, and other maritime signaling devices, not to mention binnacles, engine room telegraphs, portholes, diving helmets, etc. And finally, the collector of alarm whistles is not infrequently a collector of air-raid sirens, fire bells, and fire-fighting apparatus in general.

Emphasis on manufacturer

One of the simplest ways to specialize is to collect whistles made only by a certain manufacturer. It goes without saying that the manufacturer should be one for whose products the collector has a certain innate affection or fascination. Even so, it pays to choose the manufacturer with care. Crosby and Lunkenheimer are particularly good choices because their products were historically important and can still be found with relative ease. Moreover, in the case of Lunkenheimer at least, the product line was sufficiently diversified to give the collection some breadth and scope. Manufacturers such as Hancock or Nathan would be considerably more challenging because their output was smaller and their product line was poorly documented. At the other extreme, the collector who unwisely chooses to specialize in the products of, say, Jarecki or Hayden & Gere can look forward to few successes and much frustration.

Only commercial manufacturers have been named in the foregoing paragraph, but it is equally possible to specialize in the output of a particular railroad shop. As discussed in Chapter 3, certain railroads preferred to make locomotive whistles to their own specifications, and these shop-built whistles have a long and honorable history. Notable among these railroads were the Southern, the Baltimore & Ohio, the Santa Fe, and the Pennsylvania. One could do worse as a collector than to attempt to acquire one specimen of every type of whistle produced by the great Altoona Shops of the PRR. Not even the Railroad Museum of Pennsylvania has succeeded in doing this, so the task would afford considerable challenge. Note too that shops which built whistles for locomotives were likely to have built whistles for other railroad purposes as well, such as smaller whistles for steam cranes and snowplows and larger ones for roundhouses and engine terminals. The latter are particularly interesting from the historical and sociological points of view because their sound would have regulated the lives of thousands of nearby workers and their families.

Specializing in shop-built whistles also offers one of the few opportunities within the hobby to acquire rare or unique items. In shops where pride of workmanship prevailed, the foreman would sometimes commission a whistle from his own workmen, in preference to buying one from an established manufacturer. Proof of this pride is that the whistles were sometimes signed by the men who made them or repaired them. Their design usually adhered to the stylistic conventions of the time, e.g., in the 1870's, conical tops, elaborate acorns, extended bases, and bells of rolled sheet stock, but occasionally the design was so idiosyncratic as to border on the bizarre. Whatever their appearance, the singular character of these whistles is revealed by the absence of makers' markings, and not infrequently by non-standard dimensions, such as a bell of 7" or 9" diameter. It is a fortunate collector who can add one of these "one-off" whistles to his collection. He can rejoice in the virtual certainty that no other collector has one exactly like it.

One of the unexplained curiosities of the mind of the collector—and I speak here not only of the whistle collector but of avid collectors in general—is the Gestalt Impulse, or the urge to acquire complete sets. This impulse is familiar to everyone who ever collected copper pennies as a kid: the excitement of seeing the slots fill up one by one, and the final thrill when the rare and elusive 1909 S VDB is obtained at last. It functions not merely in the coin collector, the book collector, and the stamp collector, but just as strongly in the whistle collector who favors the output of a particular manufacturer. A surprising number of collectors set as a goal the acquisition of, say, Lunkenheimer plain whistles in every size from 1" through 10", and feel a profound sense of triumph and closure when they have succeeded. Having acquired one of each size of plain whistle, they then move on to chime whistles, etc., so that the game perpetuates itself almost without end.

Emphasis on regional significance

When a collector chooses to specialize in the whistles of a certain region, that region is usually the one in which he spent his childhood. Hence his choice is strongly coupled to feelings of nostalgia or sentiment, which, as we have seen, are among the most powerful of motivations. Taken together, this motive and this focus have resulted in some extraordinary collections. One of the legendary American collections, amounting at this writing to more than 500 whistles, was amassed by David M. Fultz of Greensboro, North Carolina, who has spent thirty-five years tracking down and acquiring all the whistles that played a role in his childhood.

Clearly, the collector who elects to follow this route must be endowed with extraordinary patience. Mr. Fultz relates numerous instances in which he waited a decade or more to acquire a coveted whistle: waiting for the whistle to be replaced with another form of signal, waiting for the mill or factory to close, waiting for the owner to agree to sell or—let us be frank—to die. If the patience of Job is demanded, so is the perseverance of Inspector Javert. It takes a bulldog tenacity of mind to keep track of all these whistles and pursue their acquisition in the face of repeated refusals and disappointments. Finally, a measure of good luck is helpful. Sometimes a wanted whistle turns up quite unexpectedly at an auction or flea market or even a garage sale, and the only way to take advantage of these happy occurrences is to attend them all.

It might be thought that only persons who grew up in an area rich with whistle sounds would choose to engage in this form of specialization, but that is not necessarily so. Despite the powerful effect of childhood imprinting, some tastes are acquired later in life. One can readily imagine the casual or indifferent collector who moves to a coastal city or fishing village, and finds himself captivated by the variety of maritime noisemakers. Or the industrial archaeologist whose researches in the urban environment lead to a consuming interest in factory whistles. The varieties of collecting experience are as diverse as collectors themselves, and one never knows how or where motivation will arise.

Emphasis on historical era

Finally, it is possible to organize a collection around whistles of a certain period. There are two difficulties with this approach, however. The first is that the earlier the period, the more difficult it is to find examples. The second, as discussed in Chapter 5, is that whistle designs tended to change so slowly that it is virtually impossible to date some whistles with precision.

Consider, for example, the predicament of the specialist who wishes to acquire only whistles manufactured during the Civil War period. Such whistles certainly existed but are now exceedingly rare. Powell and Crane among others were established in that era, the former under the name Union Brass Works, the latter under its own name. Also established was the Miles Greenwood Co. of Cincinnati, a maker of brass goods regrettably destroyed in the first days of the war. The problem is that we do not know in detail what their products looked like, because there are no extant catalogs prior to 1866. The author has in his collection a locomotive call whistle allegedly manufactured by Greenwood prior to 1861, but the evidence of its age is entirely circumstantial, e.g., the character of the knurling and other details of machine shop practice.

A more plausible cutoff date is the turn of the 20th century. This was a time of considerable freedom of experimentation in the design of whistles, as evidenced by the sudden flurry of whistle-related patents ca. 1895. It is a relatively simple matter to distinguish 19th century whistles from 20th century whistles, in part because of the rapidity of design changes and in part because of the abundant documentation available from trade catalogs. The collector who chooses to specialize in 19th century whistles pursues such rarities as flat-top Powells, produced until 1898, Crosby plain whistles, produced from 1888 to 1897, "Circle-S" whistles from the Cincinnati Brass Works, predecessor of Lunkenheimer, and Lunkenheimer round-top "baldies" without acorns, produced prior to 1898. The era also offers a number of interesting locomotive whistles. Prior to the invention of the single-bell chime whistle in 1877, these were almost exclusively plain whistles with vertical valves. After Crosby popularized the single-bell chime, the horizontal valve began to appear in locomotive whistles, although bells tended to be quite short, typically less than 6" high.

It is difficult to identify a later era of comparable interest. During the great heyday of whistle manufacture, which may be taken roughly as the years 1900 to 1930, the design of whistles changed quite slowly and there is little reason to prefer one period to another. Perhaps the most likely focus for a historically oriented collection in the 20th century is the acoustic signaling devices of World War II. The distinctive ones were for the most part marine whistles, such as the ubiquitous Liberty Ship and Victory Ship whistles. The collection might well branch out to include the familiar steam horns and steam sirens of warships. It is the latter that produce the unforgettable "Whoop! Whoop! Whoop!" of a destroyer, featured on the sound track of every World War II naval epic Hollywood ever made.

Emphasis on celebrity status

Some whistles are more famous than others, either because they belonged to famous people or because they served in famous applications. As an example of the first kind of fame, consider the whistle designed and used by Casey Jones. What collector would not aspire to own the whistle belonging to this most celebrated of American locomotive engineers? (It still exists, and it is not for sale.) Fame of the second kind attaches to whistles from the great "name" trains such as the *Twentieth Century Limited,* or the great ocean-going passenger liners such as the *Normandie* or the *Titanic.*

This is not an area in which the novice can expect to participate, nor can it plausibly be made the focus of a collection of any size. It is more likely to be the province of a long established collector who now seeks to crown an extensive collection with a few prize specimens. Despite the fact that celebrated whistles have been out of service for fifty years or more, they still come to market occasionally as their owners die or seek to convert accumulated treasures into cash. Within recent years the personal whistle of Joe Dennis, the most accomplished of all whistle talk artists, was sold, as was the whistle from a Union Pacific "Big Boy," the mightiest of all steam locomotives.

The likelihood of discovering a celebrated whistle at a yard sale or antique shop is essentially zero, about the same as the likelihood of finding an authentic Stradivarius in the attic. All famous whistles that are not in museums are by now sequestered in private hands, and it may be presumed that their owners know their worth. Hence prices tend to be extraordinarily high. Prices in excess of $25,000 have been reported (or at least rumored) for several of the big three-bell Smith-Hyson chimes that once served on ocean liners. More recently the rather ordinary 10" x 30" plain whistle from the Great Lakes excursion steamer *Tashmoo* was sold at auction for more than $10,000. Clearly such whistles are the crown jewels of a collection, not its foundation stones.

Here, more than in any other area of collecting, documentation is of utmost importance. Oral and anecdotal histories simply do not suffice to establish provenance. Authentication demands bills of sale, or letters of transmittal or guarantee, or photographs of the object in use, or other equally convincing evidence of origin and ownership. Sellers of such goods occasionally show great reluctance to part with such documentation, possibly to demonstrate that they once owned the celebrated object. It is the buyer's responsibility to insist that the documentation accompany the whistle as part of the sale. Absent proper documentation, the whistle is no more valuable than others by the same manufacturer.

Methods of acquisition

Acquisition is the essential activity of the collector, outweighing in importance everything that precedes or follows it. How does one acquire steam whistles? Methods of acquisition are as varied as collectors themselves, but certain avenues are tried and true, and these are discussed in detail below. Bear in mind, however, that these are only the usual sources of whistles, and the collector should not overlook such unlikely sources as yard sales and gun shows.

Field exploration

Few thrills compare with the discovery and acquisition of a whistle from a primary source, entirely through one's own efforts. It embodies all the excitement of the hunt, and the recovered whistle can be borne home as proudly as any trophy of the chase. To engage in this form of acquisition, carry binoculars and a notebook in your car at all times. When entering an unfamiliar town or city, drive slowly through the industrial district, scanning every rooftop. Seek out scrap yards, sawmills, paper mills, pumping stations, meatpacking houses, vulcanizing plants, breweries, laundries, and hospitals. Pay special attention to structures with tall chimneys, as these often signal the presence of a boilerhouse beneath. Follow the railroad tracks insofar as possible, examining engine terminals, roundhouses, car barns, freight offices, and trackside factories. Find the harbor or waterfront if there is one, looking for

ship chandlers and shipbreakers. One's instincts improve with practice in this pursuit, and at least one highly successful collector claims that he can "smell the whistles" on entering an unfamiliar city.

This method of acquisition has resulted in some notable success stories. A well known collector in Texas, for example, had the wit to observe that the cotton-growing areas in his home state were dotted with abandoned cotton compresses, large installations once as ubiquitous in the South as granaries in the Grain Belt. In the old days, after raw cotton was ginned, it was sent to one of these compresses to be baled for rail shipment. The baling machinery was powered by a reciprocating steam engine, which in turn was powered by a boiler. The installation was typically fitted with two whistles, a large one to signal the operation of the press and a smaller one to convey instructions from the press back to the boiler room. In later years the baling was performed at the gin itself, leaving the compresses idle and derelict. In a series of weekend trips this enterprising collector sought out and visited as many old compresses as possible, and was able to harvest several dozen large whistles at very low cost. No one else had thought to explore these abandoned compresses.

In another instance an observant collector was able to harvest a rare three-bell Powell chime from its improbable location atop the Hudson Psychiatric Center in Poughkeepsie, New York. Why there? Because he knew that psychiatric hospitals, like medical and surgical hospitals, generate enormous amounts of dirty linen, and usually incorporate a steam laundry.

There are certain rules that every field collector should obey, and the first of these is to avoid trespassing. If caught and challenged, do not offer the tired excuse that you did not know you were on private property. Private property is almost always well marked. *All* whistles are on private property except those few incorporated in public displays, and these are not generally available for acquisition. Ignore this advice and you may find yourself raising bail instead of carrying home a whistle. Always get permission before entering private property.

If a desirable whistle is discovered, the next step is to identify its owner, if indeed ownership is not self-evident. Often the simplest way to do this is to inquire at neighboring establishments. Failing that, take the address to the office of the city clerk and ask to see the tax rolls. Before contacting the owners, draw on your experience as a collector and make your best estimate of the value of the whistle. If bargaining ensues, offer half that amount as your initial offer. The day is past when whistles could be had for two cents on the dollar. An insultingly low initial offer may disincline the owner to take you seriously, putting an end to your negotiations. Be prepared to pay cash, as many people are unwilling to accept a personal check from a stranger. Finally, and most important, get a dated bill of sale and *written* permission to remove the whistle from the premises. These will stand you in good stead if you are confronted by guards or watchmen.

The last step is to harvest the whistle itself, which may have been standing unused on the roof for decades. There is a certain protocol associated with this that you would do well to observe. First, give the owner every possible assurance that you will do no damage to his property. If removal of the whistle leaves an open pipe, cap it or plug it in accord with his instructions. Do not employ a cutting torch lest the sparks set fire to his building. Do release him from all liability should you fall off, or through, the roof. Second, take steps to insure your personal safety. Work with a helper, and tell at least one other person what you intend to do and when and where you intend to do it. Wear a tool belt and take lots of tools, to minimize the number of trips up and down the ladder. Don't forget a length of strong rope. Sometimes the most difficult and dangerous part of the entire process is lowering the recovered whistle to the ground. Be especially careful at that critical moment when the feed pipe is almost sawn through and the whistle begins to wobble on its support. You dare not yell "Timber!" and let it crash to the roof like a felled tree. You must lower it gently and prevent it from rolling off the roof. This is where a helper is essential. Finally, when the whistle is safely stowed in the trunk of your car, tell the owner that you have completed your work and are leaving the premises.

Buying at flea markets and swap meets

Success in finding whistles at flea markets and swap meets depends strongly on the character of the event. The usual flea market, in which the sale tables are dominated by eight-track tapes, depression glass, dull knives and rusty tools, is highly unlikely to yield a desirable whistle. Specialized flea markets, on the other hand, such as those accompanying gas engine and tractor shows, threshermen's reunions, and railroadiana fairs, are still a potential source of whistles, although no longer as fertile as they were decades ago. With a little luck and much patience a collector can still find bargains at these events.

Buying at flea markets requires some minimal preparation. Slip a small refrigerator magnet into your shirt pocket, to distinguish painted brass from painted iron. Carry a six-inch pocket scale or a small measuring tape to make critical measurements. If your collection is already large, bring a one-page summary of your holdings so that you do not inadvertently duplicate an item. If you have business cards identifying you as a whistle collector, bring those too, but do not give them to dealers while bargaining is still in progress. Bring a writing instrument and a small folding notebook for taking notes. Finally, bring cash—lots of cash—because dealers are extremely unlikely to accept personal checks or credit cards. Safeguard your bankroll as if you were a tourist in a strange land. Regrettably, there are still pickpockets who work crowds, and they know that the crowds at flea markets are likely to be cash-rich.

Flea markets too have their own etiquette, and a foreknowledge of these customs can work to the advantage of the buyer. First of all, arrive precisely at the time of opening. As the morning wears on, the aisles fill with "waddlers," casual or unfocused buyers who impede the flow of traffic and occasionally snatch a bargain from under your nose. Do not, however, arrive before opening time and demand entry. Dealers despise early birds, and frequently give notice that they will not be admitted. If interested in an item, do not walk away from it until you have either reached an agreement with the dealer or decisively rejected it. By standing next to it and examining it—*pretending* to examine it, if necessary—you are asserting your territorial right. As long as you stand there, you retain a figurative hold on the item that prevents other buyers from moving in. Walk away from it and you lose first option. Buyers often flock to an item that had aroused no interest until it was relinquished by someone else. These reactions are deeply rooted in crowd psychology and operate quite reliably.

It goes without saying that whistles bought at flea markets are sold "as is, where is." *Caveat emptor!* Once money has changed hands, the deal is irreversible. Therefore it behooves the buyer to scrutinize the potential purchase with utmost care. Chapter 7 contains an extensive discussion of whistle defects and the difficulty of repairing them. Read that section carefully and commit its substance to memory. Use that information—silently!—to decide on a fair market price. Unfortunately some defects are not visible until the whistle has been disassembled on the workbench—an element of risk that adds to the excitement of buying at flea markets. Some superficial disassembly during examination will usually be tolerated, but always ask the dealer's permission first. Does the acorn unscrew? Can the bell be removed from the base? The answers to these questions may indicate the level of care the whistle has received from previous owners.

All flea market prices are negotiable, but only if certain rules are observed. The cardinal rule is to maintain an agreeable demeanor at all times. Begin by asking the dealer his very best price. This is often 90 to 95% of the marked price. Prices generally decline as the market nears its close, but to defer purchase for this reason is to risk loss to another buyer. Do not attempt to negotiate a lower price by denigrating the whistle, disparaging its condition and pointing out its defects. In all likelihood the dealer neither knows nor cares about the defects, and a confrontational attitude will only arouse his animosity. What he knows is that sooner or later a less knowledgeable customer will come along and buy the whistle. For the same reason, do not complain that a whistle is a common variety obtainable from many other dealers. If it's that common, buy it elsewhere. Finally, refrain from commenting on obvious falsehoods, as when a 2" whistle is asserted to have come from a steam locomotive. Let your answer be reflected in your decision to buy it or not to buy it.

Remember too that the moment of sale is the last possible moment to learn the whistle's history. Generally speaking, dealers are ignorant of a whistle's provenance, but occasionally some useful scraps of information can be gleaned. Do not rely on memory; write his remarks in your pocket notebook. They form the basis for further research.

When a sale has been successfully concluded, ask the dealer to remove the whistle from the display table and hold it until you depart. Almost every dealer will agree to this. This spares you the need to walk back to your auto after every purchase. At large flea markets the parking lot is usually remote from the sale area. If the way is long, the day is hot, and the whistle is heavy, you may regret your purchase before you arrive. Note too that if you visit another dealer with a whistle already in hand, you are immediately marked as a whistle collector, which may well put him on his guard and make negotiations more difficult. And finally, carrying a whistle about exposes you to numerous unwanted questions of the "Werdja giddit?" and "Wudja payfurt?" variety.

Buying at auctions and estate sales

Broadly speaking, auctions and estate sales are the most fertile source of whistles for the ambitious collector. Auctions that consist exclusively or even primarily of whistles are very rare, however, and most whistles will be found embedded in auctions of other railroadiana or even household goods. Auctioneers are well aware of the great popular appeal of whistles, and frequently defer them to the end of the sale in order to sustain buyer interest throughout the event. Auctions which contain a large selection of whistles can draw attendees from as far as a thousand miles away. Such people are understandably reluctant to go home empty-handed, and their presence frequently results in spirited bidding. Spirited bidding, unfortunately, is often synonymous with high prices, and in general, great bargains are not to be found at popular auctions.

Nevertheless the novice collector will benefit from attending auctions even if he does not buy. He will have the opportunity to see and examine a variety of unfamiliar whistles. He will make the acquaintance of prominent members of the whistle-collecting fraternity, and overhear their shop talk. Above all he will familiarize himself with the manner in which auctions are conducted, and thereby prepare himself to participate in future auctions. It is not true that if you scratch your nose at an auction you may inadvertently make a $1000 purchase, but the hesitant beginner may need to learn this for himself.

Preparation for an auction is largely similar to preparation for a flea market, with one important difference. Almost every major auction is accompanied by a catalog listing which items are to be sold and in what order. The best auction houses will make this catalog available in advance of the sale. The cost is often extravagant but it is worth paying, because a catalog is both a great time-saver and a convenient place to record sale prices. A cumulative record of sale prices, conscientiously kept, is the most valuable guide a bidder can have. Bear in mind, however, that most catalogs are prepared by the auctioneer, not the seller. Hence the accuracy and completeness of description depend entirely on the knowledge of the catalog compiler. Many a "whistle" in the catalog has turned out to be an organ pipe or a safety valve when held up for bids.

Examine the auction notice carefully for the phrase "10% buyer's premium added" or words to that effect. This deceptive piece of language is actually a disguised price hike, a practice that originated at high-end houses such as Sotheby's and Christie's and has since trickled down to every corner of the auction business. It signifies that 10% will be added to the amount of your bid, the difference going to the seller. Obviously this scheme rewards sellers and penalizes buyers. Most old-line auctioneers recognize this practice for what it is, and dislike it. Nevertheless they feel powerless to resist a trend that is sweeping their industry, and reluctantly go along with it.

Be aware too of the distinction between a consignment sale and an estate sale. A consignment sale contains the offerings of several sellers and is subject to state sales tax, whereas an estate sale consists exclusively of the property of a single seller (who by law must be dead) and is exempt from state sales tax. If the state imposes heavy taxes, as do New York, Pennsylvania, and California among others, and a buyer's premium is also in effect, the buyer could conceivably find himself paying as much as 18% more than he bid—not a negligible increase!

Bidding at auctions is a game and an art, like poker, and those deficient in natural gifts can become adept through long practice. What makes the game especially interesting is that the bidding floor is occasionally swept by that collective feeding frenzy known as "auction fever." (Of course it is part of the auctioneer's job to encourage such frenzy.) These moments are the stuff of folklore. Every experienced auction-goer can tell tales of lots selling for two or even three times their normal market value, merely because participants found themselves caught up in the excitement of the moment. More rarely the reverse happens. A sort of fatigue or lethargy settles on the crowd and lots are knocked down for half their usual market value. In either case the lesson is that auction prices tend to be much more volatile than prices set in calmer surroundings. Expect surprises.

The makeup of the audience can also have a profound effect on auction prices. Auctions attended primarily by dealers tend to produce lower prices, because dealers are buying for resale and try to keep their acquisition costs low. If at all possible, arrange to be the only private collector in an audience full of dealers. By contrast, record high prices tend to be set at auctions attended by little old ladies. Experienced collectors, unless they are caught up in blind pursuit of some elusive Holy Grail among whistles, do not like to overpay under any circumstances. Unwillingness to overpay is in fact one of the defining traits of an experienced collector. But the buyer who has his (or her) heart set on a certain whistle, and has no other whistles competing for attention or resources, will sometimes bid it through the roof.

Bidding techniques are as varied as bidders. When bidding on a wanted item, some bidders like to participate from the very beginning, in the hope that enthusiasm will wane while bids are still low. Others like to start at 50% or more of their predetermined ceiling, in order to scare off casual bidders and identify the serious competition. Still others like to hang back until the bidding slows nearly to a halt, and then jump in with a "killer" offer, unlikely to be topped. One piece of advice we have found useful is to avoid round numbers such as multiples of $50 or $100. Many bidders secretly set their ceilings in round numbers, and in consequence many a whistle that could not be had at $400 can be had at $415.

Should friends bid against friends? It must be admitted that some collectors have the souls of barracudas and would bid against their own mothers, but most prefer to settle these matters beforehand. A quiet conference among friends, before the action heats up, will establish who wants what and how badly. In this way unwelcome contests can be avoided and friendships remain intact at the end of the day. Whistles come and go, but friends are irreplaceable.

Buying from antique dealers

According to one definition, any artifact more than fifty years old is an antique. Hence almost all whistles are antiques and should be found at antique shops. Not so. Antique dealers as a group are the least fertile of all sources of whistles. Moreover their prices are high, since they buy for resale and they tend to resist bargaining.

Nevertheless it is possible to obtain an occasional whistle from an antique dealer. The secret is to avoid the trendy upscale antique shops and to patronize the shops at the bottom of the pecking order. (Unfortunately one's spouse may have exactly contrary inclinations.) The sort of establishment the whistle collector seeks is one where he has to kick things aside in order to pass down the aisle. Furthermore, the whistles in such a shop (if any) will not be neatly displayed at waist level or eye level; they will be on the floor at knee level or ankle level, amid all the other odds and ends. Move slowly, and keep your eyes on your feet. Explore every pile and reach under every display case or counter.

One of the more productive means of dealing with antique shops is to establish an ongoing relationship with the proprietor. On your first visit leave a business card identifying yourself as a whistle collector. Prepare a one-page sheet with pictures of various types of whistles, each identified by name and number. Be sure to make clear the difference between a plain whistle and a chime whistle. It might also be prudent to include pictures of items that novices frequently mistake for whistles, such as safety valves and air horns. Make a number of photocopies of this sheet on brightly colored paper and leave one with each dealer you visit. Most shopkeepers welcome this kind of information because it gives them a point of reference should they call you about a whistle. It also gladdens their hearts to know that they have a probable customer for a whistle should one become available.

The etiquette of the antique shop is much like that of the flea market. If you want the dealer to continue working on your behalf, it is important to maintain his good will. In particular, don't haggle over minor defects or flaws, especially if you know they can be remedied. The dealer is not a whistle collector, and most of what he knows about whistles he probably learned from you. Sometimes a dealer, less fearful of betraying his ignorance than most, will ask you what a whistle is worth. Do not "low-ball" him; give him an honest reply. On occasion a dealer may offer you a whistle of substandard quality or one you do not want for other reasons. If the cost is not excessive, buy it anyway. You can always dispose of it by other means, and meanwhile you have assured his ongoing cooperation in your search.

Buying from fellow collectors

Whistle collectors do sell whistles from time to time. Usually this is done for one of three reasons. Either the collector is disposing of duplicates, or he is attempting to upgrade his collection, or he is raising money to finance a major purchase. Only rarely is it done in response to the entreaties of a domestic partner to "get rid of some of those things; they're crowding us out of the house." Under continuing pressure of this kind, the truly dedicated collector will either enlarge the house or contemplate getting rid of the partner!

Buying from collectors offers the opportunity to acquire rare and unusual whistles that would seldom if ever appear on the open market. On the other hand, collectors as a group know more about the value of the whistles they sell than any other class of seller. Thus it will be more difficult to obtain a bargain from a collector than from anyone else. A little skepticism is not inappropriate. If the whistle offered is a duplicate, you can be sure that the collector has reserved the better one for himself. More generally, one would like to know whether the collector has a reputation for fair dealing. The best way to learn this is to inquire of other collectors. They will be quick to inform you whether the collector is honest or not. Fortunately dishonest collectors constitute only a very small minority within the hobby.

The collector who is in the process of upgrading his collection will frequently prefer a trade to an outright sale. This permits both parties to maintain the size of their collections. Furthermore, trades are virtually the only method of obtaining whistles that the owner does not wish to sell outright. Every serious collector covets certain whistles in the collection of another. How to acquire them? One can of course offer a price far in excess of their true value, but this goes against the grain. A far more promising approach is to offer an exchange for something the other collector covets. It is important to remember when trading that both parties are seeking the advantage. Even swaps, in which each party feels he has gotten the better deal, are much to be desired but seldom achieved. In all other cases some means must be found to balance the scales. One means is to add cash to the transaction: my Powell and $150 for your Nathan. Another means is to add more whistles: my Hancock and my Crosby for your Lunkenheimer, your Buckeye, and your Wabco. By one means or another it is usually possible to reach a conclusion satisfactory to both parties. Readiness to engage in such trades is the best possible justification for acquiring surplus or duplicate whistles. Every serious collector has a small stock of whistles that he secretly regards as trading stock, and not as part of his permanent collection.

On rare occasions an entire collection comes to market, either because the collector's interests have changed or—sadly—in anticipation of death. Usually the collection is put on consignment with an auction house to be sold item by item, but sometimes it is offered *en bloc* to the collecting fraternity. The most important consideration in such cases is to get there first. This is where carefully cultivated relationships with fellow collectors pay off. Such news travels *very* fast. If you are not well connected to the grapevine, you will not hear of the opportunity until it is too late to take advantage of it. A substantial amount of capital will be required. All major collections are well into the five-figure range, and some are in the six-figure range. Creative financing may be required, such as a second mortgage on the house. Do not imagine that the seller will agree to sell you only those parts of the collection you want. He wants to get rid of it all at a single stroke, or else he would not have taken such a drastic step. You must buy it all. Those items surplus to your needs can then be reserved as trading stock or sold to other collectors.

Buying through traditional media

One of the most straightforward and effective methods of acquiring whistles is simply to advertise for them. A generalized or a specialized approach can be employed, and each has its merits. In the generalized approach, one chooses a community newspaper serving a heavily industrialized area such as a mill town or a port city, and simply places an ad in the "Wanted" columns of the classified section. A small display ad with one or two pictures will draw more attention than a text-only ad, but it will also cost more and will not necessarily produce better results. In the specialized approach, one places an ad in the local swap paper, usually a weekly publication. These cater primarily to sellers, but also have a "Wanted" column.

Still better results might be obtained by advertising in specialty publications. The most specialized of all is *Horn & Whistle*, the quarterly journal of the Horn & Whistle Enthusiasts Group. Classified ads appear in each issue, and subscribers may advertise free of charge. *Trains* magazine is a good source of whistles, especially locomotive whistles. It also lists major auctions of railroadiana throughout the country. Its classified rates are quite high, but it has a larger subscriber base than any other railroad-related publication. Other steam-related publications are *Iron Men Album* and *Engineers and Engines*. The readers of these magazines, however, are already familiar with the value of steam whistles, and therefore are unlikely to offer bargains. Perhaps the best chance of finding bargains is to advertise in publications in collateral areas of the mechanical arts, such as *Hemmings Motor News* and *Gas Engine Magazine*, or in broad-spectrum hobby papers, such as the weekly *The Antique Trader*.

One can also adopt a purely passive approach and merely scan the specialty magazines, seeing what others have to sell. In this case it is a decided advantage to pay the extra fee for First Class delivery if the publication offers this service. Ordinarily magazines are mailed Second Class, and the delivery time varies widely with distance from the point of mailing. Those extra few days in transit can make the difference between winning and losing a desirable whistle. For the same reason it is advisable to respond to ads by telephone instead of by mail. A call can elicit information that might otherwise take a week to obtain. It also overcomes the widespread reluctance of some people to write letters, and it tends to keep negotiations brief and well-focused. Always remember, however, to take the called party's convenience into account when calling. Calling during the supper hour or after 10 p.m. can cost you the sale.

Electronic commerce and virtual auctions

Increasingly the Internet has become a vehicle of commerce that hobbyists and collectors cannot afford to ignore. Whistle-related marketplaces on the Internet are of two basic kinds. First are the hobby-oriented or antique-oriented bulletin boards and chat rooms established by the major online services. It would be pointless to name such bulletin boards here because they tend to be as evanescent as mayflies, but they are easily found with the aid of the powerful search engines now available. Participation is free, and in consequence no regulations govern either buyers or sellers. Many whistles have been successfully bought and sold through such bulletin boards, but the process is not without risks. It is at least as risky as buying at flea markets, with the added disadvantages that one can neither examine the goods beforehand nor look the seller in the eye. Therefore the prudent shopper should negotiate the safeguards necessary for his own protection before any money changes hands.

Within recent years a new and highly seductive sales medium has appeared and enjoyed explosive growth. This is the online or virtual auction house, a profit-making corporation with protocols resembling those of a conventional auction house. The number and diversity of items to be found there is unmatched by any other venue. Moreover shopping can be done painlessly, without leaving the comfort of one's home. As a result online auctions now con-

stitute the largest antiques and collectibles market in the world. In particular, their practices have utterly transformed the buying and selling of whistles, at least at the lower end of the market.

The online auction business is utterly dominated by eBay Inc., whose Internet address is <www.ebay.com.> eBay resembles nothing so much as an enormous nationwide garage sale. At this writing it boasts a revolving inventory of more than two million lots, of which nearly a third are classified as antiques or collectibles. The majority of these items are the same dreary goods to be found at most flea markets, but certain categories can be quite fertile. No category is more active than "steam whistle." A quick search under this title typically turns up thirty or more listings of potential interest to the whistle collector. Thus more than a thousand whistles a year are bought and sold on eBay, dwarfing all other public sales venues. It is probable that more whistles are traded on eBay than on all other auctions and consignment sales combined. In most cases the listing is accompanied by a color graphic. Buying and selling is limited to registered users. The registration procedure is straightforward but embodies fairly stringent rules for the protection of all parties. The seller pays a nominal fee to post his advertisement, and pays a somewhat larger fee—although still very much less than a customary auctioneer's fee—when his item is sold. The buyer is responsible for all shipping and handling fees.

In addition to the very low commissions charged sellers, three additional features make trade at eBay attractive to buyers. The first is a "feedback forum," i.e., a tabulated and statistically analyzed summary of comments, both favorable and adverse, on the performance of registered users. Such information is not ordinarily available through any other channel of acquisition. The comments suffer from outrageous grade inflation—no one gets less than AAAA++++ —but the mere existence of this grading scheme provides a powerful incentive toward ethical behavior. The second attraction is a proxy bidding scheme that remembers (and keeps secret) your maximum bid, but raises your actual bid only insofar as necessary to top competing bidders. Thus one need not stay glued to the computer throughout the bidding process, which typically lasts a week. Finally, unlike a conventional live auction, many lots are offered simultaneously. This permits a degree of foresight in allocating one's resources that is not possible when lots are presented and auctioned serially. Most experienced auction-goers have had the experience of lacking the funds to bid on a coveted item because they were all expended on a previous item. This is less likely to occur when the next twenty or thirty items are presented in parallel.

Electronic auctions also have some major disadvantages. The first of these is that, for the most part, sellers are not whistle specialists. This leads to an unusually high proportion of erroneous, misleading, or deceptive descriptions. Relief valves, pop valves, cab signals, explosion whistles, and auto exhaust whistles are all identified as steam whistles, battered wrecks are said to be in excellent condition, filth is called "patina," steptops are endowed with 19th century origins, patent dates are cited as dates of manufacture, and everything larger than an inch or two in diameter is alleged to have been removed from an old steam locomotive. The cautious buyer will insist on a picture of the item before the sale, and generous return privileges after the sale if it is not as described.

Electronic auctions are also infested with "snipers," persons who enter pre-emptive bids in the final seconds of an auction. Bidding in a conventional auction does not cease until all bids have been heard, but an online auction terminates at a fixed and inflexible time on the clock. Certain unscrupulous buyers have turned this difference to their advantage, lurking in the electronic shadows and then jumping in with a winning bid just as the allotted time expires. Thus no competing bidder has an opportunity to make a counteroffer. This encourages all other bidders to withhold their bids until the last possible moment and transforms the bidding process from an open contest into a secretive game of "Beat The Clock." It is not unusual for the selling price of a whistle to double or even triple in the final two minutes of an auction. This disreputable practice has become so widespread that there now allegedly exist software packages that will automate your sniping. There are procedural remedies for this abuse, but so far the major online auctions have not chosen to apply them.

But by far the largest disadvantage of electronic auctions is the attraction they hold for inexperienced newcomers ("clueless newbies"), who flock to the more popular categories like moths to the candle flame. Having no prior experience, and therefore no sense of prevailing market values, they succumb to auction fever and tend to drive prices sky-high. Sellers of course welcome their participation, but it is a disaster for buyers. Indeed, bids are often in inverse ratio to the buyer's experience. When a whistle sells for two or three times its usual price, it will often be seen afterwards that experienced buyers have bid low, whereas the highest bidder or bidders are market virgins. (This is known as the Gautreaux Effect, after the collector who first remarked it.) Until the newbie market is satiated—if indeed it ever can be—there are few if any bargains to be found at electronic auctions. Online auction houses offer the whistle buyer a splendid opportunity to acquaint himself with a wide variety of whistles in a short time, and to observe the cut and thrust of market forces. What they do not ordinarily offer is low prices.

Curatorship and its responsibilities

If you own one whistle you might be a retired sea captain or a nostalgia buff. If you own three whistles you might be an amateur historian, an ardent rail fan, or a budding collector. But if you own five or more whistles you can no longer conceal your true nature, not even from yourself. Like it or not, you have become a curator. "Curator" comes from a Latin root meaning "care," and a curator is someone who cares for the items in his charge, not merely in the passive sense of feeling affection for them, but in the active sense of bearing responsibility for their continued safety and preservation.

Fortunately steam whistles do not require a great deal of care. If kept under cover and protected from the elements, they will not deteriorate. It is possible to maintain a large collection and do absolutely nothing to it or with it. On the other hand, this *laissez-faire* attitude deprives the collector himself of one of the principal joys of collecting: the opportunity to express his affection for whistles by taking an active interest in their history, use, and preservation. Absent this interest, one can scarcely be said to *collect* whistles; one merely *owns* them.

Beyond mere ownership lie the responsibilities of curatorship. Broadly speaking, these include identification and dating, attribution or provenance, restoration and repair, documentation and cataloguing, protection against fire, theft, and other hazards, appraisal, evaluation, and insurance, and ultimately, disposition. Each of these topics is discussed below:

Identification and dating

The material in Chapter 5 is intended to assist the reader in tasks of identification and dating. Careful comparison of the whistle at hand with the figures and text in that chapter will serve to identify the manufacturer of most whistles. In this connection, the most valuable asset the collector can have is an extensive file of manufacturers' catalogs. Original catalogs are now hard to find, and very expensive when found, but the novice collector will discover that established collectors are usually willing to share photocopies of their files. Certain key items, such as the comprehensive Fairbanks catalog of 1906, have been reproduced and circulated so many times that virtually every owner of a large collection now has a copy. One can also carry out independent research at the libraries of the great industrial museums, only a few of which have been thoroughly mined for whistle-related literature. Finally, every collector must recognize that there will always be a residue of "mystery whistles" that defy identification. These may amount to as much as 5 or 10% of a major collection, and represent experimental designs manufactured in numbers too few to catalog, one-of-a-kind or home-made whistles imitative of commercial designs, whistles built in railroad shops or roundhouses for special purposes, or even patent models.

The issue of dating is rather more problematic, inasmuch as whistle designs tended to evolve slowly. In extreme instances, such as the Lunkenheimer Fig. 441 plain whistle, the design remained essentially unchanged for five decades, and in the absence of supplementary information it is not possible to ascertain the date of manufacture with any greater precision. Nevertheless most whistles exhibit variations in certain small details over the years, and these can give important clues to the date of manufacture. Pay particular attention to the nature and location of the manufacturer's markings, the shape of the valve cover, the lever, and the acorn, the manner in which the center stud joins the languid plate, and the contour of the bowl. Very often slight variations in these properties suffice to date a whistle, when carefully compared to the manufacturer's catalogs. As in every other area of connoisseurship, experience brings greater knowledge and facility.

There is one manufacturing detail that is particularly useful in dating old whistles, and that is the manner in which the bell is fabricated. Almost all chime whistles from 1887 onward had one-piece cast bells, readily identified because the inside surface of the bell is rough to the touch whereas the outside surface is machined smooth. The principal exception is the Kinsley line, in which the bell consists of a sleeve of drawn brass tubing slipped over an internal bronze casting. The earliest plain whistles, ca. 1860, also had cast bells, but these were generally so short in relation to their diameter that they could be easily machined both inside and out. The next epoch in the fabrication of plain bells consists of a cylinder of rolled brass or bronze sheet, riveted or soldered to a cast top cap. (This is the method whereby organ pipes had been fabricated since the fifteenth century.) These reveal themselves to the exploring finger by a smooth inner surface interrupted by a lap or butt seam. Often the seam is visible from the outside as well, owing to the use of flush rivets or a slightly different coloration of the joining material. Rolled sheet bells predominated from roughly 1870 to 1880. These dates are curiously late, inasmuch as the process for drawing seamless brass tubing over a steel arbor had been brought from England to the U.S. as early as 1848, and commercialized by the American Tube Works in Boston in 1850.[8] The final epoch in the fabrication of bells for plain whistles begins about 1885, with the use of seamless drawn tubing of brass, bronze, or copper for the cylindrical portion of the bell. By contrast, all-iron extra longbell whistles, such as the Lunkenheimer on p. 71, retained their rolled sheet construction throughout the entire brief period of their manufacture, from roughly 1912 to 1920. The prominent row of round-head rivets that secured the seam echoed the esthetic of steam boiler design and gave them a distinctly paleotechnic appearance.

Patent dates are a source of some confusion. Over the years many whistle manufacturers stamped their products with various patent dates, often in a changeable or inconsistent manner. The most steadfast in its practices was Crosby, which stamped "PAT. JAN. 30, 1877" or some variation thereof on every large chime whistle it ever manufactured. (This was of course the date of the seminal Einig patent on the single bell chime, as previously discussed.) Confusion arises because ignorant or deceitful sellers frequently represent the patent date as the date of manufacture, or nearly so. The result is a voluminous traffic in spurious "19th century" whistles. There is no reason whatsoever to be deceived by such claims because stamped dates are clearly designated as patent dates, not dates of manufacture. In fact, given the sluggish pace of innovation among whistle manufacturers, the date of patent can precede the date of manufacture by as much as 50 or even 75 years.

Replicas, reproductions, and forgeries

Contrary to the situation in the fine arts, and despite the felonious inclinations of an occasional rogue dealer, the whistle collector is rarely troubled by replicas and reproductions.[9] The basic reason for this is that the inducements to fakery are too meager; the potential rewards do not outweigh the necessary effort. A steam whistle, and especially one with a built-in valve, is a rather complex device. To reproduce a whistle demands the capabilities of a competent foundry and a well-equipped machine shop. This reproduction would then enter a market wherein, at least at present, the proceeds of sale would scarcely exceed, if indeed they even equaled, the cost of manufacture.

Regrettably, however, there is an occasional forgery, and these are confined almost entirely to the realm of railroad locomotive whistles. Railfans tend to be highly specialized collectors, focusing their attentions narrowly on a favorite railroad or two; thus they assign unusual value to artifacts marked with the railroad's name or initials. Knowing this, an unscrupulous seller can easily stamp such initials into an otherwise unmarked whistle, and thereby attribute it to the sought-for road. More experienced collectors call such forgeries "made-to-order" whistles, and the potential buyer can be rightly suspicious of attributions for which the only evidence is a set of stamped initials. Major railroads almost never marked their whistles in this fashion, and on those occasions when a railroad whistle was marked with the road name, the marking was almost always in the form of embossed lettering integral with the casting. It is also helpful to know as much as possible beforehand about the types of whistles favored by the road of interest. For example, one can easily doubt the authenticity of a whistle with horizontal valve allegedly originating from a road that used only whistles with vertical valves.

The practiced eye can also easily discern the signs of cheapjack manufacture. There was a period in the 1980's when ship chandlers carried Taiwanese copies of the familiar 2" Kinsley and Crosby chime whistles, intended primarily for sale to boat owners. The bodies of these whistles were yellow brass instead of red bronze, and the alloy was of such low quality that they practically crumbled to the touch. Moreover the machining was so careless that in at least one instance the air passages from inlet to bowl had not been drilled out; the whistle could not even be blown! More recently the Mu Diang Works in China have begun to produce five-chime steptop locomotive whistles modeled on the Star Brass version of 1920. These are not marked with the country of origin, and the foundry work is exceptionally crude. Nevertheless the sound is indistinguishable from that of the prototype, and the price is a third or quarter of comparable steptops on the American market. Given this inducement, several collectors have satisfactorily cleaned them up and adapted them to domestic pipe thread standards and lever operation.

Other instances of apparent fakery appear to owe as much to ignorance or stupidity as to criminal intent. In 1989 a Texas dealer sold by mail order a whistle described as a Nathan longbell steptop. On receipt the whistle proved to be a shortbell model into which a 4" length of bell from a similar whistle had been crudely spliced. The effect on the sound was disastrous, for one lowers the pitch of a multi-tone whistle by *multiplying* all the chamber lengths by a constant factor, not by adding a constant length to them. Furthermore, the quality of workmanship was so poor that the spliced bell promptly fell apart in service. Suit was brought against the dealer and a judgment obtained. This whistle was eventually restored to its original condition, but only after a long and difficult repair.

Attribution and provenance

Discovering the history of a whistle or, as a professional curator would say, learning its *provenance*, is usually a more difficult problem than identifying its maker. "Provenance" is a French word meaning "place of origin," and it is vitally important in the world of fine arts and masterworks generally. If you bring an old violin to a musical instrument dealer and assert that it was made by Antonio Stradivari, the dealer understandably would like to know where it has been for the last three hundred years. That record of prior use and ownership constitutes the violin's provenance, and it plays a major role in authenticating the instrument, supporting or refuting the claim of origin. The provenance of a whistle serves a somewhat different purpose. Almost every whistle is authentic in the trivial sense that it is not a fake or a replica of the maker's genuine article. The real interest lies in the historical record itself, which tells where the whistle served and for how long and in what capacity.

The problem is that the provenance of most whistles, and especially smaller whistles, is simply not known. They carry no documentation whatsoever and there is no record of their history. It is a rare—or at least a highly discriminating—collector who can say with certainty where even half of his whistles came from. The cause, of course, is that until recently a whistle was not regarded as an object of great value or historical importance, and there was no more reason to record its prior owners and users than in the case of a safety valve, a pressure gauge, or any other boiler accessory.

Large maritime and industrial whistles are more likely to have traceable histories than smaller whistles. In the first place, their obvious size and importance earn them more attention and respect. In the second place, they tend to move around less. Once a factory whistle is mounted atop the boilerhouse, it is likely to remain there as long as the boilers are in service. When a large ship is scrapped, the whistle is likely to be preserved, perhaps to serve again on another ship, or perhaps to be retained as a souvenir by the shipbreaker. But in neither case is the whistle likely to be lost or forgotten, and the fortunate collector who acquires it has a good chance of reconstructing its history.

On the other hand, there is no shortage of anecdotal claims. Every whistle purchased from a former owner is likely to be accompanied by a story: "I got it from a guy who said it was used on an excursion steamer on Lake George." Or: "The old man said he took it from the paper mill where he worked and kept it in his barn for thirty years." Vague allegations of this kind may pique the interest of the buyer, but they are virtually impossible to verify. Hence they fail utterly to meet professional standards of documentation. They are of interest primarily when they are manifestly false. When a seller claims that a whistle 2" in diameter was used on a mainline steam locomotive, one has reason to doubt his veracity.

Unfortunately, false attributions abound, though most of these appear to be motivated more by wishful thinking than by the wish to deceive. Consider for example the distinctive three-chime dome-top whistles built in the shops of the Pennsylvania Railroad. These were used on class D-16, J-1, and M-1 locomotives, but most notably on class K-4 Pacifics. Four hundred and twenty-five of these great passenger locomotives were built, and the wailing minor triad of their whistles was familiar to everyone who lived along the Pennsy main line. So popular were they that virtually every three-chime Pennsy whistle that comes to market, regardless of its actual origin, is attributed to class K-4. There is an old joke among fine arts dealers that of the 873 pictures van Gogh painted during his lifetime, more than a thousand are in the United States. Similarly, among the 425 whistles originally fitted to Pennsy K-4 Pacifics, at least 600 are in the hands of collectors. The same is true of many other celebrated locomotives. For example, what collector would not take pride in owning an original whistle from a Union Pacific 4000-series "Big Boy"? At one point in the late 1970's two entirely dissimilar claimants for this honor were on the market simultaneously. As the Hungarian nobleman is reputed to have said of his family's most cherished relic, the skull of the patriot Rakoczy, "Only mine and the one in the National Museum are genuine."

The marking of railroad whistles, and especially steptop whistles made in railroad shops, is a confused and confusing subject, made more so by the railroads' failure to adhere to a common practice. Hence these markings are often mysterious to the novice, and misinterpretations abound. Nevertheless two general propositions can be asserted with confidence. The first proposition is that only embossed markings, i.e., those cast into the whistle at the time of manufacture, are wholly trustworthy. Stamped numbers are always suspect, because they could have been added at any time, by any person, for any purpose. We have already remarked the unfortunate (but fortunately rare) practice of stamping road initials "to order" to pique the interest of specialized railfans.

The second general proposition is that a number embossed on a whistle is never the number of the locomotive on which it served. The beginning collector, eager to establish a provenance for his new acquisition, sometimes leaps to this conclusion but it is invariably false. In the first place, locomotives were often renumbered during their service lifetimes. In the second place, whistles are mere boiler accessories, and were regarded as interchangeable parts. They were never assigned to a particular locomotive, but moved from one locomotive to another in accord with need. Only the most senior of engineers, in the most indulgent of managerial climates, enjoyed the privilege of replacing the whistle normally mounted on an engine with his personal whistle.

The majority of embossed markings on shop-built steptops are pattern identification numbers. Examples are the "X 6532 A" that appears on the top plate of the PRR three-chime whistle, and the "LB 9299" that appears on the bell of the Southern Pacific six-chime steptop. Every foundry maintains a storeroom full of patterns for the castings it produces. The patterns are identified by metal tags mounted in a conspicuous place, so as to be readily visible when the patterns are stacked on storage racks. If the molding sand is sufficiently fine, one can sometimes see reproduced in the finished casting the heads of the small escutcheon pins used to fasten the tags to the wooden patterns. The number of the pattern is often preceded by initials indicative of the function of the part, such as 'LB' for long bell or 'SB' for short bell.

Embossed foundry markings on a Southern Pacific six-chime steptop. "LB" stands for long bell; "9299" is the pattern number. Photo by the author.

Other embossed markings that occasionally appear on steptops are either the initials of the railroad itself or (rarely) the name or initials of the maker. Bear in mind, however, that most railroads did not initial their shop-built steptops at all. Larry Spreckelmeier, one of the nation's pre-eminent authorities on locomotive whistles, has furnished the following list:

- AT&SF 6-chime: road initials, pattern numbers, and "LFM"
- Atlantic Coast Line plain and 3-chime: road initials and pattern numbers
- Baltimore & Ohio plain, 3- and 6-chime: road initials sometimes cast into fulcrums
- Boston & Maine 6-chime: road initials and pattern numbers
- Burlington or Colorado & Southern 5-chime: pattern numbers only
- Canadian National 3- and 5-chime: road initials, pattern numbers, and "McAVITY"
- Canadian Pacific 3-chime: road initials, pattern numbers, and "STAR BRASS MFG. CO."
- Denver & Rio Grande Western 5-chime: road initials and pattern numbers
- Great Northern 5-chime: road initials and pattern numbers
- Illinois Central 3- and 6-chime: pattern numbers only

•Kansas City Southern 4- and 5-chime: road initials, pattern numbers, and "LFM"

•Louisville & Nashville 3-chime: pattern numbers only

•New York Central 6-chime: road initials and pattern numbers

•Norfolk & Western plain: pattern numbers, road initials cast into valve disc

•Northern Pacific 5- and 6-chime: road initials and pattern numbers

•Pennsylvania Railroad plain and 3-chime: pattern numbers only

•Southern Pacific 6-chime: pattern numbers only.

•Southern Railway: pattern numbers only

•Union Pacific Star Brass 5-chime: road initials on lever, irregularly

•Wabash 3-chime: pattern numbers only

("LFM" stands for Locomotive Finishing & Manufacturing Co., a supplier of accessories to many railroads.)

Despite the suspicion that attends them, not all stamped numbers are devoid of meaning. These markings may consist of dates, initials, or merely strings of digits. Dates of manufacture are sometimes seen on shop-built whistles that have a long and prideful history of association with a particular workplace, such as a locomotive backshop or roundhouse. The whistle may be stamped again each time it was repaired or modified. Needless to say, these dates are important clues to its service life, and must not be obliterated by a misguided conservator. Initials may be those of a prior owner or user, possibly a locomotive engineer who was presented with the whistle on retirement. These too are valuable, especially if the engineer was a well-known whistle artist. Strings of digits are more difficult to interpret. If neatly done at the time of manufacture, they may constitute a serial number or production number, as discussed in Chapter 5. If obviously done by hand at a later date, they might conceivably record the locomotive from which the whistle was taken. As discussed above, this was never done by the railroad itself, but perhaps by the first private owner as a reminder of its origin. Other combinations of digits may represent the accession number of a subsequent owner, or merely a code (such as a Social Security number) to identify the owner in the event the whistle is lost or stolen.

Many whistles lead several service lives. The author has in his collection a six-chime steptop originally fitted to SP 4-10-2 No. 5025. After that locomotive was scrapped, the whistle passed through several other hands before coming into mine. It was then loaned to the Wilmington & Western, a tourist railroad in northern Delaware, where it was used for several years on 4-4-0 No. 98, a 1907 Alco. (An application for which it was ludicrously ill-suited.) What is the provenance of this whistle? Originally of course it was "ex-SP 5025," but now its provenance includes "ex-W&W 98." After several more exchanges, it is quite possible that the original use will have been forgotten altogether.

Like the violins of Stradivarius, the national stock of whistles, and especially chime whistles and large whistles of all types, is essentially fixed. Moreover, the supply of *available* whistles is declining, owing to progressive sequestration in private collections. Hence whistle collecting has entered an era of "depletion psychology" in which a few individuals compete for an ever-diminishing supply of goods, exchanging the same items over and over among themselves at ever-increasing prices. One of the consequences of this depletion psychology is a truncated or secondary provenance, one relating exclusively to prior ownership, not to use. The fact that the whistle was once a functioning utilitarian device seems to have been forgotten. One hears dialogues like the following among serious whistle collectors:

> "What happened to Abel's 12-inch Crosby?"
> "Baker bought it at the estate sale after his death. Had to sell a banshee and a Liberty Ship whistle to pay for it."
> "Isn't that the same whistle Charley used to own?"
> "Yes, but he traded it to Abel some years earlier for a three-bell chime."

And so forth. If the names of the whistles in the foregoing dialogue are replaced by van Gogh, Renoir, and Monet, and the names of the collectors by Getty, Guggenheim, and Rockefeller, the result is a scenario which every museum curator and director of accessions would recognize.

Given that most whistles come without histories, what can the collector do to preserve what remains? He can of course undertake to research its past, recognizing in advance that the trail is probably cold and the search will probably be fruitless. Few collectors will make this choice. But he can at least resolve that nothing more will be lost in the future, by preserving every scrap of anecdotal evidence, however flimsy or uncertain, and by carefully recording the details of his own stewardship, including specifically the modifications made during repair and restoration. Though he cannot reverse the clock and recover the past, he can assure that it will advance no more while the whistle remains in his care.

Restoration and repair

These topics properly belong under the heading of whistle conservation, a subject so large that an entire chapter is devoted to it. See Chapter 7 for this extended discussion.

Documentation and cataloguing

One of the main responsibilities of a curator is to prepare and maintain a careful catalog or inventory of his holdings. The format of this catalog can be as simple as 3" x 5" file cards or as elaborate as a computerized database. The use of a computer is strongly recommended because of its flexibility. Entries can be sorted or classified according to any listed property, such as bell diameter or date of acquisition. How many Crosbys do I have? How many 5" chimes? A few keystrokes give the answer. Furthermore, specialized reports of any kind can be extracted from the main body of the database. These can be shared with other collectors, to excite their envy or to initiate trades. Condensed versions can be prepared for field use, as when visiting flea markets. "Here's a nice 3" Lunk chime at a reasonable price, but I've forgotten whether the one I already have is a 3" or a 3-1/2"." A one-page condensation of your inventory will tell you the answer. Be sure to back up the database and keep

the backup copy in a remote location, such as a safety deposit box.

Regardless of the manner in which data is stored, every entry should contain at least the following items of information:

1. A unique number or alphanumeric symbol assigned to the item;

2. The manufacturer's name and year of manufacture, if known;

3. A basic description of the whistle type or class;

4. The provenance of the whistle, insofar as it is known;

5. Significant dimensions, especially the bell diameter and length;

6. The material(s) of which the whistle is constructed;

7. A record of any markings or inscriptions;

8. A description of its condition, including defects;

9. A record of the means whereby the whistle was acquired, including the name and location of the seller if relevant, and the date and cost of acquisition;

10. A record of repair and restoration efforts;

11. A record comparable to (9) for deaccession of the whistle, if applicable.

This list may seem excessive, but in fact it barely meets professional standards of documentation.

W 92

Manufacturer: Nathan Mfg. Co., New York, age unknown

Type: Five-chime short-bell steptop, type 963-A-1070

Provenance: War Dept 2-8-0 No. 614, Fort Eustis, Virginia

Dimensions: Bell 6-1/2" dia. by 11-3/8" tall, 2" male NPT inlet

Construction: All bronze except steel center stud and nut

Markings: 'NATHAN' embossed on side of bowl

Condition: Valve gutted, lever absent; rough finish on bell

Accession: Mark Smith, February 22, 1995; $750.

Restoration: No restoration undertaken

Deaccession: Held

A representative record from the author's railroadiana inventory database.

One may even wish to add certain other items of information, such as whether the whistle contains an integral valve, the size and type of the inlet fitting, and the note or notes sounded in use.

In a museum environment, this written record would be supplemented by one or more careful photographs of the artifact. Photographing whistles is a branch of the art of table-top photography, which in turn is a branch of studio photography. Many excellent reference works exist on these subjects, and the reader will be well repaid by a visit to the local library. We give here only the briefest possible summary of recommendations:

Use diffuse illumination. Proper lighting is overwhelmingly the most important consideration in photographing whistles, especially if the surface has been polished to a high luster. Contrary to what one might expect, the best illumination is diffuse light of near-perfect uniformity, or "flat" lighting as photographers call it. A polished whistle will *look* shinier when photographed under flat light than when photographed in bright sunlight. Fortunately there is a natural source of diffuse illumination available at no cost, and that is sunlight on an overcast day, preferably a day so cloudy that the disk of the sun can barely be discerned. The next best thing to

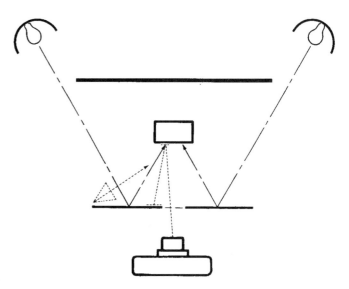

A simple way to provide diffuse illumination. The lamps are hidden from the camera behind a white backdrop. All the light that falls on the subject is bounced off a large white card. The camera looks through a small hole in the card.

an overcast day is open shade, the light found in the shadow of a large obstruction. The worst lighting is electronic flash. Unfortunately this is the choice often made by novices.

If artificial light is preferred, there are many schemes for producing diffuse illumination in the studio. The simplest is to employ only "bounce" lighting, i.e., light reflected from diffusing surfaces. Alternatively, a semi-transparent tent or cubicle can be constructed around the subject. Illuminate this cubicle from the outside and poke the camera lens through a small hole in the wall of the cubicle. This gives complete control of reflections, because the subject "sees" only softly glowing white surfaces in every direction. Consult standard references for further details of this technique.

Position the whistle before a seamless white background. This is simply achieved by purchasing an opaque white window shade, preferably washable and as wide as possible, at the local hardware store. Fasten it to the wall with ordinary shade mounting brackets about four feet above a table top. Pull the shade out onto the table so as to make a smooth large radius curve at the inside corner, and set the whistle in the middle of the table top. If an indication of scale is wanted, include a ruler or a familiar object such as a hammer. When properly lit, so that the vertical and

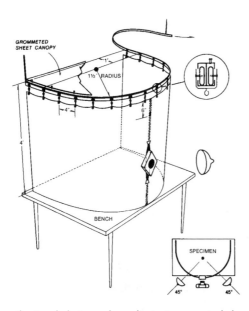

How professional photographers eliminate unwanted glare and reflections when photographing shiny objects. The object is completely enclosed in a translucent white cubicle. Illumination shines through the walls of the cubicle and the camera peeks through a small hole.

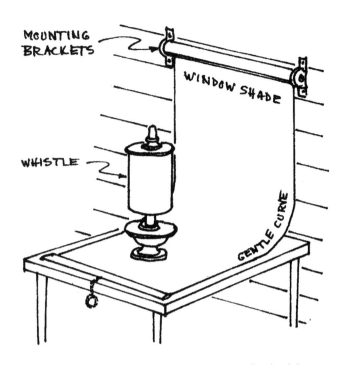

MOUNTING BRACKETS

WINDOW SHADE

WHISTLE

GENTLE CURVE

An ordinary white window shade serves as a seamless backdrop.

horizontal surfaces of the shade appear equally bright in the viewfinder, the transition between them will be almost invisible. Furthermore, the shade will be out of focus almost everywhere, obscuring its surface imperfections. This arrangement approximates quite well the expensive backgrounds used by commercial studio photographers.

Use black-and-white film. Except in rare cases (e.g., a copper bell) color values are not important to the depiction of whistles, and in fact tend to obscure detail. Black-and-white film offers superior contrast latitude, greater exposure tolerance, greater amenability to modification in the darkroom, greater suitability to reproduction, and superior permanence. Almost any slow speed fine-grain emulsion will do. Good old Kodak Plus-X, a standby for two generations, is perfectly suitable. It has relatively fine grain and adequate speed (ASA 125), and can be purchased at any photo shop. Equally suitable are Ilford FP-4 and Ilford Delta 100. One step up from Plus-X is Kodak T-Max professional film (ASA 100) with finer grain and greater latitude at a very slight increase in price. Slightly faster, but with somewhat coarser grain structure, are Kodak Tri-X and Ilford HP-5. More specialized emulsions are not needed.

Use a lens of normal focal length. Wide-angle or telephoto lenses are wholly unnecessary for this work. Similarly, perspective-control lenses are seldom needed because keystoning can be eliminated by proper placing of the camera. Only when photographing small details, such as an inscription or a patent date, might a macro lens be necessary. Even then a close-up focusing attachment is as satisfactory as a separate lens.

Use a tripod and a remote shutter release. Aperture ratios of the order of f/11 or f/16 will be needed to obtain adequate depth of field. These, coupled with relatively low ASA ratings, lead to exposure times that can be as long as one second under artificial light. Hence a tripod is mandatory. A long extension release cable will minimize shaking of the apparatus during exposure.

Protection and insurance

A major collection deserves to be safeguarded like any other asset of such magnitude. The task of safeguarding it in turn comprises techniques for preventing loss and techniques for recovering loss. Techniques for profitable disposition (or "deaccession" as it is called by professional curators) are discussed in the following section. One means of preventing loss is to conceal the existence of the collection from all except a few trusted friends. While probably effective, this approach seems unacceptably reclusive. It deprives the collector of almost all the joy of sharing his experiences with like-minded members of the whistle-collecting fraternity, and it prevents him from participating in such public demonstrations as whistle blows.

Another method is to surround the building in which the collection is housed with chain-link fence, razor wire, and guard dogs. The usefulness of these measures is highly doubtful. In my experience whistles are seldom stolen from private homes or outbuildings on private property. Instead they are stolen from public places, and especially those where crowds are present. Many more whistles have disappeared from unattended autos in parking lots or vendors' tables in flea markets than from homes. Another perilous situation occurs at auctions, where some bidders make a practice of accumulating their purchases in a heap at their feet. They then leave their seats briefly to buy a hot dog or talk to an acquaintance, with predictable consequences. The remedies in all cases are self-evident.

Given that common sense can prevent many thefts, what can be done to assist in the recovery of stolen goods? One useful technique is to stamp an identifying name or number on each item. It is essential that the item be *stamped* with machinist's number and letter punches, not merely engraved with a vibratory engraver. A marking engraved with the usual vibratory engraver can be completely effaced, but a stamped marking actually deforms the underlying metal, and can be recovered by acid etching even if filed away. What should the stamp say? The state police usually advise stamping your auto license number, because they are used to recovering stolen cars. This is bad advice. People move from state to state and change license numbers. Use your initials instead, or better still, your Social Security number, which is uniquely yours and never changes. Where to stamp it? Unless your name is Casey Jones, don't stamp it in a highly visible location on the bell or the bowl of a whistle, because that will diminish its value to a subsequent owner. Stamp the underside of the pipe nut if it is large enough to accommodate eleven characters. If not, stamp the inside of the bell cover or the underside of the spreader plate. If the bell cover is thin, be sure to support it adequately when stamping. Otherwise you will be dismayed to see your Social Security number appear in reverse, in raised relief, on a badly dished cover.

A sizable collection demands a careful inventory. A method of taking inventory often recommended for household goods is to photograph everything with a video camera. Despite its simplicity, this method has numerous shortcomings. In the first place, most people are inexperienced in the use of a video camera. Merely panning over the walls of the den or hobby room does not yield a useful record. Furthermore, unless one has access to a video frame grabber, it yields no still pictures to show the police when they ask what was stolen. Finally, it is almost useless in dealing with insurance companies. Insurance is at best a means of recovering loss, not preventing loss. It will never replace the treasured whistle melted down in a fire or stolen from the back of your pickup, but it will provide the consolation of roughly equivalent monetary value.

For these reasons I much prefer a written inventory. The best of all inventories is one prepared in accord with the instructions in the preceding section. In addition to the uses enumerated there, it is also the key to obtaining adequate property insurance at reasonable cost. Do not assume that your collection is automatically covered by the personal property clause in a standard homeowners' insurance policy. Many underwriters demand separate floater policies for possessions of unusual value, such as fine arts, jewelry, firearms, cameras, musical instruments, and coin and stamp collections. Coverage under these floaters invariably costs more than straight property insurance. A thorough inventory is a powerful bargaining tool in convincing the underwriter to assign a lower (i.e., less expensive) classification to your whistle collection. Make sure he or she understands what the nature of the collection is and what its approximate value is. (Be realistic!) Make sure that you understand what type of policy is required and what type of documentation is required in the event of loss. In my experience most underwriters will accept the inventory itself as the required documentation, both as proof of ownership and as record of loss in the unhappy event of fire, theft, or natural disaster.

Deaccession and disposition

Most whistle collections tend to grow with time. It follows that accessions must outnumber deaccessions. Unless one is a dealer regularly engaged in buying and selling whistles for profit, the deaccession of a whistle is a relatively infrequent event. It usually arises for one of a small handful of reasons, all of them basically derived from the desire to upgrade the collection. Perhaps the whistle is a duplicate of one already represented in the collection, or perhaps it was accepted merely to earn the good will of a dealer whose favor one seeks, or perhaps it can be offered in trade against the acquisition of a more desirable whistle. Deaccessions of this kind are more properly viewed as part of the acquisition game, and are not the focus of this section.

Instead we are concerned here with the final disposition of a collection. The collector may have tired of the hobby and turned his interest elsewhere, or he may move to a new residence too small to accommodate his holdings, or he may need to raise money, or he may die. There are only two occasions when arrangements for final disposition can be made: before and after the death of the collector. The first occasion has everything to recommend it and the second occasion has absolutely nothing to recommend it. As with most matters related to the close of life, advance planning and directives are the keys to security and peace of mind. The best possible outcome is to make the desired disposition of your collection while you are still alive and in full possession of your faculties. Only you can provide the background information that ensures that the next owner will preserve the historical information so painstakingly gathered, and only you can reap the emotional rewards that come from the knowledge that you have done everything in your power to preserve the artifacts themselves. The worst possible outcome is to die without having made any provision at all. Your ghost will watch from above as the accumulated treasures of a lifetime are knocked down in your widow's general estate sale, along with the lawnmower, the socket wrenches, and the broken reclining chair. You will have stolen more from your heirs than any thief might have stolen from you.

There are only three basic methods of disposing of a major collection: bequeathing it to heirs, donating it to an institution, and selling it. All three may be used in varying proportion, as appropriate. Direct bequeathal of all or part of a collection to one's heirs is a process that contains no mysteries. Nevertheless it would be prudent to ascertain beforehand that the intended beneficiary in fact wants the bequest, and that you are not burdening him or her with the proverbial white elephant. Bequests should be unconditional. Do not bequeath your prized Nathan steptop to your nephew Ricky on condition that he not marry his girlfriend Linda. Efforts to exert control from beyond the grave are contemptible in principle and almost always futile. They lead to contention and ill will, not to mention legal entanglements.

Donating all or part of a collection is largely a matter of choosing the right recipient, which depends in turn on asking the right questions beforehand. The coordinated effort of all parties is required. The donor must have thought through what he wishes to accomplish by means of his gift, and the beneficiary must be capable of honoring those wishes and be willing to do so. Many a naive collector dreams of a room in a major museum devoted to the display of his collection, the polished whistles ranked lovingly in glass-enclosed cabinets, accompanied by a tasteful bronze plaque acknowledging his benefaction to an admiring public. This is extremely unlikely to occur. In the first place every major museum has many more items in its storerooms than it has on display. At the Smithsonian Institution, for example, the ratio of stored items to displayed items currently exceeds twenty to one. In the second place, few if any private collections meet the standards of authtication and documentation demanded by professional curators. About the best the average collector can hope for is the acceptance of a few well-documented pieces for a study collection, kept behind locked doors and accessible only to scholars.

Far better outcomes will result from lowering one's sights. The Smithsonian may not want your collection, but a small regional museum might, especially if it emphasizes items of local interest. As an example, perhaps you live in a town that once had a prosperous forest products industry. If you have the whistle from the sawmill or the paper mill in that town, the local Historical Society would probably be delighted to have it, and would give it a place of honor. Similarly, marine whistles would be welcomed in port cities and locomotive whistles in railroad towns, if they can be tied in some way to vessels or engines that frequented those places. Do not overlook antiquarian associations devoted to traction engines, threshing machinery, and the like, many of which maintain small displays. These sometimes have the advantage over conventional museums that they can furnish live steam, at least on occasion. This assures the donor that his whistle will occasionally be heard as well as seen.

Selling a major collection is a major undertaking. The simplest and most lucrative solution is to sell it as a single lot to a private collector. How does one find potential buyers with heavy purses and keenly honed acquisitive instincts? If you have been an active collector for many years, you probably already know which other collectors merit this description. They should be advised of the intended sale by personal letter. Nevertheless it also pays to advertise the sale, because potential buyers sometimes emerge from surprising places. In one recent instance, a valuable collection of marine whistles in the U.K. was purchased by a consortium of hitherto unknown Ukrainian businessmen. The appropriate vehicles for such advertisements, generally speaking, are the same hobby and antiquarian publications whereby whistles are acquired. Be sure to establish whether the potential purchaser is buying on his own behalf or for resale, as a dealer. Offers by dealers tend to be 25 to 50% lower than offers by individual collectors.

Most large collections, however, are sold at auction, generally item by item. It is prudent to choose the auction house in advance, because auctioneers differ widely in their skill and areas of expertise. The auctioneer who sold Holstein heifers yesterday and will sell pizza ovens tomorrow is unlikely to get the best price for your cherished three-bell Lunkenheimer today. Fortunately there are several competent auction houses that specialize in railroadiana, and still others that specialize in industrial artifacts. If you attend auctions regularly, you probably already know which ones are professionally conducted and which ones are mere tailgate affairs. Do not hesitate to engage an auction house remote from your home if it appears to offer other advantages. Truly dedicated collectors—the ones you want bidding on your goods—will unhesitatingly drive five hundred or a thousand miles to attend a really alluring auction.

It is essential to negotiate beforehand with the auction house regarding its fees and other business practices. Consignment fees typically range from 12% to 20%, with the smaller percentage applying to larger consignments. Recall too the spreading practice of adding a buyer's premium. A buyer may view this as an unwelcome and deceptive surcharge, but a seller is more inclined to look on it with favor. At this moment it is important to remember the buyer's

point of view, because some knowledgeable buyers are so offended by the practice that they refuse to participate.

Another matter concerning which a clear understanding must be reached beforehand is that of reserve prices. The collector who relinquishes his collection with reluctance, and still feels highly possessive about it, will often wish to assign a minimum bid to each and every item. This is almost always a bad idea, and will be strongly discouraged by most auctioneers. The usual custom is to permit minimum bids on a few of the most precious items only. The collector must then resign himself to the fact that some items will sell for far less than his estimate of their worth, but others will sell for far more, so that an approximate parity is achieved in the end. Finally, an understanding must be reached regarding the admissibility of mail or telephone bids. These often result in a larger return to the seller. On the other hand it is destructive to the momentum and excitement of a live auction when a spirited round of bidding is followed by the announcement that the lot has been awarded to an absent bidder. The deflating effect of such an announcement may dampen the response to subsequent lots.

Regardless of the method whereby a collection is sold, the one absolutely essential item is a proper catalog. This is the last, and in some ways the most important, reason for preparing a thorough inventory, as urged in the previous section. It is a simple matter to convert an inventory into a catalog. It is only necessary to delete the "Accession" entries to create a catalog immeasurably superior to those that usually accompany sales or auctions. The catalog sets the tone of the entire event, as the staff at Sotheby's and Christie's will attest. Catalogs compiled *post mortem* by a grieving widow or an auctioneer tend to be inaccurate and uninformative, whereas an attractive catalog compiled by someone who obviously knows his business will add many thousands of dollars to the proceeds.

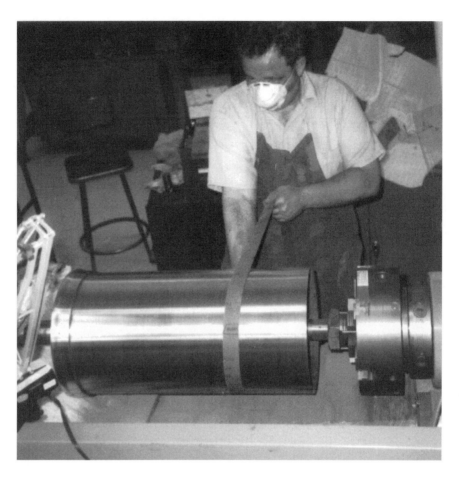

The author polishing the bell of a 12-inch plain Ashton whistle. Photo by William Rule.

7 Restoring and Conserving Steam Whistles *

He who loves the workman and his work, and does what he can to preserve and improve it,
it shall be accepted of him.

—John Adams

The task of the conservator

Primum non nocere. "First do no harm." Hippocrates considered this the cardinal rule in the practice of medicine, and it applies as well to the art of the conservator. In the most general terms, the task of the conservator of steam whistles is to leave the artifact in better condition than he found it, with its defects remedied, its structure made manifest, its appearance improved, its history reconstructed, and its market value increased. The conservator who fails in any of these requirements, or worse still, damages the whistle in his care, has betrayed his trust.

There is one respect, however, in which the duties of the whistle conservator are simpler than those of conservators in certain other fields: his tasks do not include the arresting of decay. Old whistles are not subject to self-destruction. Unlike old structures, old manuscripts, and old frescoes, they do not have to be stabilized before anything else can be done. Once the whistle rests on the conservator's workbench, it is safe from further deterioration. No thieves will carry off its parts, no careless workmen will damage it, no steam will corrode its metals, no rain will rust or discolor it, no frost will burst its innards. Restoration can be carried out as time permits. Few artifacts in the realm of industrial archaeology are so accommodating in this regard.

The conservation of steam whistles can be carried out with varying degrees of thoroughness. Ranked in accord with the order in which these activities are usually undertaken, and the amount of effort they require, they are *repair, restoration*, and *enhancement*. To *repair* a whistle means to restore it to serviceability through the replacement of missing parts, the mending of broken parts, and the reinforcement of weakened parts, usually without much regard for

appearance or historical authenticity. Broadly speaking, this is what would have been done by mechanics during the service life of the whistle. To *restore* a whistle means to return it as nearly as possible to its condition at some earlier time in its existence. That time is usually chosen to be the moment of its manufacture, but there are important exceptions. If the whistle once belonged to a famous locomotive engineer, for example, and bears the indiciae of his service, such as his initials engraved on the bowl or a lever customized to his specification, it would be a disservice to the historical record to obliterate these alterations. In such cases the restorer's aim should be to recreate the whistle as it was at the height of its service life, while in the care of a prideful owner. To *enhance* a whistle means to improve its appearance or functionality beyond its original state, and thus beyond what the manufacturer intended. This concept is so foreign to the usual notion of conservation, as practiced in the fine arts for example, that it cannot be understood without further discussion. That discussion must be slightly deferred, however. There are persuasive arguments both for and against enhancement, and its advisability should be carefully weighed by the conservator before it is undertaken.

It goes without saying that the boundaries between these various types of activity are not perfectly distinct but shade continuously into one another, especially when they are carried out more or less simultaneously. When the conservator replaces a hopelessly rusted center stud with a new rustproof stainless steel stud, is he repairing, restoring, or enhancing? Because the distinction cannot

* In collaboration with Larrry Spreckelmeier

always be made, we shall occasionally use the word "restoration" in its most general sense to embrace any or all of the foregoing activities. Hopefully the context will make clear whether the specific or the general meaning is intended.

The conservator faced with a recently acquired whistle must begin by making a decision, or more precisely, a series of decisions. He must choose the appropriate level of restoration. Unless the whistle comes from a hitherto undiscovered cache of new old stock, or has been enshrined for years on the mantelpiece of a retired engineer, it almost certainly bears the scars of its service life. Should he leave the whistle precisely as it is, as testimony to its utilitarian career? If the whistle is damaged or non-functional, should he attempt to make it serviceable again, or should he limit his efforts to improving its appearance? Should he attempt to return it to "like new" condition? Or should he polish and refine it to salon perfection, so that it stands as a showpiece and exemplar of its type?

The answer obviously depends in large part on the intended end use of the whistle. A whistle intended exclusively for display need not function, and the task of restoration can center primarily on the replication or replacement of missing parts and the cosmetic treatment of external surfaces. But the task also includes presentation of the whistle in such a manner that it relates visually to the remainder of the collection, generates viewer interest, and effectively presents the intended historical data. Presentation can be further enhanced by the proper choice of lighting, descriptive text, and illustrations depicting specific details. Within these broad parameters the restorer still has a great deal of latitude, especially in selecting the degree of surface finish. By contrast, the restoration of whistles intended specifically for use and demonstration on working locomotives, traction engines or ships is primarily a task of repair. Functionality is of course the first requirement, with reliability and safety considerations taking precedence over accurate retention of detail. Generally speaking, these needs can be met without doing violence to the historical tradition from which the whistle springs. The greatest challenge to the conservator, however, is the whistle used both for display and for occasional demonstration at events

such as whistle blows. Functionality and safety cannot be compromised, but neither can appearance or historical accuracy. Convenience of operation can be subordinated, however, so long as safety considerations are given full weight. The bulk of the discussion that follows will deal with this demanding combination of requirements.

The most important quality the conservator can bring to this initial stage of restoration is patience. As with old autos, old guns, and even old houses, there is a strong temptation to disassemble the whistle completely as soon as it is acquired, in anticipation of a full restoration. But disassembly is essentially irreversible. Once the condition of the whistle has been altered by disassembly, significant details that relate to its history may be lost. Therefore the conservator must take time to study and reflect upon what he has before picking up his tools. Much can be learned from close scrutiny of the whistle in as-received condition, for this condition constitutes a tangible record of all that has befallen it before acquisition.

It is also advisable to undertake some background research and reading before beginning work, either in the library or with the help of other collectors. This will acquaint the restorer with the origins and lineage of his whistle, and perhaps most important, it will occupy his time and thus help to curb the urge to jump in and tear things apart. This preliminary research is especially important when, as is so often the case, the whistle has broken or missing parts. Replacement parts are seldom if ever available today, so the restorer will probably attempt to replicate them. A careful study of archival materials is necessary to achieve historical accuracy, because whistles underwent numerous subtle changes in design throughout their history. Many collectors find that their priorities change as they live with their artifact and work their way through this research phase. Typically, historical considerations become more important, while the urge to polish the whistle until it looks like a bowling trophy diminishes.

Where does one find such background information? Old catalogs from manufacturers or hardware supply houses are excellent sources of information regarding appearance and mechanical design. Such catalogs are not generally available in libraries, excepting those that specialize in industrial history.

Most experienced collectors, however, have private catalog files that they will gladly share with others. The engravings in such catalogs are never dimensioned, but the creative restorer can generally infer shapes and proportions from the illustrations and from the whistle at hand. Remember that, in one sense, a partial solution of the puzzle already sits on the workbench.

Patent drawings are also an excellent source of details. The United States Patent and Trademark Office provides public access to every patent from 1790 to the present at its central search facility in Arlington, Virginia. If the patent number or date of issue is not known, various automated search engines will assist in finding relevant patents. Hourly fees are charged for the use of these engines. Remote access in a variety of formats is available from libraries in major cities. Finally, if only the date is known, the number can be obtained through the *Official Gazette*, a bound volume listing the patent abstracts by date with number. A paper copy of any patent can be obtained at nominal cost.

When the collector has done his homework, and presumably has acquired a better understanding of what he has and its historical significance, he is ready to decide what level of restoration to undertake. Every restoration effort, even the most modest, begins with a vision of how the piece will look when completed. This vision need not be committed to paper provided it is firmly established in the worker's mind. This vision in turn will determine which techniques are applied and how far they are carried out. If carefully thought through in advance, it will also prevent the workman from falling into various traps and pitfalls, such as altering some parts in such a way that other parts no longer fit.

Disassembly

Assuming that the conservator has decided to undertake some degree of restoration and repair, the first question is whether to disassemble before cleaning or to clean before disassembling. In almost every case we recommend disassembly before cleaning, if only because disassembly reveals so many more surfaces in need of cleaning. Furthermore, a disassembled whistle is always easier to work on, regardless of size.

It is a rare whistle that comes apart with ease. Unless the whistle has recently been worked on by others, it is usually necessary to apply heat or force or both. Invest in a large smooth-jaw adjustable hex wrench, such as a Ridgid No. 25 or 35. No. 25 will accommodate hexes as large as 3-1/2" across the flats. No. 35 is even larger but is no longer manufactured, and must be sought in the secondary market. In addition, a gas torch with a broad tip will help to loosen parts and prevent breakage. A propane torch is acceptable for this work, but the required temperatures are reached more easily with an oxy-acetylene torch. If acetylene is not available, an acceptable substitute for the welding torch is a Mapp gas torch, available at most hardware stores. In any case, heat and force must be applied cautiously and appropriately, even on the largest whistles. An impatient restorer can easily ruin a whistle in a few seconds of carelessness.

If one is fortunate enough to acquire a whistle that is still piped in place, and the whistle cannot be easily unscrewed from the pipe, cut the pipe off about 6" below the hex nut. Cutting torch, pipe cutters and hacksaw are all suited to the task. Never cut off a pipe flush with the hex nut, as this will make the stub very difficult to remove. Be careful of the top-heavy load as the cut is completed, especially when working on a boiler house roof or other hazardous location.

In order to remove the stub, secure it in a pipe vise and position the whistle for heating. Absolute rigidity of mounting is the key to breaking this joint or any other. Be sure the set-up provides access to the hex nut for a large smooth-jaw wrench, not a pipe wrench. Heating the stub and hex will soften the corroded threads and allow the metals to give. A cutting torch is more effective than a welding tip and more economical than a rosebud tip. When the whistle bowl is made of brass, annealing the joint will make it softer and encourage threads to stretch rather than break. It may be necessary to reheat the work after annealing, as most pieces unscrew more readily when hot. In some cases it may be easier to grip the hex nut rather than the pipe stub. Regardless of how the work is mounted, however, grip the pipe stub sufficiently far from the joint so that it will not bind if it distorts under pressure. Finally, tapping the joint with a hammer and striker plate is often a very effective way to shock loose a frozen joint.

If the foregoing methods do not succeed in loosening the stub, saw the stub off about 1/4" below the hex nut. Using a hand-held hacksaw blade or a reciprocating power saw such as a "Sawzall," make two parallel longitudinal cuts in the inner surface of the stub, about 1/2" apart. Stop as the saw blade just begins to intersect the tops of the inlet threads on the whistle base. Care must be taken not to cut into these threads. Heat the section between the cuts and drive it inward with a punch. It will roll up and drop out nicely. Drive the remaining piece inward all around its circumference, and then unscrew or pull it out.

Generally speaking, all small component parts should be removed before the heavy work begins, to prevent damage to them. Many acorn nuts, top nuts, spring caps, fulcrums, etc., will require heating and/or gentle tapping with a hammer in order to loosen them, just as in the case of the pipe stub.

Unless the whistle is a steptop type of the Nathan style, in which case the bell can be removed merely by unscrewing the top nut, separation of the bell from the base is usually the most difficult part of the disassembly process. The worst case is a joint between dissimilar metals, such as a steel stud or center rod threaded into a brass bell or bowl. Over the course of time, at the elevated temperatures due to the passage of steam, the two metals actually diffuse into each other at the molecular level at their interface, forming a kind of natural weld. Soaking the joints with a penetrating oil such as WD-40 or Liquid Wrench is helpful, and should be done for a week or two prior to disassembly. The principal challenge to the workman is to find a means of grasping the bell. Strap wrenches for loosening oil filters, etc. are commercially available, but seldom accommodate a diameter exceeding four inches. Be careful not to apply so much torque that the bell is dented at the

Stubborn rusted pipe fittings removed from whistle inlets by the method described in the text. A longitudinal slice is carefully sawn out, and the remainder is driven inward with punches after heating. Photo by Larry Spreckelmeier.

fulcrum of the wrench. For larger bells, one of the best solutions is a makeshift wrench or split clamp, made from 2" x 8" or 2" x 10" lumber, lined with leather or rubber, and secured with lengths of threaded rod. Clamp the bell just above the arch mouths if a single-bell chime, or near the top if a plain whistle.

It is safer to secure the bell and unscrew the remainder of the whistle from it, rather than the other way around. If the split clamp has a long handle, there is a risk of applying excessive torque to the bell, and damage will almost certainly result. Prior to the use of force, apply heat to the joint to be unscrewed. The tapping process is helpful here as well. Ordinarily, a plain whistle will separate most easily at the joint between center stud and bell. This leaves the center stud still embedded in the whistle base, whence it is often difficult to remove. On the other hand, removal of this stud may be unnecessary. It will often be found that the center stud has a center-drilled dimple at its top end, used to accommodate a tailstock center during manufacture. In such cases it is a simple matter to remount the base and stud assembly between centers and refinish the upper surfaces of the bowl and spreader plate. The lower portion of the base can then be refinished by inserting the stud through the spindle hole in the headstock, provided this hole is large enough to accommodate the stud.

In the case of single-bell chimes, it is very helpful to know beforehand whether the bottom of the bell carries a male or female thread. Some single-bell chimes, such as those manufactured by Crosby and Star Brass, terminate at the bottom in a male stud cast integral with the bell. These are relatively easy to disassemble because there are no joints between dissimilar metals. Many other single-bell chimes, however, such as those manufactured by Lunkenheimer, have female threads in the bottom of the bell that engage a steel stud screwed into the base. These are often more difficult to separate. In such cases, if the usual methods of disassembly fail, drill several small (0.030"

An example of the fixturing needed to hold bell and bowl in proper alignment for the repair of a center stud torn completely out of the web during disassembly. Photo by Larry Spreckelmeier.

to 0.050") holes in the center boss. Position them so that they enter the cavity above the end of the stud. Fill the cavity with penetrating oil and let it stand a week or so. Then repeat the tapping and heating process with the bell again secured by the split clamp. If this second attempt does not loosen the joint, then there is no recourse except to carry out the remaining portions of the restoration without disassembly.

With single-bell chimes there is a strong temptation to hammer on the radial webs or dividers between chambers in order to apply torque to the bell. This may work, but it is potentially so damaging that we advise strongly against it. At the very least one risks bending or deformation of the webs. At worst the center boss will crack at the webs or tear completely out. In fact any procedure that applies excessive torque to the bell is likely to result in breakage in the region of the stud. For the whistle restorer, there is no more dreadful feeling than the realization that the last blow of the hammer or the last turn of the wrench has left him with a mutilated bell in one hand, and in the other, a bowl with a torn-out center boss still firmly inserted. This is not easy to repair. A reasonable repair can be achieved by building a clamp to hold the bell square to the bowl and welding or silver soldering the pieces. To obtain maximum strength and minimize the evidence of repair, all cracked areas should be vee'd out and all surfaces checked for squareness. Adjust as necessary with the clamping fixture. Best results will be obtained by a professional welder using TIG and Everdur rod. For a final finish the welds can be ground, roughed-up slightly with a pointed hammer, sand-blasted, and painted. If a die grinder is used, a cast surface can be simulated by letting the grinder bounce around on the area being ground. Alternatively, the repaired area can be textured by the use of

a vibratory hand engraving tool with a round tip, or even by the use of texture paint.

Removal of the spreader plate or languid is sometimes as difficult and frustrating a task as separation of the bell from the bowl. The natural inclination to insert a screwdriver in the steam slot and pry upward must be firmly resisted. Such careless or inappropriate techniques can damage the bowl, the steam slot, or the plate itself. It is important to remove the plate without bending it; yet bending is likely to result if one pries mindlessly without first understanding how the plate is attached. There are four principal types of spreader plates, the first two rather common, the last two relatively rare:

a. Plates that merely drop onto the center boss and are held captive by the bell or a jam nut.

b. Plates that screw onto the center boss with a right-hand thread.

c. Plates that drop onto the center boss and are secured to the spider ribs with screws (usually seen only in whistles 8" in diameter or larger).

d. Plates that are cast integral with the center stud (usually seen only in older whistles).

Types (c) and (d) can usually be identified by inspection, and the means of removing them are largely self-evident. But types (a) and (b) often cannot be distinguished on sight, and once again, preliminary research can pay big dividends. The principal examples are Lunkenheimer whistles of relatively recent manufacture. These have plates of type (a) or (b) with two curious fingernail-shaped depressions in their upper surface to accommodate a spanner. Inserting a drive punch in one of these depressions and tapping gently in a counter-clockwise direction will almost always loosen the plate. It should then become apparent whether the plate merely lifts off or should be further unscrewed.

In cases where the manner of fastening is not known, begin the removal by heating and quenching the plate and center boss. Using a hammer and striking block, try to shock the plate into some movement. If the whistle base has no valve, work a small diameter punch through the pipe inlet and tap gently on the underside of the plate. If this is unsuccessful, try to unscrew the plate by cleaning its surface, covering it with double-sided tape, and adhering it firmly to a surface plate, counter top or tile floor. Unscrew the bowl using the hex nut at the inlet. As always, do not use a pipe wrench with toothed jaws on the hex nut. Occasionally a plate of type (a) will rotate but will not unscrew or drop off. It almost appears as if the center boss has been swaged to retain the plate. Removing the swage is the only solution, but this will necessarily leave a mark of some kind in the center of the plate. If the decision is made to proceed, chuck the bowl and the plate in the lathe and vee out the joint with a very narrow tool. Alternatively, the surface of the plate and center boss can be ground down with a body grinder. If the bell is a chime, the resultant dip in the center will be visible in the final assembly. Sometimes a very little grinding is sufficient to relieve the interference, allowing the plate to move up when pressure is applied from below.

If all else fails, drill and tap two holes 180º apart in the languid plate, equidistant from the center boss. Holes 1/4" to 1/2" in diameter are appropriate, depending on the size of the whistle. Make a spanner wrench by inserting heat-treated screws in a sturdy piece of bar stock or pipe, matching them with the holes in the languid plate. Work the plate counter-clockwise until it begins to rotate freely. It may just surprise you and unscrew. If the plate rotates but does not unscrew, drill and tap two more holes on the same radius at right angles to the first pair, so that there are now four tapped holes evenly spaced on a common bolt circle. Insert hex head bolts and align them over the ribs of the bowl. Tighten the screws evenly in rotation, using them as small jacks to lift the plate. Additional grinding or turning may be required. Tapping while everything is under pressure will help. Heating around the boss will also help, but care should be taken as this will increase the tendency of the plate to bend under pressure. After the spreader plate has been freed, the added holes must be plugged. They can be filled with welding rod, ground, and polished. Brass pipe plugs also work nicely, and are easily fitted and finished.

Preliminary cleaning

If a whistle has been exposed to the elements for a lengthy period, it will have the typical gray-green or brown patina of weathered copper alloys. In rare instances this patina is so uniform and so attractive in color that the conservator may elect to leave it untouched. If this is the case, then superficial washing is about all that is necessary or possible. If much mechanical work is required, care should be taken to protect the weathered surfaces. Accidental burnishing or rubbing will produce brass highlights that are hard to restore to the original color.

More usually, however, the as-received surface is neither uniform nor attractive. A surprising number of whistles have been painted. There may be a coating of greasy filth gathered from the industrial environment. There may be reddish brown streaks of iron or white streaks of lime from mineral-rich boiler water, with the result that an old whistle is sometimes as colorful as an artist's palette. Nevertheless some collectors and curators feel that the condition of the surface is an important record of the whistle's service history, and should be retained as a reminder of its heritage. In most cases, however, the restorer will elect to perform at least some degree of cleaning, especially if heavy repairs are necessary. Cleaning before repair is standard railroad practice. At the great Juniata works of the Pennsylvania Railroad there was a vat of lye that could accommodate an entire steam locomotive. Generally speaking, the cleaning and finishing of copper alloys is a vast subject, embodying centuries of accumulated experience. Some of the techniques in everyday industrial use involve chemical mixtures of such appalling toxicity and hazardous potential that it would be irresponsible to describe them in a book intended for a general audience. Therefore, in what follows we confine ourselves to cleaning processes suited to the hobbyist's workshop. The reader who wishes to pursue this topic in greater detail can consult standard references such as the *ASM Metals Handbook*.[1]

Unfortunately, the surface cleaning technique that the novice usually tries first is just about the worst possible choice, and that is a motor-driven wire wheel. A wire brush held in the hand is generally too feeble to do much damage, but a wire wheel mounted in a power drill or on a bench grinder, although useful for removing weld spatter and cleaning barbecue grates, can wreak havoc on a brass whistle. If vigorously applied, it will tear the surface of the metal, leaving a wavy and distorted "lemon-peel" finish that is almost impossible to smooth out. About the only circumstances in which the wire wheel is useful are for removing rust and cleaning the external threads of steel or cast iron parts such as levers and center studs. Even then it must be applied with caution. One could begin to equip a very good whistle restoration shop by throwing away the wire wheel.

Generally speaking, the best cleaning process is the one that removes the least native material from the surface. Thus chemical methods are preferable to mechanical methods, which actually alter the texture of the surface. Light patina or tarnish can be removed with ammonia. Ammonia will be recognized as the characteristic smell of proprietary metal polishes such as Brasso. Prepare a strong solution of ammonium hydroxide in a plastic bucket and immerse the work. Good ventilation is essential because the fumes are choking. Ammonia tends to work slowly, so soaking periods as long as a week may be required. *Never*, under any circumstances, mix strong alkalis such as ammonia or strong oxidizers such as Clorox with strong acids or acid-based cleaners. The ensuing chemical reaction can release gases that are choking, or possibly even toxic.

To remove heavy green or brown patina, use a liquid toilet bowl cleaner or muriatic (hydrochloric) acid. Mix the acid with an equal volume of water for the initial trial, and adjust the proportions as necessary based on the result. *Always* add the acid to the water, never the reverse. As with ammonia, be sure the area is well ventilated as the fumes are choking. Good results have also been reported with proprietary cleaners such as KRC-7, the chief ingredient of which is phosphoric acid. Be sure to obey the recommended safety precautions. Acid-based cleaners tend to work rapidly, so the work should be closely monitored at all times.

To remove paint from whistles, use a strong water-based stripper. Brass and copper surfaces are easily stripped but cast iron surfaces are more difficult. Best results are obtained on cast iron if the stripper is applied before the piece is heated, because heating appears to drive surface coatings into the pores of the metal. Therefore, even if the whistle is hard to handle, try to strip as many of the cast iron parts as possible prior to heating them for disassembly. Painted, rusted iron is the most difficult surface to treat. Many handsome restorations have been made using a combination of polished brass and clean rusted iron. A little wire brushing and steel wool following paint stripping produce a very interesting surface. Some protective coating of the iron can also enhance the finish. A light coat of linseed oil, kerosene or motor oil will darken the color of rust and give the work an old but well tended appearance.

Steel wool is also very useful for cleaning cast or smooth brass surfaces, since it will retain the use marks, flaws and patina in low spots such as those that surround embossed lettering. Working down through the various grades of steel wool, while keeping the work well sloshed with kerosene, will produce a clean, antique appearance reminiscent of a well-maintained engine room.

Chemical treatments do not significantly alter the texture of the surface. We turn now to more vigorous mechanical surface treatments. The least abrasive of all mechanical cleaning processes is blasting with crushed pecan shells. This is the method used to clean the impellers of jet engines. In general, however, this process is not available to the amateur, and the expense of the pecan shells is prohibitive. The mildest process the amateur might employ is glass bead blasting at pressures in the range 20 to 40 PSI. This process will remove dirt, oxidation and paint, and works especially well on sand-cast brass surfaces such as bowls, valve bodies and levers. Similar results will be obtained on iron. Abrasive blast cabinets and the air compressors that run them are rather expensive for the average home workshop. Fortunately the work can often be hired out to a neighborhood auto body repair shop.

Higher pressures, up to 100 PSI, will cut faster and deeper but will also peen or work harden a brass surface. Alternatively, blasting with silica sand at pressures in the range 80 to 100 PSI is a fast way to prepare surfaces for painting, machining or repairing. The resultant surface texture is much rougher than that obtained with glass beads at lower pressure, and is hard to polish and clean. Nevertheless it is appropriate for cleaning interior valve body surfaces before grinding in valves or welding cracks. Care must be taken not to let the jet of sand strike running surfaces such as valve guides or stems. After sandblasting, threads and other mating surfaces should be cleaned with glass beads at low pressure, followed by a thorough washing with solvent. Brass is soft and will be severely affected by particulate matter ground into mechanically fitted areas.

The unnaturally uniform finish created by blasting is easily softened by rubbing with No. 1 or No. 2 steel wool and kerosene. All tool and use marks will be retained, but raised surfaces will be highlighted and recesses will develop a slightly tarnished look. Depending on the judgment of the restorer, no further surface treatment may be required.

Common defects

By the time the whistle has been disassembled and cleaned, its defects will be all too apparent, if indeed they were not apparent from the moment of acquisition. A whistle without defects is a considerable rarity, and almost every whistle that comes to market can be expected to show the scars of rigorous service. In this section we list some of the more frequently encountered defects, together with comments on the difficulty of repairing them.

Bear in mind, however, that difficulty of repair must be measured on a relative scale, not an absolute one. Whistle collectors as a group embrace the entire spectrum of competence and capability in the mechanical arts. At one extreme, perhaps, is the apartment-dweller, who possesses neither metalworking tools nor the skills to use them. To him, all repairs are too daunting to undertake, and he must necessarily purchase whatever services he requires. At the other extreme is the master mechanic with a fully equipped workshop, perhaps including even pattern-making and foundry capability. No task is too daunting for him. He could, if necessary, build a whistle from scratch, or reproduce any part of an existing one. Thus when a repair is characterized in the following paragraphs as "a simple lathe job," that means it is simple only for someone who has a lathe and knows how to use it.

Here in detail are the defects the restorer is most likely to encounter in the workshop:

Missing lever

This is probably the most common of all defects among whistles with built-in valves. Most levers were made of cast iron, a material particularly susceptible to breakage by shock. A sidewise blow is especially damaging because the lever fulcrum constrains the lever to a vertical plane. Only Lunkenheimer, the sole surviving domestic whistle manufacturer, still offers OEM replacement levers for sale. The loss of a lever is always regrettable, and especially so in the case of Buckeye levers, which are stamped with a two-digit production code. Hence their loss constitutes the loss of a portion of the historical record. Similarly, Crosby and Powell levers are sometimes elaborately embossed with curlicues and other symbols. This embossing contributes much to the appeal of the design, and is virtually impossible to reproduce.

Any competent metalworker can saw out a serviceable replacement lever from steel, aluminum or brass plate stock, to approximately the correct profile. The edges can be softened with a hand file, but the result will never be mistaken for the original cast lever. In the case of exceptionally large or valuable whistles a few expert restorers have actually cast levers from newly made patterns, complete with embossed lettering, but this task lies far beyond the capabilities of most amateurs.

Occasionally one sees locomotive whistles in which the lever has been grossly altered or modified. The modification usually takes the form of a long extension welded or bolted onto the existing lever, and is done in order to provide the engineer with more precise control of the valve opening. This in turn permits him to "quill" the whistle in a characteristic way, an art much prized by engineers and trackside hearers alike. In other cases the lever has been bent from its original shape in order to accommodate a pull cord at some odd angle. The collector/conservator must decide for himself whether the altered lever is a valuable record of railroad practice or a late excrescence to be removed as part of the restoration process.

Marred pipe nut

Only rarely does one find a whistle in which the pipe nut has not been marred by the serrated teeth of a pipe wrench. In extreme cases the pipe nut has been reduced to a cylindrical mass of chewed and distorted metal, its original hexagonal or octagonal shape almost unrecognizable. The use of a pipe wrench on milled wrench flats is a gross abuse for which a steamfitter's apprentice would have had his knuckles soundly rapped in the old days. Unfortunately the practice is even more prevalent today, as the traditions of workmanship in the steamfitting trade fade rapidly away. Moreover, smooth-jaw wrenches of large capacity ("engineers' wrenches") are now difficult to find. As noted earlier, the principal exception is the Ridgid No. 25 hex wrench, which is still carried in the Ridgid catalog.

This defect is particularly offensive to the whistle-lover because of the ignorance and slothfulness it bespeaks. If the damage is slight it can sometimes be removed by careful milling or filing of the wrench flats. But the restorer should be aware that certain manufacturers stamped the wrench flats with important information, e.g., a company logo in the case of Lunkenheimer or a production code in the case of Crosby or Kinsley. Obliterating these markings sharply diminishes the historical value of the whistle. If a trademark or serial number is seen, it is better to leave that flat unfiled than to smooth away the markings. If the damage is moderate, the scars and rounded corners can often be built up by brazing or TIG welding, followed by hand filing or milling. The ideal tool for this latter purpose is a vertical milling machine with an indexing table, but serviceable work can be done in a lathe with an indexing headstock. If damage to the pipe nut is severe, it is almost irreparable except by replacing the nut altogether.

Gutted valve

The valve is the only moving part of a whistle, and valves fail for a variety of reasons. The lever fulcrum breaks, the return spring corrodes, or the valve stem is lost. The valve seat becomes worn, causing the valve to leak, or sometimes a notch is deliberately filed in the seat in order to keep a trickle of steam flowing through the whistle in cold weather. Most factory whistles are mounted on boiler house roofs, where difficulty of access makes routine maintenance even more difficult. Occasionally an effort is made to replace a broken lever or fulcrum with a crude makeshift, but usually the built-in valve is simply abandoned. The valve openings are plugged in one manner or another, and a separate valve is inserted lower down in the steam line. After that, for reasons difficult to comprehend, the built-in valve is sometimes deliberately destroyed by knocking out the internal partitions in the valve body with a punch or cold chisel. Unfortunately, internal damage of this sort is difficult to assess at the time of acquisition, and is revealed (to the collector's intense dismay) only when the whistle has been disassembled.

Whatever the reason, many whistles come to market with their valves gutted and inoperable, their innards removed, and the valve stem opening plugged or capped. The difficulty of repair depends on the nature of the damage. Replacing a broken return spring is trivially easy, provided the access cover can be removed from the valve body. Machining a replacement stem for a horizontal valve is a simple lathe job. Machining a vertical valve stem is somewhat more difficult, because a rectangular mortise must be cut to accommodate the end of the lever. The seating surfaces of disc valves stems can be remachined on a lathe and valve body seats can be remachined in a milling machine, although it very useful to have a specialized tool for the latter purpose.

A more serious problem is presented by an absent lever hanger or fulcrum. As with levers, only Lunkenheimer offers any possibility of replacing a missing fulcrum with original stock. If the fulcrum was originally a separate part it can in principle be remanufactured, but the elaborate casting is a challenge to the patternmaker and the machinist alike. In many early whistles, however, e.g., Cincinnati Brass Works, Crane, Buckeye, Lonergan, and Lunkenheimer prior to 1903, the fulcrum is cast integral with the valve body, and when the valve fails the fulcrum is sometimes sawn off. This pointless mutilation is essentially irremediable. Also essentially irremediable is a valve body that has been internally destroyed. Either defect disqualifies the whistle for the collector who seeks only fully restorable whistles.

Other lost or broken parts

The absent lever and the gutted valve are merely two of the many accidents that can befall a whistle during its life of service. There is scarcely any part of a whistle that is not subject to loss or traumatic amputation. Among the more frequently seen defects is breakage of the protruding ears between the chambers of a Nathan-style steptop whistle. A steptop with all five or six of its ears perfectly intact is a relative rarity. Whistles without acorns or with makeshift acorns of hexagonal bar stock are also common. Additionally, acorns of traditional shape tend to have very thin walls just above the internally threaded portion. Occasionally the top of the acorn cracks or breaks off at this point. A whistle that has been "dropped on its head," so to speak, may have its acorn blunted or collapsed inward. All these defects are remediable, although some degree of authenticity is necessarily lost. Steptop ears can be built up with brazed or TIG-welded additions. Acorn tops can be restored by brazing or silver soldering, and replacement acorns can be turned on a lathe, although the hexagonal flats may present a problem to those who lack a milling machine with indexing capability. In the absence of an indexing head, acorns can be turned from hexagonal bar stock. Most of this stock is yellow brass, however, which does not afford a good color match with red brass or bronze castings. Furthermore, unless the replacement acorn is built up from two or more pieces, the diameter of the turned portion cannot exceed the width of the hex stock across flats. The width across flats is not usually the widest dimension of commercially manufactured acorns.

More serious defects sometimes occur during the harvesting of a whistle. Whenever possible, a whistle should be unscrewed from its inlet pipe. Often, however, the pipe is frozen in place, and out comes the cutting torch, or more likely, the hacksaw. The correct place to cut the pipe and the means of removing the pipe stub have already been described above. Some of the most dreadful mutilations occur when an eager (and hopelessly ignorant) harvester saws through the whistle base itself, just *above* the pipe nut. A whistle without a pipe nut is junk, fit only for parting out.

Dented bell

Dented bells are at least as common as missing levers. In the 19th century the whistle bell was often the highest point of the locomotive, and hence frequently collided with overpasses, tunnel mouths, and roundhouse doors. But it is hard to understand why so many modern whistles arrive at market with dented bells. Incredible as it seems, some holes and dents are obviously the result of gunfire. It is a rare whistle collector who does not have at least one item bearing the mark of a bullet impact. One can only speculate on the sociopathic mentality that induces some gun-bearing citizens to shoot at anything shiny. Other dents arise when exuberant hostlers sitting astride a boiler bang on whistles and bells with their tools, perhaps to loosen

Restoration of a screw-in lever fulcrum from a Crosby chime whistle. This repair is particularly difficult because the threaded portion is 'timed' so that the lever is upright when the fulcrum is fully seated in the body of the whistle. The problem is solved by re-using the original threaded portion and attaching new arms to it with carefully aligned socket head cap screws. The joint is then vee'd out for TIG welding, and a new valve stem guide silver soldered in place. Photo by Larry Spreckelmeier.

The restored fulcrum. Photo by Larry Spreckelmeier.

frozen joints, but more likely just to hear them ring. Almost every loco-motive bell that has not spent its life in a protected environment carries the marks of this destructive practice. Occasionally one encounters Liberty ship or other marine whistles bearing peculiar long braided scars on their sides. These are the result of careless scrapping procedures. When the wire ropes which guy the stack are cut, the free ends, released from their tension, whipsaw about crazily and can strike the stack-mounted whistles.

A large dent or bulge in the bell is by no means irremediable. Techniques for reshaping dents and bulges are discussed at length in the following section. In some cases the task can be quite labor-intensive, and when judging whether to undertake it one should bear in mind that a dented bell is at worst a cosmetic defect, having little or no effect on the sound of the whistle.

Misaligned bell

Accurate centration of the rim of the bell over the steam slot is essential to proper operation of a whistle. Unfortunately the bell of a plain whistle is usually supported at the top by a long center stud. Hence the forces which maintain alignment must travel up the length of this stud and down the bell again, a distance more than twice the length of the bell itself. A support system more susceptible to misalignment could scarcely be imagined, and the patent literature contains numerous schemes for providing more robust support at the open end of the bell. Nevertheless the simplest design has prevailed, and hence many plain whistles exhibit bent center studs and cocked bells, owing to shocks received in service.

This defect is easily remedied by the workman with access to a sturdy lathe. The whistle base is chucked up as securely as possible while the far end of the stud is supported by a tailstock center. Force is then judiciously applied to the stud until it runs true. If the stud is twisted or bent beyond repair, it is often possible to machine a replacement stud, knowing that it will be largely hidden from view when the whistle is reassembled. Finally, in some cases bell misalignment results largely from looseness or play in the joint between stud and bell. This can usually be remedied by attention to the fitting of the acorn nut, or by the addition of an internal jam nut.

Split rim

For reasons that are not entirely clear, the bells of plain whistles are susceptible to splitting and cracking at the rim where steam impinges. This occurs most frequently when the wall of the bell is thin, suggesting that thermal stresses are responsible. The cracks are often so narrow that they are revealed only after the bell has been cleaned. Occasionally one encounters a whistle in which crack propagation has progressed to the point that a previous owner found it necessary to reinforce the rim with a circumferential band of iron or brass. In other cases a previous owner has attempted to fill the cracks by welding or brazing. This repair is often

A victim of the sport of morons. This elderly Crosby from a Lake Winnepesaukee steamer has taken three rifle shots to the bell. A previous owner tried unsuccessfully to plug them with soft solder. It may have been a fourth shot that carried away the tip of the acorn.

The owner of this marine whistle has fastened a stout steel ring around the lip of the bell to prevent further cracking. The effect of this thick, blunt ring on the vortex pattern must be horrendous.

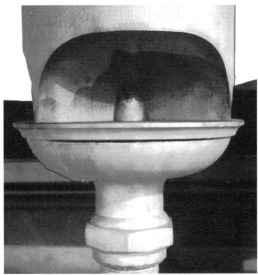

An example of frost damage caused by water accumulating in the bowl. The black line between the rim of the bowl and the bowl itself is an open crack extending halfway around the bowl. This is a difficult repair, requiring careful fixturing and great skill with the torch or TIG welder. Photo by Lin Chapman.

The languid or spreader plate of this 8-inch Crosby has been severely warped, perhaps by excessive inlet pressure, but more likely by the freezing of water collected in the bowl. This is a moderately difficult repair, demanding a powerful hydraulic press. Photo by Larry Spreckelmeier.

badly executed, with results that may be mechanically adequate but are cosmetically unacceptable.

Nevertheless, an experienced workman can usually mend cracks with a brazing torch or TIG welder, using the techniques described in the section below on hot metal repairs. If the whistle has already been banded, the new owner must decide whether to remove the band and attempt to restore the whistle to its original condition, or retain the band as a meaningful record of the whistle's life in service.

Frost damage

The bowls of vertically mounted whistles with integral valves tend to fill with water, either from rain or from condensate. If this water is allowed to accumulate until the bowl is full, and then freezes and expands, severe damage to the bowl can result. The usual consequence is a warped or broken spreader plate, but in some cases the bowl itself is cracked or deformed. Never purchase a whistle without first verifying that the rim of the spreader plate is everywhere flush with the rim of the bowl. Oldtime steamfitters sometimes attempted to forestall frost damage by drilling a small weephole near the bottom of the bowl, but this remedy is unavailing if the hole plugs with ice. A better remedy—applicable only to whistles with separate valves—is to install a small drain cock between the whistle and its valve.

Frost-damaged bowls are unusually difficult to repair. A bent spreader plate can sometimes be hammered or pressed back into shape, or even replaced, but the repair of a cracked or deformed bowl calls for heroic measures. Special jigs and fixtures and a hydraulic press are almost always required to restore the bowl to its original shape, followed by welding or brazing of open cracks. This type of repair should be undertaken only by highly experienced workmen, and then only on whistles whose exceptional value or importance merits the effort.

A different and slightly less serious type of frost damage is sometimes suffered by flat-top single-bell chime whistles. Whistles of this kind are notorious for leaking rainwater around the acorn, which then collects in the cavities above the chamber tops. Worse still, the removable top caps are sometimes lost, (or in the case of display locomotives, occasionally stolen), leaving the cavities entirely open to the weather. If collected rainwater freezes there, it can produce bulging or even rupture of the bell near its top. Repair is difficult but possible, and generally similar to the repair of bells dented from other causes.

Weathering

Weathering arises from two principal sources: the corrosive action of the steam itself and prolonged exposure to the environment. It is not generally appreciated that live steam is a highly corrosive substance, more so if the water entering the boiler has been inadequately conditioned. Live steam will leach the minor constituents from alloys not intended for steam service, leaving behind a pitted and weakened matrix of half-dissolved metal. Naturally this damage is most severe at the lip of the bell where steam impinges, and where condensate collects in drops. On very old whistles, and particularly those with brass rather than bronze bells, the lowest inch of the bell may be as eroded and pockmarked as the surface of the moon. There is no remedy for this except to cut off the corroded portion.

As discussed in the section on preliminary cleaning, all non-ferrous whistles that are exposed to the elements, and not regularly cleaned or painted, eventually develop the gray-green or brown patina characteristic of weathered copper alloys. If this patina is removed, a pitted and pockmarked surface is sometimes revealed, with defects too deep to sand or polish out. What should be done?

Fortunately, heavy weathering is almost always confined to one side of the whistle. In the case of marine whistles, the side adjacent to the stack is relatively well protected from the elements and weathers more slowly. In the case of stationary whistles exposed to salt air, the lee side of the whistle weathers more slowly. If the whistle is polished in accord with the methods described earlier, the result is sometimes surprisingly acceptable. The whistle looks used but nevertheless projects a well-cared-for appearance. If polishing does not suffice, then the collector is well advised to learn to live with imperfection. Accept the weathering, and display the whistle with the good side toward the viewer and the bad side toward the wall.

Bungled restoration

Few sights are more disheartening to the collector than a whistle bell that some well-intended but incompetent machinist has chucked between lathe centers and turned from end to end, in a misguided effort to remove surface flaws. Because cast whistle bells have relatively thin walls and are invariably out-of-round to some degree, sooner or later the turning tool breaks through the side, producing a ragged and unsightly hole. If the whistle is a single-bell chime, and the hole lies above the top of the chamber, the whistle can still be blown, but its mutilated appearance robs it of all esthetic appeal. This is a major defect, and difficult to remedy.

In general, a whistle that has suffered such damage cannot be fully restored to its original condition. The most satisfactory and least visible method of repair is a flush-mounted patch. It is also the most difficult to execute. The damaged region is cut out entirely and a patch that matches the original whistle in color and curvature is welded in at the edges of the opening. This task requires extraordinary skill in metalworking, and very few conservators are capable of undertaking it. If a flush patch cannot be managed, then the patch must lie on top of the damaged region. A band which entirely encircles the bell is easier to apply and less unsightly than a localized patch, but in either case great skill with the gas torch is necessary to prevent further cracking or warping of the bell. If the whistle is one of exceptional rarity or historical importance, and a patched appearance cannot be tolerated, it is sometimes possible to slip a thin cylindrical jacket of rolled sheet over the entire bell. Arch openings can then be filed to shape by hand, although the doubled wall visible at these openings will always betray the nature of the repair.

The lip of an ancient yellow brass bell, badly eroded by impinging steam. The rim was so ragged that it had to be trimmed off.

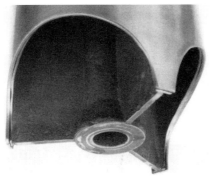

Only the double wall barely visible at the arch openings betrays the nature of the repair.

A PRR chime whistle mutilated by an inept mechanic, who went through the side wall of the bell casting while attempting to take a cleanup cut on the lathe.

The bell is repaired by wrapping it tightly with rolled and silver-soldered 16-gauge bronze sheet stock. Arch openings are then cut out and filed to shape.

Mixed parentage

Whistles tend to outlast boilers, and whistle parts tend to outlast whistles. Hence as time goes by and new whistles become increasingly rare, the stock of existing whistles becomes progressively hybridized or mongrelized, comprised of parts of mixed parentage. One of the most common forms of mongrelization is the mating of bases and bells of different origin. Many such unions are possible, owing to the standardization of threads. A Lunkenheimer bell on a Lonergan or Powell base presents an acceptable appearance, but a Lunkenheimer bell on a Nathan base looks truly bizarre to the experienced eye. No matter how carefully contrived, such a whistle can only be regarded as a curiosity, a testimonial to the frugality and ingenuity of bygone mechanics.

There is one instance of apparent part-swapping, however, that is deceptive. Several manufacturers, notably Lunkenheimer, offered whistles with iron bases and brass bells. These were alleged to offer some advantage in economy and durability, but in general they did not sell well, as most customers preferred all-brass whistles. The practice was carried even further in whistles built by railroad shops, which routinely mounted brass bells on iron bowls and iron bells on brass bowls. It has been suggested that this was done to minimize the use of brass during the war years, or alternatively, to adapt whistles to ever-increasing boiler pressures, inasmuch as cast iron is stronger than brass. Nevertheless the co-existence of both types of hybrid suggests that there was no engineering or economic principle underlying the choice of materials—perhaps nothing more than the convenience of the foundry. In any case, a mixture of ferrous and non-ferrous metals in a single whistle is not necessarily a sign of mixed parentage.

Dent removal and other reshaping operations

As noted above, it is a rare whistle that has no dents. Although dents seldom affect the sound of the whistle, many of them are visually so objectionable that they demand removal. The process is beset with two principal dangers: unrealistic expectations on the part of the restorer, and the risk of doing further damage. Not all dents can be removed so completely that no trace of their existence remains. And the greater the amount of reshaping required, the greater the danger of cracking the work.

A knowledge of the working properties of copper alloys is essential. Brass is not iron, and the customary techniques of the blacksmith are not only irrelevant, they are potentially harmful. Furthermore, most high quality whistles were not made of brass at all, which is primarily an alloy of copper and zinc, but of bronze, which is primarily an alloy of copper and tin. Crosby Steam Gage & Valve, among other firms, was meticulous in its specification of casting alloys, often using slightly different alloys for the bowl and top cover of the same whistle. A

Restoring and Conserving Steam Whistles

representative composition, used on Crosby chime whistles after 1926, consists of 86.9% copper, 8.7% tin, 2.2% zinc, 2.2% lead, and trace amounts of iron and phosphorous, presumably as impurities. The entire range of copper content in Crosby casting alloys lies between 84% and 88%, so these were copper-rich alloys indeed, of lovely roseate hue.

Generally speaking, all copper alloys, both wrought and cast, should be bent cold, not hot. Attempting to bend a bronze casting while hot is likely to result in fracture. This does not mean, however, that heat has no role in the reshaping process. Copper alloys tend to work-harden, i.e., to stiffen as a result of movement. The greater the copper content of the alloy, the greater the work-hardening tendency. The remedy is to anneal the work by heating it to a dull red. There are two schools of thought on what to do next. One school believes that the work should be immediately quenched in water or oil. The other school believes that the work should be left to cool in air as slowly as possible, even to the point of slowing the natural cooling rate by packing it in vermiculite. Metallurgical science suggests that both schools are equally right—or wrong. The atomic dislocations that are responsible for work hardening relax away while the material is held at elevated temperature, and the subsequent rate of cooling is largely irrelevant.

The simplest type of dent to remove is one which is convex outward and hence accessible to a hammer, e.g., a bulge in the side wall of a bell. These usually arise when the bell is allowed to fill with water that subsequently freezes. If the amount of bulging is small, one can hammer directly on the bulge itself. At this point we cross the boundary from science into art, and the working techniques of various expert restorers begin to diverge. Members of one school favor the use of lead hammers or plastic-faced non-marring hammers. If an ordinary hammer is used, a radius is ground on the edges of its striking face, and the face is padded with leather. This group claims that the crescent-shaped "dings" left by the edges of the striking face are virtually impossible to remove. Members of another school use only flat-faced steel body hammers, claiming that they dent the work less. Crescent-shaped dings, they aver, are the result of the craftsman's inability to hit the work squarely! Both groups agree, however, that one must work the entire

Preparation for the repair of a large bulge in the wall of a bell. The bulged area is bridged over with stiff acrylic sheet. Photo by Larry Spreckelmeier.

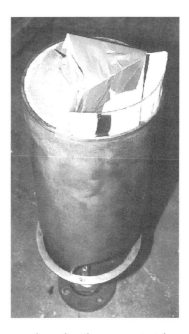

Extra spaces are plugged with scrap material, and concrete is poured behind the acrylic sheet. When hard, this will serve as backing for the restorer's hammer blows. Be sure to provide clearance for later removal of the concrete! Photo by Larry Spreckelmeier.

surface of the bulge uniformly, using small quick blows to reduce stress. When working without a backup block, be careful to prevent overbending of the surface. The process works with both cast and rolled bells, but cast bells have a greater tendency to crack if much movement is required.

If the bulged area is extensive, however, more elaborate precautions are needed to prevent overbending. Bridge over the bulged area from the inside with thin metal or acrylic sheet stock to duplicate the original radius. Fill the remaining volume with concrete to serve as backing, and then hammer the bulge inward until it feels solid. Care must be taken to block off undercuts in the cavity before filling with concrete. It is also good practice to use a release agent. Two garbage bags, one inside the other, work well. This will allow the concrete to slip out once the job is complete. Standard concrete reinforcing bar is bent into a loop and used as a handle for removing the concrete slug. Considerable pulling or hammering may be required to dislodge the concrete.

Unfortunately most dents are concave, which is why they are called dents and not bulges. Dents in plain bells up to 3-1/2" in diameter can sometimes be removed or substantially reduced without hammering by use of a tailpipe expander. These are internal expanding mandrels sold by auto parts supply houses to stretch undersize or dented portions of an auto exhaust system until they fit together. The device is inserted in the open end of the bell and expanded by turning the draw nut with a wrench. Drawbacks to their use are that they do not reach to the top of long bells, and that each expander covers only a narrow range of diameters.

Alternatively, the restorer can make a cylindrical hardwood form and drive it in. The form should be split longitudinally into two or more wedge-shaped pieces so that it can be collapsed for withdrawal. A heavy lag screw driven into the end grain will give something to grasp when pulling. Hardwood mandrels can also be used on chime bells, but their construction becomes considerably more elaborate. In this case it is important that the mandrels bear only on each other or on the central axis of the bell. Do not exert large unbalanced stresses on the partitions between chambers, lest they deform or fracture.

If the removal of large or deep dents is to be attempted, and the whistle is at least three inches in diameter, a miniature hydraulic ram is the tool of choice. These are available from well-equipped machinists' or auto body shop supply houses, typically under a name such as "Porta-Power." The essential component is a small, short hydraulic cylinder with a stroke of about 3/8", a minimum height of about 1-3/8", and a diameter slightly more than 1". Despite its small size, the cylinder carries a surprising rating of five tons. The complete tool consists of the cylinder, a hand-powered pump, and a connecting hose. The set-up should include metal shims to position the ram, and properly contoured anvils for each end of the ram to distribute the large localized forces. These are essential to prevent high spots or possible puncture. Opinions differ on whether the outside of the work should be backed up. Some favor backing the ram with an appropriately shaped piece of wood or steel, clamped in place to prevent over-travel of the metal. Others favor a free outer surface so that the motion of the metal can be closely watched, detecting cracks as soon as they appear. Both methods can be made to work.

If none of the foregoing techniques are available or suitable, then the dent must be hammered out. There are basically two ways of doing this. The first is to hammer directly on the dent, as in the case of bulge reduction described above. Needless to say, the bell must be sufficiently large in diameter and unencumbered by internal partitions, so that there is room to swing a hammer inside. The use of a steel or wood backup block shaped to the outer radius is advisable. Despite its limited applicability, this method has the advantage that no hammer marks can appear on the outside of the bell.

The other technique is called "hammering off the dent" and is borrowed from the repertoire of the auto body shop. A massive and suitably shaped backup piece or "dolly" is pressed by hand against the dent from the *inside* of the bell, and hammer blows are directed from the outside at the crease or fold at the edge of the dent. The crease gradually flattens out under the combined forces, obliterating the dent. As above, many light blows are preferable to a few heavy blows. This method is advantageous when the bell diameter is small or its interior is encumbered by partitions.

Regardless of the manner in which the bulge or dent is reduced, once the bell is reconfigured its surface must be smoothed. The process is much like that used by auto body shops to refinish a dented fender. Holding the piece rigid is the key to success. For larger whistles, make a cradle of several 2" x 6"s or 2" x 8"s, with radiused cutouts to match the bell. Pad the cutouts with strips of old carpeting. Nail the pieces together with appropriate spacers to create a sturdy fixture. If the imperfections are numerous and deep, and the wall thickness will permit vigorous stock removal, work over the repaired area with an angle grinder and a 60 or 80 grit disc. An ordinary 3" x 21" belt sander works almost as well. Care must be taken not to cut through high spots. After grinding is completed, the smoothing process continues with hand filing. Begin with a coarse file, follow with a bastard cut mill file, and then a fine file. After filing, work the surface through several grades of abrasive paper and finish with polishing on the felt wheel, as described below in the section on polishing. If the imperfections are relatively minor and the wall is thin, sanding with a random-orbit sander and 120 grit paper may suffice.

An alternative to abrasive paper is the use of a proprietary 3M product called Scotchbrite™. This comes in the form of fibrous abrasive pads of various sizes and various degrees of coarseness. The preferred tool is a modified 4-1/2" angle grinder with a 1/4" Jacobs chuck, holding 3" diameter Scotchbrite pads and their associated rubber backing discs. Work through the grades to a "superfine" pad, which leaves the surface sufficiently smooth to go directly to the buffing wheel. Eye and lung protection must be worn when using Scotchbrite.

Joining methods and hot-metal repairs

Under this title we collect that body of repair and fabrication techniques popularly called welding. This is a task that the average workshop owner or home hobbyist is seldom equipped to undertake. Yet to deliver a whistle to a welder chosen more or less at random from the Yellow Pages is to invite disaster, for the average welder is no better qualified to repair a fine whistle than the average Sunday painter is qualified to retouch the Mona Lisa. In the first place, almost all welding is done on ferrous metals, whereas almost all whistles are made of non-ferrous alloys. In the second place, almost all welding is done electrically, usually by MIG or TIG, whereas two of the joining techniques most useful for whistles, brazing and hard-soldering, demand a gas torch. Thus an entirely different body of skills is called for, more nearly like those of the sculptor or artisan than of someone whose principal occupation is patching up auto frames or hayrakes. Such skills are rare and hard to find, and the best way to learn who possesses them is to inquire of other, more experienced collectors.

If the task at hand is to join two pieces of metal, the first step is always proper preparation of the mating surfaces. Cracks should be thoroughly vee'd out, on one or both sides as appropriate, after which the surface should be cleaned by bead blasting. If the metal is iron, and color matching is desired, then electric welding is the only option. The vee channel should be overfilled and then ground to final contour. Once the surface is ground, the weld can be darkened by reheating. Selective blasting or roughening, using a mask on the area to be protected, will help match texture prior to heating. Salt water and browning solutions can also be used to bring the weld closer to the rusted color. Some experimentation may be needed. If color matching is not demanded, e.g., if the part will subsequently be painted, then brazing can also be considered as a repair technique.

If the metal is brass or bronze, then brazing, hard soldering, and TIG welding are the techniques of choice. Generally speaking, copper alloys respond poorly to carbon arc welding and resistance welding. Brazing is particularly useful for building up missing or worn areas of metal, as when filling holes, restoring a mangled pipe nut, or reinforcing a weak joint between bowl and base. The long temperature range in which the brazing rod remains semi-solid or "slushy" permits metal to be added bit by bit, much as a sculptor adds clay. The color match between brazing rod and most brasses is good but not perfect. On the other hand, hard solders (also called silver solders or silver brazing alloys) are particularly useful when metal must flow into extremely narrow interstices, as when filling tiny cracks. For example, Handy & Harman Easy-Flo™ melts at 1160°F and becomes as fluid as water at only 1175°F. Like all silver brazing alloys, it has the desirable property of "running to get warm," so judicious application of the torch will draw it into the tiniest openings. Other silver brazing alloys offer larger temperature intervals between melting point and flow point, and hence a longer working range. On the other hand, the color match with respect to the usual bronze alloys is not as good as brazing rod, although the contrast is less visible when the metal is highly polished. Finally, if color matching to red brass or bronze is the primary issue, the best choice is TIG welding with Everdur™ rod. All these processes demand forced ventilation. In particular, most silver brazing alloys contain large amounts of cadmium. Cadmium vapor is a cumulative toxin, and is released copiously when these alloys are melted. Silver brazing without forced ventilation is suicidal.

A problem common to all high temperature joining techniques is the minimization of thermal stress. Electric arc welding is less troublesome than gas welding in this respect, because the application of heat is very brief and highly localized. But to apply a hot gas flame to one small portion of a large casting is to flirt with catastrophe. The resultant thermal stresses can deform or even crack the casting, leaving the restorer with a much more severe problem than he set out to remedy. Ideally one should bring the entire workpiece as nearly as possible to the same temperature throughout. Use the largest possible torch tip and play it uniformly over the work until the last possible minute. It may even be necessary to build a makeshift firebrick oven or heat shield around the work and warm it with supplementary gas flames. Similarly, cooldown of large workpieces should be as slow and uniform as possible. In my experience (although this is disputed by others), it is best not to quench the work with cold water or oil. If necessary, pack it in sand or vermiculite while hot, and walk away for an hour or two.

Do not overlook soft soldering as a joining technique. Ordinary 50-50 tin-lead solder melts at 437°F. It is not its low melting point but its lack of mechanical strength that precludes its use in most whistles.

Nevertheless, there are situations in which great strength is not required and soft soldering is the joining technique of choice. This is particularly the case with large diameter organ pipe whistles for marine applications. The cylindrical bells of these whistles are often soft-soldered into their top caps, and there is no reason why the same should not be done with other large whistles operating on saturated steam.

Finally, there is an excellent joining technique which is almost always overlooked by the home mechanic, and that is shrink fitting. It has only occasional application to whistle repair but it might well find a place in whistle construction, e.g., in assembling a bowl to a base. A proof of the extraordinary strength and security of shrink fitting is that the tires of locomotive driving wheels were always shrunk onto their hubs. The only risk associated with shrink fitting is that the pieces may seize before they are fully mated, in which case they cannot be separated again without destroying one or the other. This eventuality can be prevented by employing the standard clearances recommended in handbooks of mechanical engineering. Note that it is immaterial whether the outer piece is heated or the inner piece is cooled. Those with ready access to liquid nitrogen may wish to explore the latter option.

Part replication

A thorough job of repair and restoration frequently demands the replacement of a missing part. With the sole exception of parts for certain Lunkenheimer whistles, spares can no longer be purchased from the manufacturer. Hence the restorer is compelled to rely upon his enterprise and ingenuity. Drawings of the missing part can be developed by enlarging catalog or patent illustrations to the appropriate size in a photocopier. It is often useful to redraw these illustrations as fully detailed orthographic projections in order to avoid surprises during the fabrication process. If no pertinent illustrations can be found, an example of the part can often be borrowed from a cooperative fellow collector. The novice will soon discover that there is a continual brisk exchange of acorns, levers, valve access caps, and other frequently missing parts among the inner circle of whistle restorers, primarily for the purpose of producing replicas.

The first step in making a replacement acorn for an old-style 10-inch Crosby. A split and doweled wooden pattern is prepared for the foundry. The outside is lacquered to keep molding sand from sticking to it. The long extension at the bottom will hold a sand core in position to make the hollow interior.

A positive pattern is made for the core, and positioned within a core box. The core box will then be filled with plaster to make a negative mold of the core. The actual sand core will then be cast within this mold.

In many instances the missing part can be fabricated in the machine shop from stock materials. This is the case for example with acorns, valve stems, and other simple turnings. More complicated parts, such as detachable lever fulcrums, can sometimes be built up from machined components by brazing or hard-soldering. In other instances, however, the missing part is so intricate and difficult to fabricate, or a built-up replacement so little resembles the original, that a new casting is called for. Consider for example an actuating lever that, as discussed before, is more usually absent than any other part. A serviceable replacement for a simple lever can be sawn or flame-cut from plate stock, but for the replacement of fancy levers (and many other whistle parts), expert restorers often find themselves drawn into foundry practice.

The molding and casting of molten metal is one of mankind's oldest technological undertakings. It is also the subject of a vast literature, reaching back at least to Agricola's *De re metallica* in 1530. It is far beyond the scope of this book to instruct the reader in the art and science of making castings. Go instead to the nearest technical library, or better still, to the nearest foundry. This is the proper starting place for any effort at part replication by casting, because there is much to learn and because shops differ in their requirements and expectations. The discussion that follows aims only to acquaint the reader with some of the most elementary considerations in foundry practice, so that he can at least converse intelligently with the foundryman.

The core box with the completed sand core embedded in it.

The newly cast acorn after being broken from the mold. Note the hole in the bottom where the core entered.

The acorn after machining and finishing, and the wooden pattern it was cast from. All photos by Larry Spreckelmeier.

Every casting begins with the making of a pattern. Occasionally, as suggested above, the pattern can be a part of the same kind, borrowed from another collector. More usually, however, the restorer must provide the pattern himself. For one-of-a-kind pieces or short runs, wood is the best material for pattern-making. Dimensional stability is the principal consideration. Mahogany and poplar are good choices in this respect. Large sections are more stable if constructed of multiple layers with grain directions at right angles to each other, as in plywood. This tends to cancel out the effects of warpage. Plywood itself is not a good choice, however, because of its knots and loose grain structure. To further reduce warp and dimensional change, seal all wood surfaces with lacquer immediately upon completion of the pattern. Lacquers dry rapidly and are not affected by the chemicals in the casting process. A simple spray lacquer primer will work well. By contrast, some enamels will cause the sand of the mold to adhere to the pattern, resulting in loss of detail in the casting.

Every pattern must be slightly oversize, because molten metal shrinks on solidification. The allowance for shrinkage depends on the composition of the metal. The usual allowance for brass and other copper-rich alloys is 0.187" per foot, or almost exactly one part in 64. Additional allowance must be made for machine finishing, of course. Every pattern must have some draft or batter, i.e., a slight taper in the direction of pull, so that it can be removed from the sand mold without disturbing the surface of the sand. All else depends on the shape of the pattern. If it has one flat side, it can be mounted on a flat surface ("match plate") and requires only an upper sand mold ("cope"). If not, the pattern must be split along an appropriately chosen parting line, with draft sloping away from the parting line in both directions. The piece is then molded between two sand molds, an upper "cope" and a lower "drag," the two molds together forming a "flask." (Note that draft and parting lines concern only the removal of the *pattern* from the sand, not the casting itself. The cooled casting is removed by breaking away the sand, which is then cleaned and reused.) Finally, every mold must be fitted with appropriate gates, vents, and risers, to permit the entrance of molten metal and the escape of evolved gases. Correct placement of these items is the fruit of long experience, and belongs to the art of the foundryman.

Many parts, such as valve bodies, have intricate inner partitions, cavities, or holes. Casting such parts requires the use of sand cores as well as patterns, and greatly complicates the casting process. Essentially, a sand core represents the negative spaces in the part, such as the interior of a valve body or the resonant chambers in the bell of a chime whistle. Cores are made in advance from sand fired with a binder, and are suspended within the upper and lower sand molds that create the outside shape of the part. Cores require only enough draft to permit removal from the core box after molding; they are broken up in order to remove them from the finished casting.

How are cores supported? In the case of a gate valve, for example, the internal cavity extends all the way through the casting. Hence the core that represents it can be supported and positioned at both ends by extensions of the core into the sand of the main mold. In the case of a chime whistle bell, however, only the lower end is open. Extensions can be used to support and position the cores at this end, but at the top or sides of the bell the cores must be supported by small rods. These rods leave small holes in the finished casting that must later be plugged or welded shut. Close inspection of a Crosby or other single-bell chime will reveal small brass plugs near the tops of the chambers.

Apart from the secondary issue of allowance for shrinkage, the making of patterns and cores depends very little on which metal is to be cast. Broadly speaking, the restorer can specify whether he wants the part cast in brass, bronze, aluminum, or iron. In most cases, of course, he will wish to utilize the metal originally used, but it nevertheless behooves him to acquaint himself with the properties of various ferrous and non-ferrous alloys. Whistles are commonly made of one of the copper-rich "steam alloys" such as red brass or bronze. Iron is less frequently employed. If given a choice of irons, ductile iron is much preferable to gray iron, due to its superior strength and fracture resistance. Localized stress on gray iron will usually result in cracking, a property that underlies the plumber's ordinary method of cutting gray iron pipe.

Polishing

Once repair and restoration have been completed, surface finishing can be carried out in any desired manner to any desired degree. The most widely practiced (and widely admired) form of finishing is the mirror-polishing of all external surfaces of the whistle. This procedure is fundamentally offensive to historically oriented conservators in other fields, especially the graphic arts. What possible justification can there be for enhancing a whistle beyond its manufacturer's intent, thereby robbing it of its authenticity? One might as well presume to "improve" the gilding of a medieval manuscript. The answer lies in the nature of brass and the workman's innate response to it. Brass "wants" to be polished in the same sense as fine hardwoods want to be smoothed and bricks want to be laid neatly in courses. Moreover there is a long tradition of polishing brass artifacts, a tradition at least as old as the Industrial Revolution itself. What lover of the mechanical arts has not thrilled to the beauty of a finely made 18th century telescope or sextant, or the fittings in a well-tended 19th century engine room? The restorer can tell himself that he is merely completing a task that the manufacturer left undone in his pursuit of lower production costs. Taken together, the temptations to put a mirror polish on every accessible surface of a brass whistle are almost irresistible.

On the other hand, as traditional conservators would agree, it is far too easy to over-finish a whistle. Polishing requires a great deal of labor and contributes nothing whatever to the performance of the whistle. More important, it removes all those traces of age and character that were the very signature of the artifact. Gone forever are the residual clues to its method of manufacture and its service history. One no longer has a whistle that proudly bears the indiciae of a long and useful life, but a kind of ageless trophy, removed forever from the passage of time.

The decision between restoration and enhancement is one that every collector and conservator must make for himself. It would be a mistake, however, to assume that mirror polishing invariably constitutes an enhancement. Industrial history offers some guidance in this regard. Early steam locomotives used an astonishing amount of brass, much of it for purely ornamental purposes such as bands around the steam dome and cylinders. A careful inventory of the parts and materials in a 4-4-0 built in 1865 by the Hinkley Locomotive Works of Boston shows 1,948 pounds of brass, or 3.6% of the total weight of the locomotive.[2] In keeping with this tradition, many early whistles were in fact machined and polished all over. As labor costs rose, however, some of these non-essential manufacturing steps were eliminated. One of the first changes was the elimination of polished bowls. Bowl castings were machined as necessary for fit and function but no further. Parting-line flash was ground away, but sand-cast surfaces were otherwise left rough. Whistle bells were the last to succumb to cost-saving measures because much of the visual appeal of a steam whistle is attributable to the appearance of the bell. Hence it is usually safe to assume that the bell had a high degree of finish, although not necessarily a mirror polish. The Lunkenheimer bell is still machined and polished today, as were British locomotive whistles up to the demise of steam.

Further changes arose as a consequence of the Depression, World War II, and above all, as a result of the gradual rise in boiler working pressure. All those factors inclined toward the replacement of brass with economical and durable cast iron—and cast iron cannot (or at least should not) be polished. A polished iron casting is not merely an offense against the nature of the material; it is a falsification of historical fact. The lesson here is that the decision whether to polish must take into account not merely the type of whistle but also the era and historical tradition from which it springs. The conservator must at least be aware which path he is pursuing and have thought through the consequences of his actions.

If the decision is made to polish, the conservator must have in mind beforehand a firm notion of precisely which surfaces are to be polished. If anything at all is to be polished, it is almost certainly the bell and the acorn. The next logical candidates are other surfaces likely to have been machined during manufacture, e.g., the top plate (if one exists), the outside of the bowl, and the lip of the bowl and the outer rim of the spreader plate on Lunkenheimer whistles. A pleasing contrast can be obtained by polishing only machined surfaces and leaving the remaining parts with a clean sand-cast surface. The lever can be polished if it is a brass casting, although this usually constitutes an unwarranted enhancement. The most extreme enhancement consists of polishing every surface, including rough cast surfaces. A few restorers have even mirror-polished steptop locomotive whistles in their entirety, something that was never done by any manufacturer. (It is noteworthy that no restorer has ever undertaken this task a second time.) Special consideration must be given to parts that underwent heavy repairs or were replicated by casting. It is difficult to give these parts an antique appearance consistent with the remainder of an unpolished whistle, and sometimes the only solution is to polish them and then artificially tarnish them. Tarnishing and patinating solutions are available at many antique shops and gun shops, and produce a very agreeable dark brown color.

As with cleaning, the techniques for producing a bright finish on copper alloys are legion. Once again the reader is referred to the *ASM Metals Handbook*[1] for an exhaustive discussion. Some of these, such as the "bright dip" solutions widely used in industry, are acid mixtures of frightening ferocity. Here we describe only mechanical (i.e., non-chemical) methods suited to the home workshop. The first step in producing a high polish is to smooth out all surface irregularities with successively finer grades of abrasive. Irregularities to be removed may be tool marks remaining from manufacture or repair, or the natural surface texture of a sand casting, or corrosion due to weathering or steam impingement, or dents and dings acquired in service. The abrasive may take the form of ordinary metal-working sandpaper or 3M Scotchbrite™, as previously mentioned. Depending on the initial degree of roughness, it may be necessary to start with abrasives as coarse as 80 or 100 grit, or in still more recalcitrant cases, a file, body grinder, or hand-held belt sander. 120 grit begins the series of wet-or-dry metallurgical papers in aluminum oxide or silicon carbide. Successive members of this series are 180, 240, 320, 400, and 600 grit. Ideally every member of this series should be employed in turn, although in practice it is often possible to skip alternate grades because brass is relatively soft. Switch to the next finer grade only when a uniform finish has been attained with the

previous one. Professional finishers endeavor to turn the work through 90 degrees between grades, so that the scratches produced by one grade are at right angles to those produced by the previous grade. This greatly assists in determining when the use of each grade has been sufficiently prolonged.

Abrasive papers may be used dry, but many workers prefer to slosh kerosene or water on the work to lay the dust and wash detritus from the surface. Whether or not a liquid is used, inhalation of the dust can produce severe respiratory problems. Wear a high-quality dust mask and position a ventilating fan to blow the dust away from you. The so-called lead grade respiratory masks made by 3M are particularly effective. If the part being polished has axial symmetry, it can be chucked in a lathe and the paper merely held against it as it revolves. This process is messy and the slurry of abrasive particles is highly detrimental to the ways of the lathe, so a basin or absorbent cloth should be positioned below the work to catch the runoff, and the sanding session should be followed by a thorough cleanup of the machine.

As an aside, it is sometimes useful to catch and save the dust produced during the sanding process. It can be washed, dried, and stored in a glass jar. The cleaned dust can then be employed as a filler in a clear epoxy body to produce a sort of cold-cast brass, useful for filling holes and defects in much the same way as Bondo is used to make cosmetic repairs on the sheet metal of auto bodies. The advantage of this method is that perfect color matching is assured, since the filler came from the very whistle under repair. The disadvantage is that the repair will not withstand live steam.

The worker who has conscientiously carried the sanding process through 600 grit will find that the resultant surface already has very nearly a mirror finish. It is possible to stop work at this point, and many restorers do. The luster is not as perfect as the specular surface obtained by buffing, but it will satisfy most viewers, and the surface is in some respects easier to maintain than a fully polished surface. When it tarnishes, it is only necessary to chuck it up again and give it a few quick swipes with the 600 paper.

Mirror polishing or buffing for luster is done on a cloth wheel using very fine abrasives embedded in a waxy base. The usual abrasives, in order of increasing

Restoring and Conserving Steam Whistles

fineness and decreasing cutting ability, are emery (black), tripoli (brown), white rouge (white), and jewelers' rouge (red). Safe and effective polishing demands proper equipment and proper technique. A long-shaft buffer of at least 3/4 HP is recommended. Wheels should be spiral-sewn cotton, although for the ultimate luster a layered rather than a spiral-sewn wheel is sometimes employed in the final step. Wheels of 6" or 8" diameter are usually used for non-commercial work. The 8" wheel will produce faster results owing to its higher surface speed, but may require a more powerful motor. Several wheels stacked side by side on a common shaft produce a suitably wide surface. Always wear eye protection, a dust mask and gloves.

Occasionally the wheel will seize the part and throw it violently to the floor. This is usually the consequence of attempting to turn the part in the hands while maintaining pressure against the wheel. Hence professionals polish a spot, back off slightly from the wheel while rotating the work to a new spot, and then reapply pressure. Until this rhythmic technique becomes second nature, novices are advised to polish over a soft rubber mat or a grassy lawn if possible, so that damage to the part will be minimized if it seizes. Furthermore, on dry days the buffing wheel can build up a substantial static charge on the work. The novice who is unaware of this possibility, and accidentally makes contact with a grounded metal part, can be startled into dropping the work or injuring himself.

If the work is too large to bring to the wheel, then the wheel must be brought to the work. Many very large whistles, locomotive bells, etc., have been polished with a buffing wheel on the end of a flexible shaft, as used in auto body shops. In the absence of a flexible shaft machine, a wheel mounted on a mandrel in a sturdy electrical drill will suffice. Still another alternative is the Big Daddy™ hand polisher, consisting of an arbor-equipped motor mounted beneath a board shaped much like a fraternity paddle, with a sturdy loop handle directly behind the motor. Two hands are used to guide the polishing wheel, one on the handle of the paddle and the other threaded through the forward loop.

If a true 600 grit surface has been obtained on a brass part, it is often possible to reduce the polishing stage to a single operation using only jewelers' rouge.

The direction of travel of the wheel should be perpendicular to the marks left by the abrasive paper. If the material is stainless steel, use white rouge instead. If the sanded finish is less than perfect, it may be necessary to precede the use of rouge with tripoli, which provides a slight cutting action. The coarsest of all buffing compounds, black emery, has no place in whistle restoration other than rust removal from cast iron. Even this task is best achieved by other methods of surface preparation. Do not interchange compounds on the wheel; dedicate one wheel or set of wheels to each compound. A wheel that has once been contaminated with a coarser compound will never again be usable with a finer one. Polishing technique can only be acquired by practice. The most common error made by the novice is to attempt to polish out an imperfection such as a pit by bearing down heavily on the wheel. This produces a depressed area around the imperfection that actually looks larger than before in reflected light.

Once a mirror polish has been obtained, its luster must be preserved. This is especially important in the case of whistles blown on steam. Elevated temperatures greatly increase the natural rate of surface oxidation. After as little as a minute or two of blowing, a highly polished whistle will be covered with an iridescent coating of oxide, as brilliant as a soap bubble, the color and extent of which exactly indicate the surface temperature attained. One means of restoring luster is to re-polish the whistle periodically with one of the proprietary brass polishes. The best of these is an exceedingly expensive compound called Simichrome™, made by Happich of Germany. (This is what antique auto buffs use on their million-dollar Duesenbergs.) The process is labor-intensive, to put it mildly. The collector who owns fifty mirror-polished whistles and attempts to keep them all shiny with paste polish will soon begin to doubt the wisdom of his choice of hobby.

Alternatively the surface can be coated with a transparent lacquer. The lacquers sold to the general public in spray cans will provide a measure of protection, but they are neither impervious to moisture nor permanent. Periodically the piece must be stripped and recoated. Much more durable coatings are employed by the makers of builders' hardware and band instruments, but the solvents these coatings contain are so hazardous that the EPA has put stringent limitations on their sale and use. The man in the street can neither buy them nor apply them safely. The best hope for the collector who wishes to avail himself of these coatings is to approach a commercial metal finisher licensed to apply them, and attempt to work out a deal. If only a few whistles are involved, the unit cost is likely to be high.

Other surface finishes

Occasionally it is desired to recreate the tarnish or patina the whistle had before restoration was begun, either to simulate age or to mask newly repaired portions. This can be accomplished in several ways. Gunsmiths can furnish commercial chemicals that produce an antique brown or blued surface. Still other products are available that yield an oxidized green appearance. Heating while brushing with salt water also works well. These finishes have the advantage that they require little or no maintenance, except perhaps an occasional rubdown with an oily rag.

On other occasions a painted finish is appropriate. This is often the case with whistles of all-iron construction, such as two-bell horizontal gongs, Barnes patent "mailbox" whistles, or the iron bells of some steptop locomotive whistles. Levers are sometimes painted, as are the webs or dividers of single-bell chime whistles. In all these cases the key to success is correct preparation of the metal surface. What is required is a pickling solution, i.e., an acid etch which permits the finish to adhere tightly. Pickling solutions are specialized, and different formulations are used on iron, steel, brass, etc. These chemicals are always used when repainting cars, and are available at any automotive paint supply store. They leave a durable and professional-looking surface that retains its natural texture. A good grade of exterior spray paint, either flat or satin luster, is usually all that is needed to complete the job. The use of a primer coat is unnecessary if the surface has been properly prepared, and is undesirable in any case. When a painted surface is nicked or worn, the base metal shows through, and this is generally preferable to the sight of a brightly colored primer.

Larry Spreckelmeier pulls the lanyard on an 8-inch two-bell Union Water Meter gong, Jones, Michigan, 1996. Photo by Diana Spreckelmeier.

8 *Blowing Steam Whistles*

Blow, winds, and crack your cheeks! . . .
. . .And thou, all-shaking thunder,
Strike flat the thick rotundity of the world!
—Shakespeare, *King Lear*

Unlike paintings, stamps, coins, baseball cards, and many of the other artifacts prized by collectors, steam whistles are active devices, intended for use. A steam whistle standing mute upon the mantel may retain its visual appeal, or evoke a wealth of nostalgic associations, or arouse the curiosity of scholars, but it is nevertheless devoid of aural appeal. Steam whistles are cherished primarily because of the sounds they produce, and a soundless whistle is a ghost, a spectre, a phantasm, deprived of its reason for existence. Hence much of the activity among whistle enthusiasts is devoted to the search for means of hearing them in action.

Protecting your hearing

Before discussing the various means of blowing whistles, however, it is essential to address the issue of personal safety. Whistles make very loud noises. They are *intended* to make very loud noises, and loud noises can damage your hearing. When noise is too loud, it begins to kill the nerve endings in the inner ear. As the exposure time to loud noise increases, more and more nerve endings are destroyed, a process called sensorineural hearing loss or nerve deafness. Nerve deafness is *cumulative*. The longer the exposure to damaging noise levels, the greater the hearing loss. Nerve deafness is *permanent and irreversible*. Even in this age of medical miracles there is no medicine, no surgery, and no hearing aid that can completely restore hearing lost because of damaged nerves. It is particularly important to refute the notion that one can toughen up the ears by repeated exposure to loud noise. If your ears have become

accustomed to loud noise, it is because hearing damage has already occurred.

Hearing damage can be caused by other factors as well, such as disease, but noise-induced hearing damage differs from other forms of hearing damage in that it is completely preventable. The means of prevention is to reduce the sound level entering the ear through the use of some external form of ear protection. We will shortly discuss the various types of ear defenders, but first let us get some feeling for the sound levels that characterize our everyday aural environment.

Sound levels cover an enormous range from 0 decibels (abbreviated dB) to 140 decibels or even more. (See the Glossary for a definition of the decibel) This range spans a ratio of 100 trillion to one in intensity, a tribute to the extraordinary adaptive capacity of the human ear. Here are some representative sound levels, all approximate of course:

0 dB Faintest sound heard by human ear

30-40 dB Whisper, quiet library, rustling of leaves

55-65 dB Normal conversation, sewing machine, computer keyboard

70-80 dB Average radio or vacuum cleaner

90-100 dB Power lawnmower, table saw, heavy truck traffic

100-110 dB Chain saw, pneumatic drill, snowmobile

115-130 dB Sandblasting, rock concert, auto horn at close range

130-140 dB Gun muzzle blast, drop forge, jet engine

What sound level causes hearing damage? Obviously this question can only be answered in a statistical sense. Individuals differ widely in their susceptibility to hearing damage because of age, sex, genetic differences, medication, and numerous other factors. Furthermore, the amount of damage depends on other factors as well, such as the spectral composition of the sound and the duration of exposure. There is evidence that very intense sounds of very short duration, such as gunshots or explosions, produce acoustic trauma of a type different from (but every bit as damaging as) hearing loss induced by more or less steady noise. And finally, the answer depends on which criteria are used to define the extent of hearing damage: the occurrence of tinnitus (ringing in the ear), the loss of high frequency acuity, impaired speech intelligibility, or some other criterion altogether.

Nevertheless there is broad general agreement among hearing specialists that sound levels below 85 dB are tolerated indefinitely by most people without damage. For unprotected ears the allowed exposure time is cut in half for each 5 dB increase in the average noise level. Thus at 90 dB, eight hours per day is the maximum permissible exposure to protect 90% of the population; at 95 dB exposure is limited to 4 hours, and at 100 dB to two hours per day. 115 dB for fifteen minutes per day is the maximum permissible exposure for unprotected ears. (It follows that most rock concert attendees, not to mention band members, have already suffered irreversible hearing damage.) Levels of 140 dB produce intense pain and almost instantaneous damage in unprotected ears, and can be permitted only with the most effective types of hearing protection.

It will recognized that many, if not most, whistles fall within the dangerous range. The average locomotive whistle will produce a sound level of 110 to 115 dB at a distance of 100 feet, and indeed is required to do so by FRA regulations. Hence a steamfitter who works several hours per day among large whistles at a major whistle blow is committing audiological suicide unless he provides himself with appropriate hearing protection.

Hearing protection devices come in two principal types: ear plugs and ear muffs. Earplugs are small inserts of a spongy or waxy substance that fit into the outer ear canal. They are shaped before insertion by rolling between the fingers to provide a snug seal, so that the entire circumference of the ear canal is blocked. They are inexpensive and disposable, and available in a variety of shapes and sizes. Properly fitted they attenuate incoming sounds by 15 to 30 dB. The amount of attenuation is frequency-dependent, and higher for low frequency sounds than for high frequency sounds.

Earmuffs resemble the large professional headphones worn in recording studios except that they are completely passive and therefore lack a dangling electrical cord. They are held in place by an adjustable headband, and their essential feature is a large squishy pad, often fluid-filled, which completely surrounds the ear ("circumaural"). The effectiveness of earmuffs depends critically on the completeness of the seal between this pad and the skull; hence they are not always suitable for persons with long hair or heavy eyeglass frames. Properly fitted earmuffs attenuate incoming sounds by 15 to 30 dB, about the same as earplugs, except that earmuffs work better at high frequencies than low. Simultaneous use of earplugs and earmuffs usually adds 10 to 15 dB more protection than either used alone. Earmuffs are sold in tool stores, industrial supply houses, and gun shops, and are widely used by woodcutters, hunters and shooters, and airline ground crew members.

Finally, note that the time-honored practice of stuffing the ears with cotton is completely inadequate as hearing protection. Cotton balls in the ear canal provide at most 7 dB of noise reduction.

Blowing on steam

A steam whistle ought to be blown on steam, as God and man intended, but this is no longer easy to achieve. The day when live steam was available at every laundry, brewery, factory, and roundhouse is long since past. A few very fortunate collectors have privately owned steam supplies, sometimes in the form of a stationary boiler, but more usually in the form of a restored traction engine. These few are their own masters, and need no instruction in the art of whistle blowing. Another small segment of the whistle collecting population consists of persons associated with various shortline steam tourist railroads, of which approximately 60 exist in the United States. These happy volunteers can almost always prevail on members of the locomotive operating crew to mount a favorite whistle on the steam dome for a run or two, and thus hear their possessions in the working environment for which they were intended.

Most collectors, however, have no such resources at their disposal, and thus must rely on communal whistle blows. There are currently about a dozen such events each summer in the United States. At this writing almost all of them take place east of the Mississippi and north of the Ohio. The best known of these, and the nearest thing whistle enthusiasts have to a national convention, is the annual Boot Hill blow at Jones, Michigan. Other more or less regularly scheduled blows are held at the Railroaders Memorial Museum in Altoona, Pennsylvania, Bergen Tech in New Jersey, the Rough & Tumble Engineers in Kinzers, Pennsylvania, the Pratt Institute in Brooklyn, and the Cass Scenic Railroad in Cass, West Virginia, plus several others of a more ephemeral nature.

The organization of a successful whistle blow is a major undertaking, demanding long and careful preparation. Furthermore, events of this kind are attended not merely by the whistle-blowers themselves, but also by their wives, girlfriends, railfans, and the general public. Thus the organizers must give attention not merely to engineering requirements, but also to the fundamentals of showmanship, presenting an entertaining and instructive experience that will enhance the hobby in the eyes of the public.

The first requirement, of course, is to assure an ample supply of steam, which in turn is likely to govern the choice of venue. Perhaps the smallest boiler that will suffice is that of a traction engine. Traction engines range up to about 65 HP, which is more than adequate for drawing a four-bottom plow, but inadequate for the prolonged blowing of large whistles. Whistles up to about 4" in diameter can be accommodated by a 65 HP traction engine. A 6" whistle of conventional design, however, draws 60 or more pounds of steam *per minute* at usual inlet pressures, and a prolonged blow will quickly drop the pressure of a traction engine boiler. Furthermore, traction engines are typically limited to boiler pressures in the range 100 to 120 PSIG, which means that larger whistles will not attain the sound volume for which they were designed.

The next larger category of boilers consists of stationary boilers for reciprocating engines and truck-mounted boilers to supply process steam. The latter are available in ratings up to 250 or even 500 HP, and will blow 6" and 8" whistles satisfactorily. 10" and 12" whistles can be accommodated if some loss in pressure can be tolerated, and if the boiler is given sufficient time to rebuild pressure between blows. Portable boilers of this description can often be rented in major cities. Rental rates tend to be daunting, however; one must not only hire the boiler itself, but also someone to run it, in the event that there is no qualified fireman in the organization. Other boilers are the property of antiquarian organizations such as threshermen's associations and industrial museums. The resourceful organizer of a whistle blow would do well to contact such organizations regarding the use of their facilities. Another source of abundant steam is one of the forementioned shortline steam tourist railroads. Even a small road locomotive carries a boiler rating of 1000 HP or more. Occasionally management can be persuaded to fire up a locomotive for a whistle blow, on days when the locomotive is not in tourist service. There is usually a sizeable fee for this service, and it is fully justified, because qualified crew members must be on duty to tend the locomotive for many hours before and after the whistle blow itself. The Cass Scenic Railroad of West Virginia has been especially accommodating in this regard. In addition Cass is favored with a location at the bottom of a valley surrounded by high hills, providing the participants with multiple echoes which greatly enhance the aural experience of whistle-blowing.

Finally, the ultimate source of steam is a major centralized electrical generating station, whose colossal steam generators can carry ratings as high as

600 MW (800,000 HP), dwarfing all other types of boilers in both size and capacity. In these times of deregulation of the electrical industry, the likelihood that a group of amateur whistle enthusiasts can successfully negotiate an agreement with a major generating plant is small, and possibly zero. Nevertheless, it has happened at least once. In June, 1983 the Marysville, Michigan plant of Detroit Edison made a steam line available to the Lake Huron Lore Marine Society for a whistle blow, with memorable results. Regrettably this practice was not continued in later years.

Boot Hill whistle blow, 1997. Two steamfitters labor to mount a small gong whistle on the manifold between blowing periods.

A few words of caution are appropriate at this point: A steam boiler is inherently a dangerous device because of the vast amount of stored energy it contains. The industrial history of the 19th century is marred by hundreds of boiler explosions, most of them with tragic consequences. Efforts to codify the construction, maintenance, and inspection of steam boilers constitute one of the most successful chapters in the progress of mechanical engineering. Attempts to operate a boiler in ignorance, or worse still, in defiance of these regulations, are not merely foolish and illegal; they are all too likely to be catastrophic. If you are not a qualified stationary steam engineer, or if your boiler has not met the applicable inspection and certification requirements of the American Society of Mechanical Engineers (ASME), you have no business anywhere near its controls.

Once an adequate supply of steam has been secured, the next requirement is a proper manifold for distributing it. In order to ensure blowing at full volume, it is essential that the manifold have at least the diameter of the inlet of the largest whistle to be connected to it. Since 12" diameter whistles typically have 3" NPT inlets, this mandates a manifold having a minimum internal diameter of 3", or better still, 4". The manifold should be fitted with one or more full-bore shutoff valves at its inlet, and a condensate drain at its low point. A 4" manifold rated at 200 or 250 PSIG, and having, say, ten 3" tee outlets, is not an ordinary item of commerce, and is neither easy nor inexpensive to fabricate. The services of an ASME-certified welder are demanded. Fortunately it need only be built once, and the expense can be shared by an *ad hoc* group or club of enthusiasts. It is also surprising what quantities of time, effort, and material will be donated by other parties interested in the mechanical arts once they catch the spirit of the enterprise.

Two decisions must be made with respect to the design of the manifold. The first is whether to lay it on the ground or elevate it to waist height. A waist-high manifold undeniably makes the mounting and demounting of most whistles more convenient. On the other hand some whistles, notably marine whistles, are exceedingly large and heavy, and it may take three or more men merely to lift them into position. An elevated manifold is also a beam, structurally speaking, and must be sufficiently stiff to carry many hundreds of pounds between points of support. The prevailing practise appears to favor ground-level manifolds. The second decision is whether or not to fit each outlet with its own shutoff valve. As in railroad usage, this permits the exchange of individual whistles without dropping pressure in the entire line. But large-diameter shutoff valves are costly, and a worker who attempts to change one whistle while others nearby are in operation exposes himself to intolerable noise levels and the risk of scalding by live steam. Again, prevailing practice does not favor individual shutoff valves. In fact, the enforced silence when the manifold is shut down for whistle replacement is usually welcomed by workers and spectators alike.

The organizers of a whistle blow must also be prepared to supply almost all the tools and small parts used in the steamfitting trade. It is particularly important to have on hand a number of smooth-jaw hex wrenches of large capacity, such as the Ridgid No. 25 and No. 35, the latter regrettably no longer manufactured. Ordinary pipe wrenches with serrated jaws can be used on pipe fittings, but their use on the pipe nut of a whistle which has been lovingly polished to high luster by its owner will provoke mayhem at the least and homicide at the worst. These wrenches can be conveniently stored on a centrally located "headache rack" of the type used by truckers. Organizers should also have on hand adapters of every description between various pipe sizes. Participants have presumably been told beforehand the size of the manifold outlets, and advised to bring the appropriate adapters for their whistles, but some invariably forget or misunderstand the instructions. It would be unfortunate if a would-be whistle blower were turned away for lack of a simple reducing bushing. In addition, caps or plugs should be available for all unused manifold outlets, so that a round of blowing can proceed without a full complement of whistles mounted. All of these auxiliary fittings must be made of black iron. Galvanized fittings are not permitted in steam service because the zinc coating can flake off under thermal or mechanical stress, and the flakes can foul injectors or valves. Finally, a few stiff wire brushes are needed to clean the threads of whistles and fittings that have fallen on the ground.

Mark Phillips demonstrates the use of the "leverage stick" to attain finer control of a whistle valve.

A refinement that organizers can easily provide, and which will be much appreciated by whistle blowers, is a device for multiplying the mechanical advantage of the whistle lever. This so-called leverage bar permits extremely fine control of the valve opening, and hence facilitates the quilling of the whistle. The simplest possible version of this device is shown in the adjoining figure. The operator stands with one foot on a footboard, the underside of which contains protruding nails to anchor it to the ground. At the front of this board is hinged a long lever with a number of transverse holes, and the whistle cord is hooked to an eye bolt through one of these holes. The mechanical advantage produced thereby ranges from about two to about four times. In a more elaborate version of this contrivance, the lever hangs downward from the top of a pipe framework that surrounds the operator, giving him the sensation that he is seated within a locomotive cab.

A few horn enthusiasts invariably show up at whistle blows. Discouraging their attendance can only lead to ill will within the fraternity; on the other hand, they can scarcely lay first claim to the available facilities. Hence thoughtful organizers will find a way to provide them with the steam or compressed air they seek, without allowing them to intrude on the principal event, perhaps by sequestering them on one side of the area. A particularly appropriate way to provide them with compressed air is to employ a Westinghouse steam-driven cross-compound compressor, if one is available.

As previously emphasized, some form of hearing protection is needed by all participants. Steamfitters can be expected to provide their own high-quality circumaural earmuffs, but members of the general public often forget to bring appropriate protection. Fortunately they tend to take up positions much further removed from sound sources, and hence require less attenuation. Simple non-reusable earplugs can be purchased for less than 20 cents per pair in quantity, and organizers can well afford to pass these out *gratis* as a gesture of good will.

Finally, of vital importance to the organizers of a whistle blow is assurance that local noise ordinances will not be violated, or if violation is anticipated, that an appropriate waiver has been granted. It is embarrassing, to say the least, to have a carefully planned whistle blow shut down in mid-course by the police, and to receive a citation as a public nuisance. Most such complaints are generated by nearby residents who have either not been warned of the forthcoming event or who have failed to notice such warnings. Thus it is essential that the organizers secure advance clearance for their plans from all relevant departments of the local infrastructure, and that they publicize their event among the citizenry to the maximum extent possible.

This completes the list of essentials for a whistle blow, but certain amenities are also needed to make the experience a pleasant one. For obvious reasons, whistle blows tend to take place at relatively isolated locations. Generally speaking these locations lack both toilet facilities and eating facilities; hence considerate organizers will provide portable toilets and some sort of food concession. Both requirements are obviated, however, if the blow is held at an established fairground, tourist railroad, or museum. Whistle blows also tend to take place in sun-baked and treeless open fields. A simple awning or tent to shield the fairer members of the crowd will be much appreciated.

A whistle blow of any size requires a protocol, and this must be established beforehand and enforced throughout by the organizers. The simplest form of schedule is that which results naturally from the use of manifolds without individual shutoff valves. A batch of whistles is mounted and these are blown one by one by their owners. The manifold is then shut down, this batch of whistles is replaced with a new batch, the manifold is pressurized again, and the process repeats. This leads automatically to a schedule in which about half an hour of blowing is followed by half an hour of silence, a pleasing ratio. Allowing an hour for lunch, the cycle can be repeated six or seven times in a day. In order to minimize confusion during changeover, it is important that participants know well in advance when their turn comes. This is easily achieved by drawing lots beforehand to assign positions within a rotation. Alternatively, if the whistle blow is embedded in some larger event, such as a threshermen's reunion, blowing may be restricted to specified intervals, such as the first five minutes of the hour, or morning, noon, and evening whistles. Apart from such special occasions, however, unregulated whistle blowing *ad libitum* must not be allowed. This tends to go rapidly out of control as the participants strive to outdo each other, and the resultant cacophony quickly exhausts the patience of both participants and neighbors.

As remarked earlier, every whistle blow is improved by attention to the basic principles of showmanship. The key to maintaining the schedule and sustaining public interest is to appoint an announcer or master of ceremonies. He must be provided with a powerful public address system in order to be heard over the prevailing din, and before each whistle is blown he must be furnished with a proper description by its owner. Most important, he must have no other duties. The announcer who shuttles back and forth between the microphone and the monkey wrench will not perform either job properly. Nothing is more destructive to the interest and attention (and ultimately the support) of the general public than a whistle blown without an accompanying narration, because the announcer was occupied elsewhere. "What the devil was that?" asks the listener, and rightfully so. Similarly, it is the announcer's task to sustain public interest during the long changeover period. One of the more fruitful ways to pass the time is to interview the owners of those whistles about to be blown. These interviews give the owners an opportunity to share their knowledge and pride of ownership, while the master of ceremonies exercises his skills in eliciting a meaningful commentary.

The question of fees is vexing. Whistle blowers love their hobby and freely make great sacrifices for it, but somehow expenses always seem to exceed anticipation. In my view, a properly organized whistle blow merits an admission fee from all who attend. I believe that an additional hookup fee is justified for those desiring to blow their whistles. In exchange the organizers of the event should not only satisfy all the considerations discussed above, but should bear full responsibility for publicizing the event, reserving blocks of rooms as necessary at local hotels and motels, arranging banquets and other ceremonial functions, placing and removing directional signs on nearby roads, managing vehicle parking, and in general presenting their hobby to the public in a professional manner. The participants in turn have an obligation to tune up their whistles to the best of their ability before mounting them on the manifold. The middle of the blowing period is not the time to repair a leaking valve or straighten a bent center stud.

Blowing Steam Whistles

Blowing on compressed air

The great majority of steam whistle enthusiasts, however, neither own steam boilers nor attend one of the national whistle blows where live steam is provided. The only means whereby the members of this majority can hear their whistles in action is to blow them on compressed air. This entails three important differences. The first is the absence of that glorious ascending plume of white condensate, the signature of an operating steam whistle, the sight of which contributes almost as much to the thrill of whistle-blowing as the sound itself. A second difference arises because the velocity of sound in air is only about 85% of its velocity in saturated steam. Hence the frequency at which a given whistle speaks on air is only about 85% of its frequency on steam. All pitches are lowered by about three semitones, or approximately a minor third. E flat becomes C, C becomes A, and so forth. A 5" whistle on air sounds very much like a 6" whistle on steam. Chime whistles do not become discordant, however, because all pitches are *multiplied* by the same factor, precisely as if they were transposed to a lower key. Some steam proponents also claim that the timbre or overtone structure of a whistle is altered for the worse by blowing on compressed air, although there is no experimental evidence in support of this claim. Blowing on steam does produce a very slight initial ictus or "chiff," as the air within the bell is displaced by steam. This chiff is of course absent when blowing on air. Others claim that whistles which quill on steam cannot be quilled on air, or at best quill very poorly. This assertion has never been subjected to a controlled test, and its validity is questionable.

The third major difference is that a very large reservoir is required for sustained blowing on air, much larger than a steam boiler of comparable capability. The reason is that compressed air is a single-phase thermodynamic system, whereas steam in equilibrium with boiling water is a two-phase system. For those whose grasp of physical chemistry may have weakened somewhat since school days, a two-phase system is one in which two different forms of the same substance (liquid and gaseous water in this instance) can coexist in varying proportions at the same temperature and pressure. As steam is extracted from a boiler, more water flashes off into steam but the pressure within the boiler does not change. The volume

ratio between liquid and gaseous phases is very large. Each cubic foot of boiling water becomes approximately 1600 cubic feet of saturated steam. Hence a boiler of modest proportions can deliver many times its own volume of steam, even when the difference in pressures is taken into account. Air, on the other hand, remains a gas at all relevant temperatures and pressures. There is no phase change, and therefore no volume multiplication. You get only as many cubic feet of gas out of an air tank as put into it in the first place.

The rate at which a typical steam whistle consumes compressed air is enormous, hundreds or even thousands of times larger than the conventional air-operated tools familiar to most mechanics. Unfortunately very few manufacturers provide engineering data of this kind, but two who do are Lunkenheimer and Kahlenberg. Table 1 (next page) gives air consumption data extracted from Lunkenheimer's 1912 catalog. The type of whistle under consideration is its standard plain whistle, Fig. 441 or 442 in the catalog. Table 2 gives data on plain whistles taken from a relatively recent but undated Kahlenberg technical bulletin.[1] Unlike the Lunkenheimer line, a gauge pressure of 100 PSI is specified for all Kahlenberg whistles.

Note that the units of air consumption in the third row of the following tables are cubic feet per *second*, not cubic feet per minute (CFM). These numbers must be multiplied by 60 to get the usual rating in CFM. Thus for example a 6" Lunkenheimer plain draws 720 CFM at the very modest inlet pressure of 70 PSI. It would draw almost twice as much at the inlet pressures for which it was designed. It is obviously impossible to meet demands of this magnitude on a continuous basis with any compressor likely to be available to the hobbyist. They must be met from air previously stored in a reservoir, or *receiver* as it is called in the trade. The usual compressed air installation in a shop or garage consists of a large compressor coupled to a small receiver, the latter often just large enough to smooth out pulsations in the airflow. By contrast, the compressed air installation in a whistle enthusiast's workshop usually consists of a relatively small compressor coupled to an enormous receiver. A 120-gallon tank, the largest usually supplied for

TABLE 1. AIR CONSUMPTION OF LUNKENHEIMER WHISTLES [2]

Bell diameter, inches	1	1.25	1.5	2	2.5	3	3.5	4	5	6
Air pressure, PSIG	40	40	40	40	50	50	50	60	60	70
Consumption, CFS	0.41	0.43	0.45	0.91	1.8	2.7	5.1	6.8	8.6	12
Normalized flow rate	0.45	0.47	0.49	0.99	1.66	2.49	4.71	5.44	6.88	8.47

TABLE 2. AIR CONSUMPTION OF KAHLENBERG WHISTLES [2]

Bell diameter, inches	1	1.5	2	2.5	3	4	5	6
Air pressure, PSIG	100	100	100	100	100	100	100	100
Consumption, CFS	0.93	1.37	2.18	3.65	4.58	7.03	10.75	13.98
Normalized flow rate	0.48	0.72	1.14	1.90	2.39	3.67	5.61	7.29

non-industrial installations, is barely sufficient for fifteen seconds' blowing of the usual steptop locomotive whistle. This has led some amateurs to install 300-, 500-, or even 1000-gallon air tanks in their backyards. This is "serious tin", as compressed air engineers say. An hour's pumping to fill the tank is followed by a minute's blowing to empty it, and the dedicated enthusiast considers this a satisfactory exchange.

How can the hobbyist learn the air consumption rate of an unknown whistle, and thus judge the size of receiver he needs? He can of course look up an analogous whistle in one of the foregoing tables. But if he wishes actually to measure the flow rate, he quickly runs into a problem. These enormous flow rates lie far beyond the range of any conventional paddlewheel flowmeter. Nevertheless the flow rate can be estimated well enough for practical purposes by measuring the time required to deplete a receiver of known volume from a known initial pressure to a known final pressure. The author has derived the necessary equation under very simple and plausible assumptions.[3] The equation can be inverted to find the size of reservoir needed to produce a blow of specified duration with a specified pressure drop in the reservoir.

Air tanks or receivers are almost as dangerous as steam boilers. They are classified by the ASME as "unfired pressure vessels," which means that they differ from boilers only in that they are not subjected to open flame. In all other respects the demands on them are comparable. Like boilers, the code that governs their construction, maintenance and inspection has been developed through nearly two centuries of engineering experience, and the user disregards it at his peril. Under no circumstances should any hobbyist employ a non-code receiver. i.e., a tank that does not bear the seal of ASME certification. This seal takes the form of a metal plate securely welded to the tank, on which are stamped the serial number of the tank, various instructions regarding its use, and the letter 'U' within a square shield. The sale of non-code tanks is illegal in Arkansas, New Jersey, Oregon, Massachusetts, and Puerto Rico, as well as in numerous municipalities across the nation. In addition, code tanks must be used wherever OSHA compliance is required.

Particularly to be discouraged is the practice of using propane tanks as air receivers. Large propane tanks are attractive because they are readily available and considerably cheaper than ASME-certified air receivers, but they fall short in other important respects. The first consideration is that an air tank is subject to rapid cyclic pressure changes as it is repeatedly filled and emptied. These mechanical stresses ultimately induce metal fatigue, which is taken into account in the design of the tank. A propane tank, by contrast, is filled infrequently and emptied very slowly; metal fatigue is not an important design factor. Hence the walls of ASME code air receivers are at least 50% thicker than those of propane tanks of corresponding size. Furthermore, as everyone who has put his hand on an interstage cooler knows, compressed air is hot, because it has been compressed adiabatically (i.e., without the transfer of heat). This influx of hot gas produces additional localized thermal stresses which are absent in propane tanks. Finally, compressed air is wet, because the water vapor in the air condenses under pressure. This leads to progressive rusting of the tank bottom from the inside, out of sight, another factor absent in propane storage. Hence ASME code air receivers must be fitted with bottom-mounted drain cocks and inspection ports, whereas no comparable requirement exists for propane tanks. It is irrational, to put it mildly, for the hobbyist to spend thousands of dollars per year to insure his life, while refusing to spend the extra few hundred dollars to ensure his safety while standing next to an air tank containing stored energy equivalent to several sticks of dynamite.

The choice of compressor for home use is governed by the desired pressure level, the adequacy of electrical supply, the hobbyist's tolerance for long recovery times, and the heft of his purse. A single-stage compressor will provide pressures up to about 110 PSIG. A two-stage compressor will provide pressures up to about 175 PSIG, with marginally greater efficiency. A large compressor will fill the tank more rapidly than a small one, but the largest electric motor that can be accommodated on a conventional 115 V 20 A household circuit is about 1.5 HP. This corresponds to a flow rate of about 5 CFM at 100 PSIG. Five HP single-stage compressors of the type usually seen in gas stations are ubiquitous and relatively inexpensive, but require a dedicated 230 V 30 A electrical supply line.

Engine-driven compressors of the type used by paving contractors and road maintenance crews can often be borrowed from municipal public works departments. Occasionally they are declared surplus by their parent municipalities and sold at auction. These are designed to power several paving breakers or air hammers simultaneously, and typically have ratings in the range 85 to 125 CFM. At first glance these appear to be attractive candidates for whistle blowing because of their quick recovery time, but closer scrutiny shows that they are not. The compressors are invariably single-stage and limited to about 105 PSIG. Their storage tanks are small, usually 30 gallons, because their only function is to smooth out pulses in air delivery. Furthermore, the outlet ports seldom if ever exceed 3/4", because this is adequate for the demands of air tools. Hence they are useful only if the maximum pressure limitation is acceptable, if the air tank can be supplemented with a larger one, and if the outlet port can be enlarged.

The same considerations that govern the design of steam lines govern the design of compressed air lines. It is particularly important that there be no constrictions or orifices anywhere in the line smaller in diameter than the inlet of the whistle itself. This presents a problem inasmuch as the outlet ports intended for air delivery on conventional air tanks seldom exceed a nominal 3/4" pipe diameter. This suffices for whistles up to about 3" in diameter, but will seriously restrict the performance of larger whistles. However, every ASME-certified tank of 60 gallon or larger capacity has at least one 2" diameter inspection port, and the remedy is to plumb the air line to this port instead of to the usual outlet. It goes without saying that all shutoff valves in a 2" line must also be 2" or larger. If the pipe run is long, or if the whistles connected to it are exposed to the weather, pitch the line back toward the tank and install a condensate drain at the lowest point. Further information regarding the design of compressed air lines can be found in standard handbooks of mechanical engineering.

Blowing at reduced pressure

The hobbyist who has access to neither live steam nor compressed air can nevertheless hear his whistles, although in greatly diminished fashion. All that is required is a vacuum cleaner with a pressure outlet. This is a common feature of the many varieties of Shop Vac™ sold by Sears and other hardware supply houses. These outlets deliver large volumes

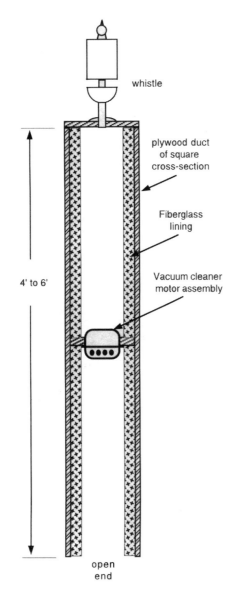

Proposed design of a noise-suppressing duct to silence a vacuum cleaner motor, for blowing whistles at low pressure.

whistle

plywood duct
of square
cross-section

Fiberglass
lining

Vacuum cleaner
motor assembly

4' to 6'

open
end

with a sliding collar at its lower end. This collar can be as simple as a cardboard tube or as elaborate as a nicely made attachment of machined brass. The most attractive collars, in the author's view, are those made from stiff acetate sheet or celluloid, because they are the least conspicuous and permit the original shape and position of the bell to be seen. Unlike plain whistles, single-bell chime whistles have fixed lip heights, and in general respond less well to the addition of collars. The whistle may sound, but the tuning may be slightly off pitch because a constant length has been added to each resonant chamber.

The principal drawback to low pressure blowing, however, is that the relatively feeble sounds produced tend to be overwhelmed or masked by the roar of the vacuum cleaner itself. One can experiment with various techniques for acoustically isolating the machine, such as placing it in an adjacent room and running the hose through the wall, but a more fundamental approach should yield better results. Extract the fan and motor assembly from the machine (or buy a new one at an industrial supply house). Build a long duct of plywood, having a square cross-section perhaps 12" on a side, and close it at one end. Line the inside walls of the duct with 1" thick fiberglass batting. Mount the fan and motor assembly on an airtight partition in the approximate middle of the duct, with the air inlet facing the open end. Drill appropriate holes for mounting the whistle (or whistles) on the closed end. The long fiberglass-lined tunnels on inlet and outlet are acoustical low-pass filters, and should produce a marked degree of noise reduction. This design is correct in principle but has not been tested in practice. Therefore the reader is warned that some experimentation may be necessary to bring it to its most effective form.

of air at low pressure, typically 80 to 100 CFM into free air, or static pressures of 2 to 4 PSIG when blocked off. This is sufficient to blow—or at least cause to sound—the majority of whistles, provided the lip height is appropriately adjusted.

Broadly speaking, high pressures call for high lip heights and low pressures for low lip heights, and this is why plain whistles are made with adjustable bells. In most cases, however, the pressures obtainable from vacuum cleaners lie far below the range of adjustment anticipated by the manufacturer, and therefore the bell must be extended downward until its lip is quite near the slot of the bowl. This is most easily accomplished by fitting the bell of the whistle

Whistle-blowing artistry *

As discussed in Chapter 3, a steam whistle, by its nature, is an extremely limited instrument of communication. Hence most areas of application have developed over the years a system of coded signals that stand for pre-arranged messages. Three of these codes are displayed in the accompanying sidebar. Those in railroad and maritime applications are quite firmly established by regulatory agencies, those in agricultural applications less so. And of course

In collaboration with David Fultz and Mark Phillips

Blowing Steam Whistles

WHISTLE CODES

Railroad code

The Association of American Railroads (AAR) prescribes the following whistle signals for railroad use. A dash (—) indicates a long blast; a dot (•) indicates a short blast.

— If stopped, air brakes are applied and pressure is equalized

— If moving, apply brakes

— — If stopped, brakes are released, or proceed

— — If moving, release brakes

• — Inspect brake system for leaks or sticking brakes

• • Acknowledgement of any signal not otherwise provided for

• • • Back up

• • • • Request for a signal, or for a signal to be repeated

— • • • Flagman protect rear of train

• • • — Flagman protect front of train

— — — — Flagman return from west or south

— — — — — Flagman return from east or north

— — • — Warning of approach to a grade crossing, bridge, or tunnel

This last signal is often called a "14L" from the paragraph in the Rule Book which specifies it. It is also sometimes called a "Q" signal because it is identical with the Morse letter Q. The final blast should be prolonged until the train is actually within the grade crossing. As late as the 1940's this crossing signal consisted of two long blasts followed by two short blasts.

Many railroads had additional signals for specific purposes, such as notifying a tower operator of the route to be lined up.

Great Lakes Maritime code

• Passing to port

• • Passing to starboard

• • • Full astern

• • • (repeated once per minute) Underway in fog

• • • • Risk of collision, intent not clear, or other danger

— Ready to cast off

(continued next column)

— • • Vessel in tow

— — • Overtaking starboard side

— — • • Overtaking port side

— — — • • Master's salute

Very similar codes are used on inland rivers and waterways, and offshore on the open seas.

Traction engine code

The Case Corporation, a major manufacturer of steam traction engines, promulgated the following whistle code for the operators of traction engines in agricultural service:

— The engine has arrived at the working place

• • The engine is about to begin work

• Stop

— — Work is over for the day

• • • Grain haulers report promptly to engine

— • • • Water carriers report promptly to engine

• • • • • etc. Fire or distress

Although not explicitly codifed, a lengthy series of short blasts signifies an emergency in almost every application.

unregulated applications were free to develop their own system of signals. There was probably little nationwide uniformity, for example, among the signals used in logging camps.

A code tells the whistle blower in broadest terms what to blow. It does not tell him how to blow it. Within this narrow latitude, however, whistle blowers of inventive inclination have developed a quite astonishing repertoire of blowing techniques. An instrument less well suited to musical self-expression than a steam whistle could scarcely be imagined. A steam whistle is designed to produce a single note, or in the case of a chime whistle, a cluster of notes, of unvarying pitch under the widest possible range of inlet pressure and volume throughput. Yet the skilled whistle artist can elicit from it sounds imitative of the human voice, birdsong, animal calls, and various orchestral instruments, not to mention a litany of eerie wailings more appropriate to the spirit world than to everyday life.

Making a whistle "talk" by artful manipulation of the whistle valve is called in the vernacular "quilling" or "twilling." These words themselves present something of a puzzle to the etymologist. The authoritative *Oxford English Dictionary* gives "the whistle of a steam engine" as one of the alternative meanings of "quill" in 20th century American usage. The name may derive from the use of large feather shafts or porcupine quills to make a primitive whistle or panpipe. It seems only a short step from the noun "quill" to the verb "to quill", and thence to the gerund "quilling," meaning "whistling." It is unclear, however, why "quilling" should mean specifically imitative or musically expressive whistling rather than whistling in general. "Twilling" is of obscure origin, perhaps onomatopoeic, like the word "whistle" itself. Note that the initial "tw-" sound appears in several other words denoting a birdlike piping or chirping, as in "tweet" and "twitter."

Whatever the origins of the words, the practice is made possible by departures from ideal performance inherent in the whistle itself. Despite the best efforts of the designer, the pitch of a whistle is not entirely independent of either inlet pressure or volume throughput. By choking or restricting the flow of steam, the skilled practitioner can "pull" the pitch of the whistle over a musical interval as large as a fourth, or in exceptional cases, a fifth. By adjusting the height of the lip of the bell, the whistle can be made to overblow or underblow, producing overtones or "wolf notes" which may or may not be harmonically related to the fundamental. By further minute adjustments of the lip height and conformation, in a manner analogous to the voicing of organ pipes, the chambers of a chime whistle can be made to speak sequentially as the valve is opened. Finally, in addition to exploiting these peripheral features of whistle performance, the whistle-blower has complete control of the tempo and rhythm of blowing. He can produce anything from a sustained wail to a series of staccato grunts. Taken together, these qualities permit a surprising variety of quasi-musical expression.

Railroad folklore has preserved the names of many of these early whistle artists. Almost without exception they were locomotive engineers from the southeastern United States, where railroads were more inclined to tolerate departures from signaling regulations. One such engineer was William Fraker, who retired in 1941 from the Mobile & Gulf Railroad after 52 years of service. "Uncle Billy" had this to say about his special short-bell whistle:

> Shortly after the close of the Civil War, an engineer on the Nashville & Chattanooga Railroad gave this whistle to an engineer on the Mobile & Gulf. Since then, it has been passed on to the best whistler upon the death or retirement of the previous owner. I got the whistle in 1906. It is made of brass, with the ring of a silver dollar, and has the sweetest tone you could hear on this side of the Pearly Gates. It is a stumpy little fellow, 3-1/2" tall, and 5-3/4" in diameter. I kept all the lost motion in the lever and valve taken up, so that the slightest pull on the whistle cord would change the notes. You might call it a "fiddling whistle." I could get most of the notes from it that you can get on a violin.

One of Fraker's favorite tunes was called *Possum and Taters*. When an acquaintance died, he would sound forth the more restrained notes of *The Lonesome Road*. Unlike most of the engineers of the day, Fraker took his whistle home when he retired. It is now the property of his son, and is one of the oldest surviving locomotive whistles.

The whistle artist best known to the general public was of course Casey Jones, whose mournful history is recounted in the ballad which bears his name. Casey's whistle was built to his own specifications in Illinois Central shops, and consisted of six individual tubes mounted in a circle on a common bowl. Sometimes called a "whippoorwill," this type of whistle in now more commonly known as a "Casey Jones," although it is doubtful that Casey originated it. According to chronicler Freeman Hubbard, Casey could make it "scream like a banshee or say its prayers." For many years Casey's whistle was displayed at his home in Jackson, Tennessee, subsequently donated to the state as a museum. When the state moved the home nearer Interstate 40, his outraged family retrieved the whistle and it remains in their possession.

Engineer D. B. Menefee of the Norfolk & Western was so fond of the whistle he designed that he left instructions to mount it on his tombstone in Limestone,

Virginia, where it can be seen today. Another celebrated whistle artist was engineer C. E. "Dutch" Eiford of the Cincinnati Southern. It was alleged that he could play the opening bars of the hymn *Oh, How I Love Jesus* on his chime whistle. Engineer John Milnar of the Minneapolis & St. Louis played a signature tune instructing his wife to bring him hot coffee as he chugged into the station at Albert Lea, Minnesota.

Perhaps the most accomplished of all whistle artists was the legendary Joe Dennis, an engineer on the Atlanta & West Point Railroad. Dennis was also the mayor of his hometown, Palmetto, Georgia, 28 miles south of Atlanta. His instrument was a 6" diameter Crosby chime whistle equipped with an extra-long lever that Dennis had forged to his specifications at the A&WP shops in Montgomery, Alabama. His specialty was to imitate a woman sobbing. An earwitness to Dennis' skill described his technique as follows:

> In the summer of 1904, a newcomer was wheeling trains around the belt line, and his whistle was unlike any I'd ever heard. I wondered who he was, and whether or not some personal sorrow was being expressed by his eerie music. It was different from the lonesome calls that faded into a whispering moan. This one, if I can possibly describe it, began with a slightly quivering whisper, slowly climbing to a high crescendo, to be followed by rising and falling notes before dropping back to a whisper. Three other blows followed, each with somewhat different melodies. The tones swelled as they scaled up and then slowly subsided to a whisper, ending with a whip-cracking finale. From where I heard the whistle, it sounded like a perfect imitation of a sobbing woman or child.

Years later Dennis was riding as a passenger on a Seaboard Air Line train when he overheard a group of young people talking about the famous whistling engineer of the A&WP. One girl claimed that she had heard that whistle and knew the sad story behind it. When the engineer was a young married man, she related, his wife would meet him at the railroad crossing each morning to hand up some breakfast as the engine rolled by. One rainy day the engineer told his wife not to meet him at the crossing that morning. After he left for work, the skies cleared, and she decided to take his breakfast to him anyway. She rushed down to the crossing and attempted to cross in front of the engine to get to his side of the cab. The engineer was running faster than usual and did not expect her, and she was struck and killed by the engine. Ever since that day, the engineer has vented his sorrow through his whistle.

Asked if the story were true, Joe chuckled and replied, "Hell, no, I wasn't even married then. My first reaction was to introduce myself and explain to the young woman that she was mistaken. But I changed my mind and let it pass. I reckon the rumor went around from one person to another until it became a legend."

Joe was still running locomotives when he died. His whistle remained in service until the last engine it was used on, A&WP No. 186, was retired. Many knew about this special whistle, and a plumber in Newnan, Georgia, a life-long railfan, arranged to buy the whistle before the engine went to the scrapyard. It now resides in the private collection of co-author David Fultz. Coincidentally, Joe's favorite steam locomotive, No. 290, still exists in the collection of the Atlanta Chapter of the National Railway Historical Society, and ran in excursion service for several years in the early 1990's.

Another celebrated whistle artist was Claude S. Jones, an engineer on the Seaboard Air Line. Jones described his famous whistle thus:

> It was a three-cell affair with the sweetest tone I've ever heard. John Watson, roundhouse foreman at Howell, made the whistle when he was working for the Southern. After he came to the Seaboard, he gave it to an engineer named Blossmeyer. I would have given about any price for it. Imagine my surprise when one day in 1910 he gave me the whistle upon my promotion to passenger service.

Jones persuaded a machinist to rig the whistle with a series of levers, and by taking up all the slack, could make the whistle respond to the slightest touch. He said it enabled him to run a musical scale and imitate the human voice. Some years later the Seaboard put out a directive prohibiting the use of special whistles on its engines. Jones pleaded with the officials, and went all the way to the chief clerk, who intervened on his behalf with the president, but to no avail. One day Jones had shot some quail during a layover and packed them in ice for the return trip to Atlanta. As it happened, the president's private rail car was attached to the train, and the porter of that car went to the cab to tell Jones that he missed his special whistle. Jones thanked him, and told him to take the quail to the president's car with his compliments. The next day, the engineer received a letter from the president stating that his train was not to be allowed to run without his special whistle.

The foregoing anecdotes all bespeak the intensely personal relationship that once existed between a locomotive engineer and his whistle. The engineer looked on the whistle as an extension of his personality and used it to express his feelings. If he felt out of sorts, he pulled harshly on the whistle cord. If in good spirits, a wave from trackside was answered with a cordial toot of the whistle. It is alleged that at one time so many engineers on the Southern Railway had their private whistles that new locomotives were purchased without whistles, because the manufacturers knew that their whistles would be removed and discarded before the engine made its first revenue trip. Some railroads had a custom of giving the whistle of engineer who died in service to his family. Several whistles still exist because of this custom, the most famous being Casey Jones' six-chime boiler tube whistle.

After World War I many railroads ceased to assign a certain engine to one man, and this effectively ended the use of an engineer's personal whistle, as it took time to change a whistle from one engine to another. Claude Jones lost track of his whistle during this period, and never saw it again. Very few engineers took their whistles home with them when they retired. Most gave them to another engineer, or simply left them on the last engine they ran. Without exception, those who didn't take their whistles with them when they retired regretted it in later years.

One engineer with the foresight to save his personal whistle was G.A. "Gillie" Speas, a 50-year veteran of the Southern Railway. After his steam locomotive was retired, he drove to Southern's huge repair facility in Spencer, North Carolina, and removed his whistle, a 6" Crosby chime, from the locomotive as it was being prepared for the trip to the scrapper. In later years Speas was invited out of retirement to run Southern excursion locomotive No. 4501 whenever it came to the Winston-Salem area, and on these occasions he mounted his whistle on the engine. It was never left on the engine, and at the end of the day it was returned to the hearth at Speas' home.

"Whistle talk" can still be heard today, not of course on mainline steam, but on various tourist railroads and railfan excursions. The whippoorwill style of Casey Jones survives in the hands of engineer A. J. Lee of the Bonhomie & Hattiesburg Southern in Mississippi. By good fortune some of Lee's work has been captured in modern stereo recordings by Brad Miller of Mobile Fidelity. Also notable are engineers Danny Seldenridge, Robert Long, and Artie Barkley of the Cass Scenic Railroad in Cass, West Virginia, and engineer Rich Melvin of the Norfolk & Western. These men in turn have inspired a still younger generation of whistle blowers, men who were born after the death of steam railroading but strive to emulate the old ways. Perhaps the most accomplished of these amateurs is Mark Phillips of Oakland, Maryland, whose demonstrations at whistle blows are always well attended.

What is required in order to quill a whistle? The first requirement of course is that the whistle itself must be inherently suited to such use. Not all whistles will quill, and in fact the design features that make quilling possible are largely mysterious, lying outside the realm of established whistle science. No one knows in fundamental terms how to design a whistle whose pitch can be pulled over the widest possible range, or conversely, how to design a whistle that cannot be pulled at all. The weight of experience, however, suggests that whistles of large scale (diameter-to-length ratio) are more likely to quill than whistles of small scale. Furthermore the whistle valve must be the right sort. Compound automatic valves, which snap open and snap shut, do not permit the exquisitely fine control of pressure and throughput that quilling demands. Finally, the mechanical linkage between the whistle pull cord and the whistle valve must be of the type that permits fine control, free of lost motion and instantly responsive to the whistle-blower's touch. This list of desirable qualities explains why skilled whistle-blowers prefer one whistle to another.

Furthermore, the whistle-blower himself must possess certain skills. Typically the engineer wraps the whistle cord once around his hand and makes minute adjustments to the steam flow by means of wrist motion. Walter Dove, road foreman of engines for the Southern Railway, was the regular engineer on locomotive No. 4501 when it was returned to excursion service in 1966. He had a good touch with the whistle, and was asked the secret of his technique. Dove replied that you needed to "have a marble in your wrist." In other words, you have to grasp the whistle cord correctly, and use wrist action to make the whistle respond. Many engineers used this technique to blow a "whippoorwill," an imitation of a bird call.

The whippoorwill is merely one member of a large repertoire of attainable effects. Many of them have been given expressive names, as in the following brief glossary:

walk: A series of short tugs on the whistle cord. Can be made to mimic a drum cadence.

chirp: A quick sharp tug on the whistle cord, causing the whistle to overblow. The effect can be enhanced by raising the whistle bell until it is on the verge of overblowing under normal conditions.

cry: A brief interruption or hiccup in the whistle sound, produced by quickly releasing the whistle cord and then quickly reopening it to the same point. Works best on plain whistles, and can be further accentuated by incorporating a chirp.

bark: Similar to a chirp but preceded by a low growl. The valve is opened just enough to cause the chimes to sound softly for a second or two. The cord is then jerked to open the valve fully, then quickly released.

scream: A rapid and sustained full pull on the whistle cord. As with a chirp, overblowing heightens the effect.

moan: A long slow ascending portamento, followed by a long slow descending portamento. More effective on whistles of deeper pitch.

whoop: An ascending portamento with an abrupt termination.

All the foregoing discussion of whistle-blowing artistry pertains to whistles of conventional design. There also exist variable-pitch whistles of several types, known variously as mockingbirds, combination whistles, or fire alarms. (See the Glossary in Appendix A for a further description.) The essential feature of all these designs is a movable piston which alters the length of the bell or resonant chamber, in the manner of an ordinary slide whistle. By this means simple monophonic tunes can be played, although fine coordination of the two hands is required to produce disjunct notes rather than a continuous portamento. Incredibly, these clumsy devices have found some favor as performing instruments. The most celebrated of these is the 3-1/2" Crane mockingbird whistle atop the New York Wire Manufacturing Co. in York, Pennsylvania. For more than sixty years Christmas carols have been played on this whistle a few minutes after midnight on Christmas Day. What the performance lacks in subtlety, it makes up for in sheer volume. On a clear night it can allegedly be heard more than ten miles in either direction along the Susquehanna Valley.

Display vehicles

There is something about a steam whistle that is inextricably linked to thoughts of travel and vehicular motion. It may be a long-forgotten association with the whistles of steamboats or railroad locomotives, or it may simply be the sense of expectancy or urgency that the sound of a steam whistle arouses. Whatever the cause, numerous whistle collectors and hobbyists have conceived of mounting a whistle or two on their personal conveyances and tootling their way merrily down the road. In a few instances these plans have actually been carried out, and in fewer still the plan has been elaborated into a self-propelled vehicle carrying a great many whistles. Thus has arisen a new and curious class of vehicle that is neither a calliope nor a fair organ, for it plays no tunes, but neither is it a trailer or a parade float, for it is self-powered. It is in fact a mobile whistle demonstration, and for want of a better name we shall call it a display vehicle.

In the 1980's the best-known exponent of this concept was the late Milo Novak of Montgomery, Michigan. Mr. Novak, a man of many eccentricities, replaced the original bed of his 1979 three-quarter ton Ford pickup with a specially made flat bed on which he mounted a 20 HP engine-driven Ingersoll-Rand compressor and an 80-gallon air receiver. He then began to mount whistles and air horns all over the truck bed and cab roof. At its zenith in 1989, the seriously overloaded truck chassis carried 55 whistles ranging in size from 1" to 10" in diameter, each with its own lanyard running to the cab. Also mounted were at least a dozen solenoid-operated air horns of railroad and marine origin, and fifteen railroad bells. One observer called his creation a "one-man whistle blow," and another calculated that if all his horns and whistles were sounded simultaneously (which in fact could not be done owing to limitations of the air supply), his truck would generate more acoustical energy than any other vehicle in the world.

In 1991 Mr. Novak's health began to fail, and the truck and its contents were acquired by Hyler Bracey of Smyrna, Georgia. Dr. Bracey repeatedly rebuilt and improved the vehicle and renamed it "Big Horn." He exhibited it with great flair at numerous rail shows, parades, antique engine meets, and other festival events. In 1995 he added a Kahlenberg S-6, the largest air horn ever built and the only one of its kind. At this point the vehicle weighed six tons and carried four ship's horns, sixteen train and boat horns, and more than fifty whistles, all individually operable. The combined load proved too great for the original Ford 350 engine and a high-torque 460 engine was installed. It became clear at this point that Big Horn could be developed no further. In 1996 Big Horn was irreparably damaged in a highway accident. Undiscouraged, Dr. Bracey then commissioned the design of a wholly new vehicle by industrial engineering students at the University of Cincinnati. The design competition was won by Kristin McKinley-Steiner with the brilliantly audacious concept shown in the accompanying figure. This vehicle was painstakingly constructed over the next three years, and made its debut in the fall of 2000. Its specifications are staggering. It weighs over eight tons, and is ten feet tall, nine feet wide, and 28 feet long. It carries 100 whistles, 22 horns, 11 bells, two sirens, a circus calliope, and a 21-bell carillon, all individually controlled by an elaborate computer system. *Son-et-lumiere* effects are provided by 20 strobe lights, 175 feet of neon tubing, 76 feet of rope lights, two smoke generators, and a 300 Watt audio system. Several other collectors, notably Fred Giltay Jr. of Ellicot City, Maryland, and Ron Beberniss of Houston, Texas, have also built display vehicles, although none of these remotely approaches either the elaboration or the cost of the new Big Horn.

Big Horn is rolled out of the shop where it was created over a period of three-and-a-half years by noted race car engineer Al Moody.

Blowing Steam Whistles

Newly completed Big Horn makes its debut. Hyler Bracey stands beneath the elliptical arches.

Maestro Bracey commands his extraordinary creation.

A portion of the whistle ranks that line the sides of Big Horn.

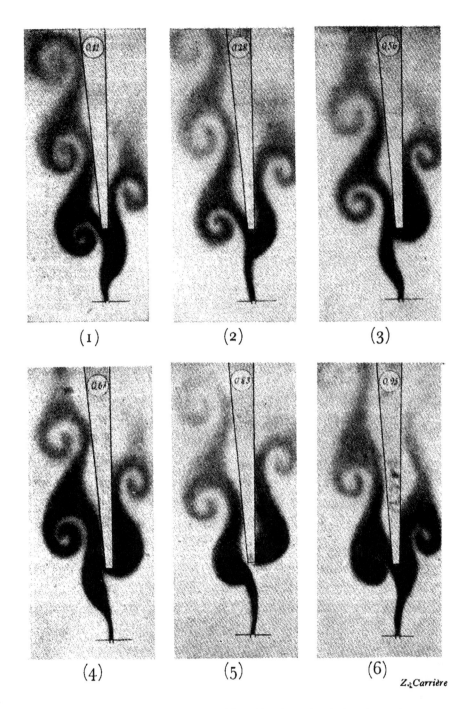

(1) (2) (3)

(4) (5) (6)

Z.ₜCarrière

Drawings by he French physicist Carrière, ca. 1925, of the eddies formed at the lip of a very large organ pipe. The number of each drawing gives the phase as a fraction of the whole period. The windstream was made visible by injecting smoke. From James Jeans, Science and Music.

How A Whistle Works

$\mathcal{9}$ *How A Whistle Works*

That there is a close relationship between the rushing wind-stream at the mouth and the proportions of the responding and resonating column within the pipe, and that they exert a mutual influence, are self-evident, but in exactly what manner this mutual influence is exerted, and what the conditions are that modify it in the way one observes in pipes of different forms, proportions of parts, scales, etc., have never been satisfactorily explained.

—George Audsley

Introduction

About a year before the U.S. entered World War II, the famous Radiation Laboratory was established at MIT. The name of the laboratory was deliberately chosen to mislead the enemy. Its true purpose was to develop a new British invention, the radio detection and ranging apparatus or "radar," into an effective weapon of war. One of the laboratory's first directors was Isidor Rabi, a tough-minded physicist from Columbia who later won the Nobel Prize for his work on atomic beams. The British had recently invented the magnetron, a new type of vacuum tube that produced enormously powerful pulses of microwave energy, and it fell to Rabi to explain the operation of this device to his skeptical American colleagues. "It's simple," he said. "It's just a kind of whistle." One of them snapped back, "Okay, Rabi, how does a whistle work?"[1]

Rabi was renowned for his sharp tongue and quick wit, but this may have been one of the rare occasions on which he was stumped for an answer. He surely must have recognized that the question is not trivial. Even today, we are not entirely certain how some whistles work. The whistle on a teakettle, the referee's or coach's whistle with its little pith ball in the chamber, and the oldest of all whistles, the human mouth, have not yet been analyzed to the satisfaction of the acoustical engineer. The steam whistle is in some ways the most mysterious of all. Despite its apparent simplicity we still cannot predict from first principles (i.e., from a blueprint) the exact pitch the whistle will sound, or which overtones it will produce, or how loud it will be.

Thus, regrettably, you will not learn from this chapter how a steam whistle works. You will learn instead how an organ flue pipe works. Flue pipes or *labial* pipes are organ pipes that do not contain reeds, such as Diapasons, Bourdons, and Flutes. Organ pipes of this type are the nearest relatives of steam whistles. The two devices are not brothers but more like distant cousins, not the same but not entirely different either. In any event we have little choice but to exploit this similarity, because the organ pipe literature is immense whereas the steam whistle literature is almost non-existent. This arises in turn because organs are old and steam whistles are relatively new. Primitive organs are depicted in Greek vase paintings as early as the second century B.C. Treatises on organ-building circulated among the monasteries of Europe in the 10th century. A sophisticated organ of 2500 pipes was built at Amiens more than sixty years before Columbus sailed for America. The design of organ pipes has been continually refined by thousands of organ-builders for half a millennium, whereas the steam whistle was not invented until about 1833 and has received almost no attention from researchers. We would handicap ourselves needlessly if we failed to make use of the vast store of accumulated knowledge concerning organ flue pipes.

On the other hand, it would be an equally great mistake to accept the analogy between organ flue pipes and steam whistles uncritically, as some earlier writers have done. Despite many similarities, there are fundamental differences between the two devices. We will have more to say about these differences later in this chapter, after we have discussed flue pipes. It would also be a mistake to assume that the organ pipe literature is static and unchanging because of its antiquity. In fact there was a long period of stasis during the first two-thirds of the 20th century, during which very few advances in understanding were made. Since 1968, however, there have been great forward strides in our understanding of the operation of organ pipes, owing largely to the work of L. Cremer and H. Ising in Germany, J. W. Coltman and S. A. Elder in the United States, and N. H. Fletcher in Australia. In the discussion that follows we will draw heavily on the work of the forenamed investigators, and especially on the authoritative treatment by N. H. Fletcher and T. D. Rossing in *The Physics of Musical Instruments*.[2] An excellent popular account of much of this material can be found in an article in *Scientific American*.[3]

In retrospect, it now appears that much of the earlier literature purporting to explain the mechanism of sound production in organ flue pipes is polluted with errors and misconceptions, many of which were merely parroted down through the centuries by one author after another. It is sobering to reflect that the operation of a device that has been in use for millennia, and that has received the devoted attention of thousands of builders and craftsmen, has not been understood until the modern era. Nor is the task complete. Many details of the mechanism of operation are still under investigation.

Recall that a plain whistle of conventional design consists of two main parts. The lower part, called the base or bowl or cup, has an annular ("ring-shaped") slot from which a jet of steam or air emerges at high speed. The upper part of the whistle, called the bell, is an acoustic resonator, whose shape and dimensions govern the pitch and overtone structure of the whistle. The jet traverses the mouth of the whistle and causes the gas within the bell to vibrate and produce sound waves. These vibrations in turn alter the course of the jet in such a way as to make the vibrations self-sustaining so long as pressure is maintained. Together, the jet and the bell constitute a *regenerative feedback system*. The interaction of the parts is quite complex and not yet fully understood. We shall endeavor to untangle this problem by first studying the jet and the resonator separately, ignoring their interaction. Then we can approach the difficult problem of combining them.

Properties of the jet

The stream of moving fluid (yes, steam and air are both fluids) that emerges from the slot of a whistle is called by mechanical engineers a *submerged jet* because it is immersed in more fluid of the same kind. Furthermore the jet is *free* because its motion is substantially unaffected by the presence of nearby objects. The jet of an ordinary plain whistle is for all practical purposes *axisymmetric*, meaning that the it has a central axis, and all cross-sections containing this axis look exactly alike. Thus it is effectively *two-dimensional*, because there are no variations of importance in the circumferential direction.

What happens to the jet of steam or air after it leaves the slot of the whistle and travels freely through the (initially) stationary steam or air that surrounds it? The question is one of considerable practical importance, because it also arises in the design of turbine nozzles, rocket engines, and many other devices. Common sense suggests that the jet must certainly spread out and slow down as it gets further and further from its point of origin and mixes with the stationary fluid that surrounds it. Broadly speaking, these expectations are confirmed by both theory and experiment, but the precise details of the spreading out and the slowing down are numerous and subtle. This is not a topic that the layperson can readily investigate, because both steam and air are invisible to the eye. Special techniques are required to make the fluid flow visible. Unfortunately, nothing can be learned from the white plume that seems to emerge from an operating steam whistle. Closer examination shows that the jet is colorless and invisible for the first few inches above the slot, and the plume becomes visible only above the lip of the whistle. This plume is not steam, but a mist of microscopic condensed water droplets. Everything of importance to whistle operation has already happened before the steam condenses, i.e., before the visible plume has formed.

The basic properties of a submerged jet are all exemplified in the behavior of a column of smoke rising

How A Whistle Works

The plume of smoke from a cigarette, illustrating the spontaneous transition from laminar to turbulent flow. From Ascher Shapiro, Shape and Flow.

from a cigarette in still, moist air. (Strictly speaking this is a *convection plume*, not a jet, because it is driven by density differences rather than pressure differences.) Careful study of the figure shows that there are three distinct regimes of flow. Regime I consists of the first inch or two of rise. In this regime the column is straight and vertical, and the flow is called *laminar*. In laminar flow, the fluid moves downstream along smooth and regular streamlines that do not change with time. It is almost as if the flow could be divided into non-interacting sheets or layers that slide over one another, and indeed the word "lamina" means "layer" in Latin.

In Regime II the plume retains its coherence, but it begins to make increasingly large sideways excursions, taking on a shape rather like a question mark. The flow is still laminar, but it has become laterally unstable. It is vitally important to understand that this lateral instability is not provoked by currents in the surrounding air nor by any other form of external perturbation. It is inherent in the nature of submerged jets. This spontaneous instability of laminar flow was analyzed theoretically in 1878 by Lord Rayleigh, a seminal figure in the history of acoustics. He was able to show mathematically that a sheet of moving fluid sandwiched between adjacent sheets of stationary fluid (i.e., a planar jet) will develop ripples perpendicular to the direction of motion.[4] These ripples will move at exactly half the velocity of the moving fluid, and their amplitude will grow exponentially with time, like compound interest. Within a very short time—approximately the time for the moving layer to travel the length of one ripple—the ripples have grown so large that the approximations that underlie the analysis are no longer valid, and a new and unpredictable regime of behavior is initiated.

Lord Rayleigh's theory is precisely borne out by the plume of cigarette smoke. After about one wiggle, the sideways excursions become so large that the laminar flow of Regime II is overwhelmed, and the plume becomes *turbulent*. It now enters Regime III, a diffuse and unpredictable pattern of swirls and eddies in which an irregular chaotic motion of the fluid is superimposed on its average downstream velocity. This leads to vigorous mixing and exchange of energy between layers. There are no streamlines, or more precisely, the streamlines shift about rapidly and unpredictably from instant to instant.

The inherent lateral instability of jets is their most important property. If the jet of an organ pipe did nothing but shoot straight upwards until it struck the lip of the pipe, the pipe would produce no sound, or at least not the sound we are accustomed to hearing from it. Even in Regime I, before sideways wiggles develop spontaneously, the jet is in a state of highly precarious stability. It is not yet unstable, but it is in a hair-trigger state of *incipient* instability. Under these conditions, it can be easily driven into instability by feeble external forces. We will shortly see where these forces originate, and how they account for the operation of flue pipes. Before we can discuss the interaction of jet and resonator, however, we must first discuss the properties of the resonator itself.

Properties of the resonator

Every volume of gas that is enclosed, or mostly enclosed, by a chamber with rigid walls has certain frequencies at which it is naturally resonant. Each of these frequencies corresponds to a particular mode of vibration of the contained gas, called a *natural mode*. Vibrations in one or more of these modes can be excited by gently perturbing the pressure of the contained gas in an appropriate way. This is exactly what we do when we blow across the mouth of a wine jug or into the embouchure of an orchestral flute. One of the classic problems of acoustics is to identify these natural modes and compute their characteristic frequencies. For an enclosure of arbitrary shape this problem cannot be solved by elementary methods, and it can be readily solved only for certain simple geometric shapes of high symmetry, such as a rectangular box. But it is important to remember that the natural modes always exist, even when we cannot easily calculate their frequencies, or when the shape of the enclosure is not simple.

The simplest of all shapes to analyze, and the one of greatest importance to our understanding of whistles, is a pipe of uniform cross-section which is open at one or both ends. The pipe must be long compared to its diameter. A length-to-diameter ratio of six or more is generally considered to fulfill this requirement. This condition insures that all the pressure differences and acoustic flows in the gas will take place in the longitudinal direction only; there will be no sloshing of gas from side to side of the pipe. The pipe need not be round; the exact shape of its cross-section is unimportant provided that shape does not change with position along the pipe. Hence the pipe retains its essentially one-dimensional character.

Most organ flue pipes meet this criterion but most whistles do not. Whistles that do are a comparative rarity, and they are called "organ pipe" whistles in consequence. Such whistles have bells six or more diameters long, and they have mouths that embrace less than the full circumference of the bell. By contrast, most plain whistles have mouths that extend around the full circumference of the bell, and the bells have much smaller length-to-diameter ratios. A ratio of two is more or less standard for plain whistles, so that whistles with longer bells are usually called long bell whistles. The fact that such relatively short bells nevertheless behave like long pipes demands explanation, but that explanation will be deferred until we have examined the long pipe itself.

If the pipe is open to the air at both ends, as are most organ flue pipes, then theory shows that to a first approximation the enclosed column of gas will resonate whenever its length is an integral number of half-wavelengths. If the pipe is closed at the far end ("stopped"), like an organ flue pipe of the Gedeckt family or the bell of a whistle, then the gas column will resonate whenever its length is an *odd* number of quarter-wavelengths. Note that all the even multiples of the lowest resonant frequency are absent in the stopped pipe. Note too that a stopped pipe of given length will have its lowest mode at half the frequency of an open pipe of the same length. In both cases the frequencies of resonance depend directly on the velocity of sound in the medium. The velocity of sound in air at standard temperature (68° F) and pressure (14.7 PSIA) is about 1130 ft/sec. It varies with the square root of the absolute temperature, i.e., about a 1% change for each 10° F change in temperature, in the neighborhood of room temperature. The velocity of sound in saturated steam at 212° F is 1328 ft/sec, or 17.5% faster than in air. The difference amounts to almost three semitones in frequency, or nearly a minor third. Hence a whistle blown on steam will sound roughly a minor third higher than when blown on air. The characteristic "chirp" of rising pitch when a whistle is first blown is due in part to replacement of the air in the bell by incoming steam.

It is also important to understand that these natural resonances of the gas column have nothing to do with vibrations of the pipe itself. A whistle is not a piano or a violin, and its bell is not a sounding board. Vibrations of the walls of the bell make no contribution to the intended sound output. (This has not, however, prevented some whistle manufacturers from asserting the superiority of their whistles because of the "resonant" qualities of the metal from which they are constructed.) For simplicity we assume that the walls of the gas column are perfectly rigid. In the real world, of course, the walls do vibrate to a very small degree, but in general the free transverse vibration of the pipe itself (e.g., when used in a wind chime) will occur at a much higher frequency than the longitudinal vibration of the gas it encloses. This is easily demonstrated by first blowing across the end of a length of pipe, and then tapping it in the middle with a wooden stick while holding it slightly less than one-quarter of its length from one end.

The most important feature of the foregoing results, however, is that all the resonant frequencies are small integral multiples of the lowest or fundamental resonant frequency. These higher frequencies are called *harmonics* because they all occur naturally in the musical scale erected on the fundamental frequency. If the fundamental (or first harmonic) is middle C on the piano, for example, then the second harmonic is C an octave higher, the third harmonic is G above that, the fourth harmonic is C two octaves above middle C, the fifth is E in the third octave and the sixth is G. The seventh harmonic is nominally B-flat, but sounds a bit flatter than that to modern ears. The eighth harmonic, however, is C three octaves

How A Whistle Works

above the fundamental, the ninth is D above that, and the tenth is E above that. Thus the intervals of classical harmony are built up, and together they form the notes of the diatonic major scale. Despite a certain amount of cultural relativism in our preference for musical scales, there is abundant evidence that the human ear naturally seeks out and recognizes harmonically related groups of frequencies. They sound consonant to us, and we prefer consonance to dissonance.

Only one-dimensional vibrating systems possess the desirable property that the frequencies of higher resonant modes are simple multiples of the lowest resonant frequency. The proof can be found among the instruments of the orchestra. The strings of violins, violas, cellos, basses, pianos and harps are all basically one-dimensional, as are the air columns of the brass and woodwinds. Only in the percussion section do we find sound generators which are essentially two-dimensional (e.g., the stretched membranes of drumheads) or three-dimensional (e.g., the wooden blocks of the xylophone), and which consequently lack a harmonically related series of resonant frequencies. The same is true of bells—ordinary bells, that is, not whistle bells. Indeed, the pattern of modes excited by striking a bell is so complicated that the perceived pitch of bells was a subject of controversy among acousticians until quite recently.

The stopped pipe is far from a perfect model for the bells of most whistles, but it is the best simple model we have. (There do not appear to be any steam whistles that employ open pipes as resonators.) Despite the apparent simplicity of the model, however, it contains a complication that must be taken into account. If one compares the actual resonant frequencies of an organ pipe with those predicted by simple theory, one finds that the measured frequencies are all slightly too low. In other words, the pipe behaves as if it were longer than it really is. The physical explanation of this effect is not hard to understand. For the sake of simplicity, we have pretended that all motion of the gas ceases abruptly at the open end of the pipe. But this cannot be the case in reality. Gas molecules emerging from the end of the pipe will knock into neighboring ones in the surrounding atmosphere, which will knock into their neighbors in turn, and so on. Thus the gas in the

immediate neighborhood of the open end will participate to some degree in the vibratory motion of the gas within the pipe. In particular, its mass must be accelerated and decelerated with every cycle of oscillation. Therefore it is customary to add a small amount, called the *end correction*, to the actual length of the pipe when calculating its frequencies of resonance.

We can estimate the magnitude of the end correction by a very simple argument. Suppose that the "extra" gas engaged by the vibration is confined to a hemisphere erected on the open end of the pipe. (This is a plausible choice of shape because it suggests the transition from purely longitudinal acoustic flow within the pipe to sound waves radiating in all directions.) The height of a cylinder containing the same mass of air as this hemisphere is one-third the diameter of the pipe. This result is astonishingly close to the exact theoretical value, which is 0.31 times the diameter for a pipe opening into empty space.[6] The end correction for other geometries, such as the mouths of chime whistles, is an enormously difficult theoretical problem that has not yet been solved, and the problem is best approached experimentally.[7]

Regardless of the precise value of the end correction, it is noteworthy that it depends directly on the diameter of the bell. This means that a tall skinny whistle will have a relatively small end correction and a short fat whistle will have a relatively large one. This has important consequences for the harmonic structure of the emitted sound, because the end correction diminishes as the frequency increases, and vanishes altogether around the fifth or sixth harmonic. Thus the effective length of a whistle bell grows somewhat shorter as the number of the harmonic grows larger—a minor effect in a skinny whistle and a major effect in a fat one. A whistle bell with a small end correction will be almost in tune for the third, fifth, seventh, etc. harmonics, whereas a whistle bell with a large end correction will grow progressively further from resonance for these higher harmonics. The result in the latter case is that these harmonics are not strongly excited or supported, and the harmonic spectrum chokes off quickly. Hence—perhaps contrary to intuition—a short fat whistle will produce a pure

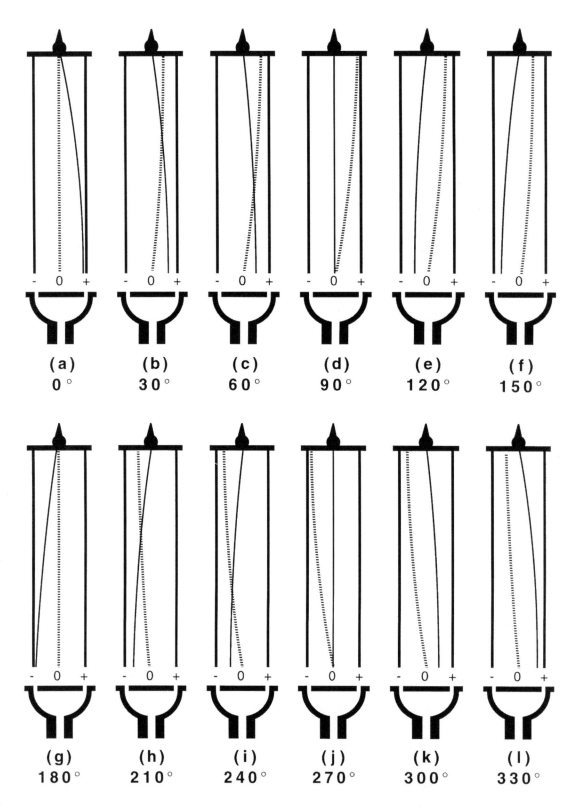

Pressure and velocity variation in a stopped pipe (whistle bell) at twelve instants during one cycle of oscillation in its fundamental mode. See text for further explanation.

flute-like tone, almost a pure sine wave, whereas a tall skinny whistle will produce a piercing nasal tone, rich in higher odd harmonics. It is important to understand that the overtones remain perfect multiples of the fundamental frequency, regardless of the proportions of the whistle. It is only the strength with which they are excited that varies with the diameter-to-length ratio of the bell.

Despite these complications, the stopped pipe is the natural starting point for a discussion of whistle operation, and therefore it is essential to understand precisely what is happening when a stopped column of gas resonates in its lowest natural mode. The sequence of events occurring during a single cycle of oscillation is shown on the opposite page. The twelve small pictures in this figure are instantaneous snapshots, like successive frames of a movie. The snapshots are evenly spaced at intervals of 1/12th of an oscillation, or if one complete cycle is regarded as equivalent to a rotation of 360°, at intervals of 30°. The situation at 360° is not shown because it is the same as the situation at 0°, and the cycle starts over. Superimposed on the outline of the whistle bell in each case are two vertical graphs. The solid line represents the net speed of gas flow as a function of position within the bell. In drawing this picture we have adopted the convention that deviation to the right of the center line of the bell represents net upward flow, and deviation to the left represents net downward flow. It is important to remember that the mode under discussion is a purely longitudinal mode. The gas flows only up and down in response to acoustic forces, even though the speed with which it does so is plotted sideways. The dotted line represents the acoustic pressure of the gas as a function of position within the bell. Here we have adopted the convention that deviation to the right of the center line represents a pressure in excess of atmospheric pressure, i.e., an acoustic compression, whereas deviation to the left represents pressure below atmospheric pressure, i.e., an acoustic rarefaction or partial vacuum.

There is much to be learned from careful study of the figure. Note that the speed of flow is always zero at the top of the bell, because the gas cannot penetrate the top plate. By contrast, the acoustic pressure is always zero at the bottom of the bell, because the gas there is surrounded by gas at atmospheric pres-

sure. (For simplicity, the slight penetration of the acoustic pressure into the region of the end correction has been neglected in these figures.) During the course of one cycle the velocity graph wiggles back and forth as if it were hinged at the top, whereas the pressure graph wiggles back and forth as if it were hinged at the bottom. The cycle begins (quite arbitrarily) at (a) with the pressure uniform throughout the length of the bell and gas rushing into the open end of the bell from the surrounding atmosphere. This inrush begins to compress the gas within the bell, and a quarter-cycle later at (d) the pressure reaches a maximum at the top of the bell. Gas now begins to leave the bell in consequence, and at (g) the velocity of outgoing gas reaches a maximum while the pressure is again uniform. The departure of the outgoing gas leaves a partial vacuum in the bell, which reaches its peak another quarter-cycle later at (j). During the remaining quarter cycle the partial vacuum draws more gas into the open end of the bell, until we return to the situation at (a). Note that the peak of the velocity graph and the peak of the pressure graph are always separated by a quarter-wavelength in space and a quarter-cycle in time. Despite all this wiggling and time-shifting, all the curves have the same basic shape, which is one-quarter of a sine wave. Scientifically inclined readers will recognize the subject of this lengthy prose description as a *standing wave*, expressible much more concisely in mathematics.

Interaction of the jet and the resonator

We begin with a historically important model of this interaction, now thoroughly outmoded but possessing some interesting features. Long before the lateral instability of a submerged jet was discovered, there was a theory of flue pipe operation provided by that universal genius Heinrich von Helmholtz, 19th century German mathematician, physician, physicist, naturalist, and philosopher. Reed instruments such as orchestral woodwinds were well understood in Helmholtz's time. He postulated that the jet functions as a sort of "aerial reed," flicking back and forth across the lip of the pipe in a manner analogous to the real reed in a woodwind. The mid-19th century

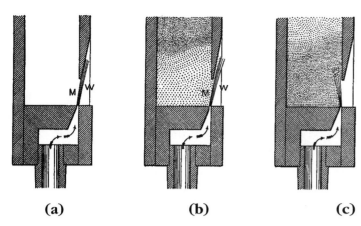

(a)   (b)   (c)

Helmholtz's "aerial reed" model of organ flue pipe operation, ca. 1861. From G. Audsley, The Organ of the Twentieth Century.

engravings in the above figure illustrate the presumed mode of operation. In (a), the jet is initially directed just outside the lip of the pipe. As it passes by, it entrains some air from within the pipe. This produces a partial vacuum just inside the mouth, as indicated in (b) by the less dense dotting in that region. Air from the atmosphere then rushes in to fill that vacuum, dragging the jet with it, as in (c). But when the air flow conveyed by the jet is added to the air drawn in from outside, the mouth of the pipe becomes overfull. The excess of pressure now forces the jet outside the lip again, and the cycle repeats.

There are certain points of resemblance between Helmholtz's speculations and the actual behavior of the jet in a flue pipe. The jet does deflect from side to side, and it does flick back and forth over the lip of the pipe. But virtually every other feature of Helmholtz's model is either wrong or grossly oversimplified. This became clear when theory was replaced by observation, and scientists learned how to make visible the actual flow of air in an organ pipe. The frontispiece of this chapter gives an example of these early experimental investigations. It consists of drawings by the physicist Carrière of the windstream in a very large organ pipe, made visible by injecting smoke into the windway. The sinuous behavior of the windstream could hardly be more different from Helmholtz's stiff and inflexible aerial reed.[8]

Pictures such as these are seductive but misleading. In fact they were misinterpreted for many years, and gave rise to an erroneous theory of flue pipe

operation. The eye is drawn immediately to the beautiful series of eddies produced alternately on either side of the lip of the pipe. This process of eddy generation is known to fluid dynamicists as *vortex shedding*. It occurs whenever fluid moves past or around an obstacle, and is familiar to anyone who has ever studied the train of eddies in the wake of a ship. It is hard to resist the inference that these elegant snail-like whorls are sound waves being born, and indeed they are, but unfortunately they are not the sound waves we hear from the pipe.

They are an altogether different type of sound wave called an *edge tone*. Edge tones are the origin of the sighing of the wind in the trees, among many other natural phenomena. The incomplete or ambiguous explanations of organ pipe operation found in the older literature frequently suggest that the sound of a flue pipe is merely this edge tone stabilized by, or somehow brought into synchrony with, the natural frequency of the resonator.[9]

Attractive though it may be, the edge tone hypothesis is demonstrably false. Perhaps the most serious of its shortcomings is that the frequency of an edge tone increases with the velocity of the fluid. (This is why the sighing of the wind in the trees rises in pitch as the wind blows harder.) But the pitch of an organ pipe is very nearly independent of the velocity of the jet, i.e., the pressure in the wind chest. Even the hypothesis that the edge tone is stabilized in frequency by the resonator will not withstand close scrutiny. Generally speaking, the edge tone is much too high in frequency and too feeble in acoustic power output to account for the sound emerging from the pipe.[10] Thus it is now generally acknowledged that the edge tone is largely independent of the natural resonances of the pipe and plays no significant role in pipe speech. It may play a role, however, in the initial ictus or "chiff," the "consonant before the vowel of speech," which lends such charm to the sound of older, unnicked pipes in Baroque organs.

It took some years to understand that the really significant feature of the Carrière drawings is the behavior of the jet *before* it strikes the lip of the pipe, i.e., before the edge tone is generated. This lateral instability, shaped rather like a question mark, has exactly the form predicted by Lord Rayleigh, and exactly

How A Whistle Works

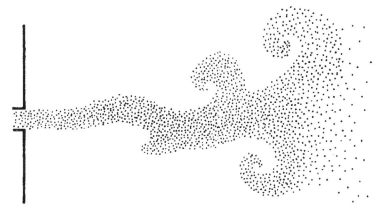

Schematic representation of a laminar jet emerging from a slit into an acoustic crosswind, causing it to break up into a series of vortices. From Fletcher and Rossing, Ref.2.

resembles the behavior of the column of cigarette smoke in Regime II, i.e., in the middle of its upward travel. The difference is that this wiggle occurs immediately when the air emerges from the windway, and does not follow an initial region of unperturbed laminar flow. What accounts for the difference? Recall that Regime I of the smoke plume is a region of *incipient* instability, preceding the spontaneous instability of Regime II. In the case of the flue pipe, instability in this normally tranquil region has been provoked by the "acoustic crosswind" issuing from the mouth of the pipe. It is emphatically *not* caused by the jet striking the lip of the pipe, because it occurs upstream from the lip.

Lateral instability of the jet in the presence of an acoustic crosswind is the key to the operation of both flue pipes and steam whistles. Almost all of the recent progress in our understanding of flue pipes has come from careful studies of the response of jets to acoustic crosswinds.[11] In a typical experiment a planar jet is exposed to the sound field produced by a loudspeaker, and the instantaneous position, pressure, and velocity profile of the jet are painstakingly mapped. It turns out that the jet is amazingly sensitive to tiny perturbations. In one experiment an acoustic crosswind in which the air molecules vibrated back

and forth less than one mm. caused the jet to make sideways excursions exceeding ten mm.[12] Effects grossly disproportionate to their causes are the sign of a nonlinear operating mechanism. Nonlinearities are notoriously difficult to treat in theory, and one of the principal impediments to our understanding of whistle operation.

The most thorough investigations of the behavior of jets in acoustic crosswinds are due to Fletcher and Thwaites.[3] A representative result of their experiments is shown in the figure below. This is a series of snapshots of the center line of a planar air jet as it flutters back and forth in the acoustic crosswind produced by an artificially driven organ pipe. Note that the bottom end of the jet is firmly anchored in the slit, like a bar clamped in a vise. As foreseen by Rayleigh, sinuous waves propagate upward with half the speed of the air in the central plane of the jet, increasing exponentially in amplitude as they go. The wavelength becomes shorter as the jet loses speed. At first, the center of the jet flicks back and forth over the undeviated center line. After little more than one wavelength, the sidewise excursions exceed the width of the jet itself, so that the jet dissolves into chaos. The arrow in this figure indicates the approximate position of the lip of the resonant chamber in a properly made organ pipe. Note

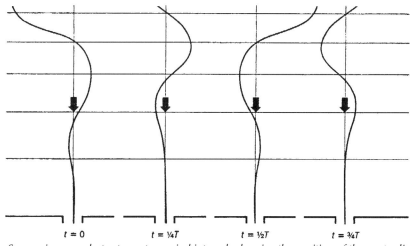

Successive snapshots at quarter-period intervals showing the position of the center line of the jet as it emerges from the slit and crosses the transverse sound field emerging from the resonator. The sound field creates a sinuous wave that moves upward at half the speed of the fluid in the jet, and grows exponentially in amplitude as it rises. The horizontal lines show the distance traveled by the wave in successive quarter-periods. The black arrows indicate the approximate position of the lip of the organ pipe or whistle bell for best operation. From Fletcher and Thwaites, Ref. 3.

How A Whistle Works

that it lies on the centerline of the undeviated jet, and at a height such that the jet executes approximately one-half of a sinuous wave before striking it. As the jet waves back and forth across the lip, it blows alternately into the pipe and out of it, just as organ builders have always asserted. It is this periodic insertion and withdrawal of gas from the mouth of the pipe that excites the vibration of the column of gas and causes the pipe to sound. The circle of action and reaction is now closed. We have identified the regenerative feedback mechanism that sustains the production of sound in the steady state. The wiggling of the jet excites the natural vibration of the gas column, and the vibration of the gas column produces an acoustic crosswind that causes the jet to wiggle.

The recognition that a regenerative feedback mechanism governs the operation of an organ pipe inevitably raises the chicken-and-egg question: Which comes first, the wiggling of the jet or the vibrations of the air column? In other words, how do the oscillations get started? The answer to this question is what engineers call the *transient solution,* and a discussion of it would take us too far afield. Nevertheless certain facts are known about the transient behavior of organ pipes. In most pipes, somewhere between 20 and 40 cycles of oscillation must elapse before the pipe settles down to steady speech, depending on the wind pressure and how rapidly the key is depressed. For pipes in the all-important midrange, this amounts at most to delays of one or two tenths of a second, entirely tolerable values in the highly reverberant environments where pipe organs are usually situated. Furthermore, most organ music is inclined to be slow in tempo, so that only in rapid passagework is slowness of speech a serious impediment to the performer. In the case of steam whistles, however —with the possible exception of calliope whistles—promptness of speech is of no concern, or in any event far less important than it is in music. As a consequence almost nothing is known about the transient state of steam whistle operation.

The differences between flue pipes and steam whistles

How much of the theory of organ flue pipes applies to steam whistles? It is impossible to answer this question with certainty, because steam whistles have been so little studied. Despite the obvious structural similarities between the two types of devices, there are some compelling differences that make the flue pipe model inapplicable in some respects and of dubious validity in others.

The principal difference is that the pressures at which steam whistles operate are typically hundreds or even thousands of times greater than the pressures at which organ pipes operate. Wind pressures in a pipe organ are measured on a water manometer, and pressures of three to ten inches of water are usual. It is an unusual stop that is voiced on as much as 20 inches of water. But pressures in a steam whistle are measured in pounds per square inch gauge (PSIG), and one lowly PSIG corresponds to roughly 27 inches of water. Hence an inlet pressure of 150 PSIG, for example, is 400 to 1300 times greater than the pressure applied to an ordinary organ pipe. The pressure matters because both air and steam are *compressible* fluids, unlike water, for example, which is essentially incompressible. At organ pipe pressures, the compressibility of air can be safely ignored, and the density of the gas never changes as a result of its motion. Under these conditions the pressure and the velocity of the moving air are related by an extremely simple equation called Bernoulli's Law, known for hundreds of years.[13] This law makes the dynamics of fluid motion easy to understand and relatively easy to compute.

At the pressures typical of steam whistle operation, however, the compressibility of the working fluid matters very much. As the pressure rises, Bernoulli's Law becomes increasingly inaccurate.[14] At a mere 15 PSIG—about the lowest pressure at which steam whistles customarily operate—it has become totally inapplicable, and the equations of fluid motion have become enormously more complicated. This changes drastically the dynamics of the jet. At about 15 PSI the velocity of steam in the slot of the windway has become equal to the velocity of sound. At all higher inlet pressures the velocity remains locked or frozen at Mach 1, a condition known as *choked isentropic flow.* Thus, though it may be hard to believe, a steam whistle is a sonic or even a supersonic device. Those familiar with the design of supersonic aircraft know what an important difference that is. To say that the jet of a steam whistle is basically like the jet of an organ flue pipe is to say that the aerodynamics of an F-16 are basically like the aerodynamics of a Cessna trainer.

Furthermore, the changes in density that occur during the flow of a compressible fluid cause changes in temperature. These changes in temperature bring the thermodynamic properties of the fluid into the picture, and further complicate the equations of flow. It is not an exaggeration to say that the study of the flow of compressible fluids is about half fluid mechanics and about half thermodynamics. None of these considerations apply when the compressibility of the fluid can be ignored, as in organ flue pipes.

A still further consequence of the difference in operating pressures is that the fluid flow in an organ pipe is (or at least can be) laminar, whereas the flow in a steam whistle is necessarily turbulent.[15] The jet of a steam whistle does not merely *become* turbulent, like the plume of cigarette smoke in Regime III; it is *born* turbulent. Do turbulent sonic and supersonic jets also develop spontaneous lateral instabilities? The evidence at hand suggests that they do, just before they dissolve into utter chaos. The mathematics of this problem is so difficult that much of the evidence comes from computer simulations. The figure shows four successive stages in the time evolution of a supersonic submerged jet. Sidewise wiggles, called *Kelvin-Helmholtz instabilities*, develop spontaneously, although they are quite different in detail from the instabilities predicted by Lord Rayleigh.

This is an ongoing area of research, bearing on numerous applications in ordnance, aerodynamics, plasma dynamics, and space flight. On one hand, certain qualitative features of jet behavior, such as spreading out and slowing down, are expected to be "robust," i.e., to survive the transition from low velocity to high velocity regimes. This expectation is supported by the observation that whistles continue to whistle in the same way (with appropriate adjustments of lip height) as the blowing pressure is lowered right down to zero. On the other hand, it is well known that high velocity flows can exhibit features that have no equivalents at low velocity, such as the formation of shock waves. Shock wave formation is the principal means whereby a supersonic jet loses energy and becomes subsonic, yet with the exception of such oddities as the Hartmann whistle and stem-jet whistle, the role of shock waves in whistle operation is almost totally unexplored.[16] The last word has not yet been written. Perhaps when we understand the rocket ships of the 21st century, we will at last understand the humble steam whistle.

A final difference is that the shapes of many whistles do not conform at all well to the simple model of a long closed pipe. (See next page.) We have already remarked that the bells of most whistles are too short to meet the usual criterion for a "long" pipe. There are innumerable plain whistles, principally locomotive whistles of older design and manufac-

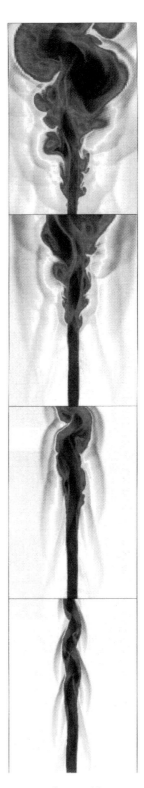

Computer simulation of four stages in the progressive growth of lateral wiggles ("Kelvin-Helmholtz kink instabilities") in a turbulent Mach 3 supersonic jet. (Read from bottom upward.) Simulation visualized using Spyglass Transform, by Michael L. Norman, NCSA and Dept. of Astronomy, Univ. of Illinois, and Philip L. Hardee, Univ. of Alabama, Tuscaloosa.

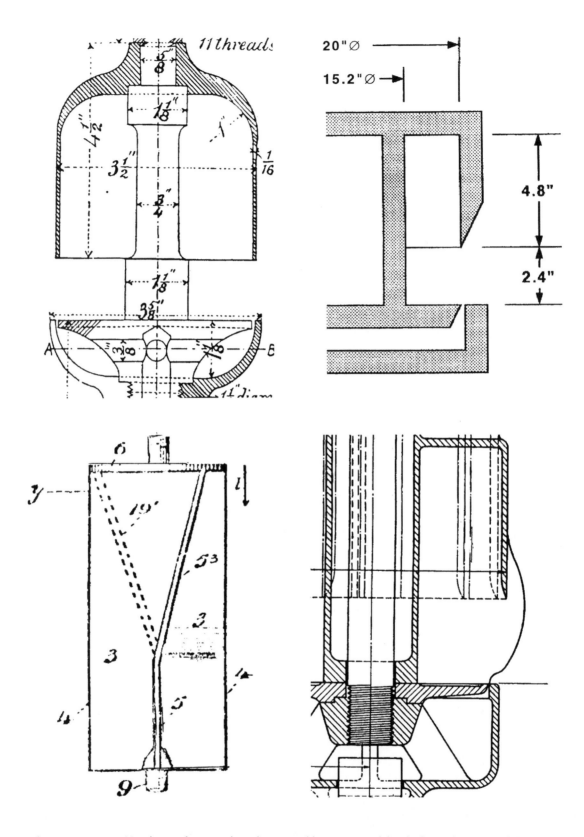

Some resonant cavities that conform poorly to the stopped long pipe model. Clockwise from upper left: An English "egg cup" locomotive whistle, ca. 1895; a toroidal high-efficiency whistle from U.S. Patent 4,429,656; the shortest flute from a Nathan five-chime locomotive whistle; the twisted and tapered cavities of a Kinsley four-chime whistle, from U.S. Patent 520,418.

How A Whistle Works

ture, in which the bell is scarcely taller than it is wide. The English "egg-cup" whistle, widely used on European locomotives, is representative of this type, as are the toroidal high-efficiency whistles of R. J. Weisenberger. The reason these short bell whistles work more or less in the manner of long pipes is that they possess axial symmetry. They can be made to oscillate in a purely longitudinal mode because all parts of the lip or rim are excited uniformly. If excitation were not uniform (as might occur if the bell were not perfectly centered on the slot), then some sort of mixing with other modes would certainly occur, and "wolf notes" would be produced.

Recall also that the definition of a long pipe implies a uniform cross-section. A striking example of the effects of a non-uniform cross-section is provided by the familiar Kinsley four-chime or "quartet" whistles, the subject of U. S. Patent No. 520,418. As shown on the previous page, all four chambers of these whistles have the same length and the same mouth area, hence the same end correction. Therefore, according to the closed pipe model, they should all sound the same pitch. But they do not; they sound a melodious chord instead, because the ingeniously twisted and tapered internal partitions give the chambers differing internal volumes. Chambers of such complex shape defy calculation of the resonant frequency from first principles. We can only imagine the lengthy trial-and-error process that led to the final design.

Finally, there are other whistles, principally single-bell chime whistles, in which the resonant chambers lack even axial symmetry. For example, the shortest chamber of the widely used Nathan five-chime short-bell steptop locomotive whistle has the shape of a pie wedge with a truncated apex, approximately 3" high, 3" wide from corner to corner, and 2" deep in the radial direction. It mocks common sense to assert that this peculiarly shaped chamber is appropriately modeled on a long stopped pipe of uniform cross-section, or that its ancestor is an organ flue pipe. About the most that can be said about such resonators is that they are cavities of complex shape, and do not conform to any simple model. It must be remembered, however, as was emphasized at the very start of this section, that natural frequencies of resonance always exist, regardless of our ability to calculate them by means of simple models.

Unanswered questions about steam whistles

Given the apparent plausibility of the modern explanation of whistle operation in terms of flue pipes, it might seem that no major unsolved mysteries remain. On the contrary, numerous areas of controversy remain. A controversy of minor practical importance, but considerable importance to theorists, concerns the exact mechanism whereby the jet transfers its energy to the gas column in the resonator. This dispute dates back to those two titans of 19th century acoustics, Helmholtz and Rayleigh. Helmholtz believed that the principal mechanism of excitation was the volume flow contributed by the jet. Therefore, in order to transfer energy from the jet to the gas column as efficiently as possible, the jet must enter the pipe at the instant when the acoustic pressure just inside the mouth is at a maximum. Lord Rayleigh, on the other hand, argued that the principal mechanism was the transfer of momentum from the jet to the fluid within the resonator, and therefore the jet must enter the pipe at the instant when the acoustic flow is a maximum. Coltman makes an apt comparison to pushing a child on a swing.[10] Since acoustic flow represents energy of motion or kinetic energy, and acoustic pressure represents stored or potential energy, Helmholtz's hypothesis corresponds to pushing the swing at the peak of its arc, when potential energy is a maximum, whereas Rayleigh's hypothesis corresponds to pushing the swing at the bottom of its arc, when kinetic energy is a maximum.

A simplified model of the interaction between jet and resonator, due originally to Elder,[17] shows that at low blowing pressures and high frequencies coupling via volume flow (i.e., the Helmholtz mechanism) dominates. This conclusion probably holds for the majority of organ pipes. But for steam whistles, it seems probable that coupling via momentum transfer (i.e., the Rayleigh mechanism) prevails. An experimental test is clearly called for.

A far more serious deficiency of the flue pipe model is that it offers no insight into the mechanism of quilling. If the sounding pitch of a whistle is governed by the physical dimensions of the resonator, how can that pitch be made to vary over wide limits merely by throttling the steam input? The range of variation is certainly not small. Ommundsen[7] cites the case of a 5" Star Brass chime in which the pitch of the shortest chamber rises from D at 50 PSI to F at 150 PSI, a difference of roughly 20% in frequency. A similar result was observed with an 8" Crosby chime. Moreover, these commercially manufactured whistles were not designed to maximize quilling ability; in fact, quite the reverse. Using whistles specially designed for the purpose, the great whistle artists described in Chap. 8 managed to produce pitch variations as large as a fourth (a frequency ratio of 1.33:1) or even a fifth (a frequency ratio of 1.50:1).

How is this possible? What features of whistle construction contribute to quilling ability? As a matter of experience, the most important factor appears to be a very wide scale. William Fraker's whistle was actually oversquare, 5-3/4" in diameter but only 3-1/2" tall, and in general, the shorter and fatter the whistle, the more readily it quills. There is support for this observation from organ building practice. The organ stop that most nearly resembles the proportions of an ordinary steam whistle is the Tibia Clausa, a covered wooden flute stop of very wide scale. So broad is the scale of this stop that the uppermost members of the rank are almost cubical in shape. Furthermore, the Tibia Clausa is more sensitive to pressure variations than any other stop. When fitted with a tremulant device, as it often is in theater organs, a ±5% pressure variation can produce a pitch vibrato of a semitone.

Another large class of unsolved problems relates to the proper position for the lip of the bell. This question has two parts: first, what is the proper height above the steam slot, and second, what is the proper lateral or radial alignment with respect to the steam slot? As every whistle-blower knows, these adjustments have a significant effect on the emergent sound. There is no shortage of rules-of-thumb or folklore surrounding these questions, but there is a conspicuous shortage of well-founded theory.

Consider first the matter of lip height or cutup, i.e., distance downstream from the slot. There are several lines of argument that bear on the issue of lip height:

(a) The argument by analogy to organ flue pipes. The metal Diapason and Principal stops that provide the foundation of organ tone typically have lip heights approximating one-quarter of their diameter. Roughly the same proportion is observed in many wooden stops of flute-like tone, although it would do an injustice to the inventiveness of organ builders to assert this as a general rule. Applicability of this argument to steam whistles is dubious at best, since it is well known that the optimum lip height for a whistle depends on the inlet pressure.

(b) The argument by analogy to heating and ventilating ductwork. Note that a lip height equal to one-quarter of the bell diameter ($h = 0.25d$) makes the cylindrical surface of the mouth equal to the cross-sectional area of the bell. Hence, it is argued, the sound waves suffer the least possible discontinuity in area as they make the transition from axial to radial travel, rather like a right-angle bend in ductwork. Indeed, whistles of British origin frequently have a large concave radius where the center stud joins the spreader plate, as if to make the transition smoother. This apparently absurd argument may have a germ of still unrecognized truth in it.

(c) The argument by appeal to authority. The eminent Canadian horn and whistle designer R. E. Swanson, whom we have already met in connection with the experimental determination of end correction, asserted flatly that the correct lip height for plain steam whistles with axial symmetry is 0.35 times the bell diameter.[18] So far as is known, he made no allowance for variations in inlet pressure or other factors.

(d) The argument from manufacturers' recommendations. It is very hard to quarrel with this purely empirical approach, based on field experience. We will shortly display the recommendations of Lunkenheimer for its line of plain whistles, and compare them with the results of other arguments.

(e) Finally, there is the argument from first principles, which endeavors to determine the optimum lip height through an understanding of the mechanism of interaction between the jet and the resonator. The fundamental effect of increasing the lip height is to increase the time it takes for the jet to traverse the height of the mouth. This in turn will alter the phase relation between the sinuous excursions riding on the jet and the vibrations of the sound field. According to this model, the optimum lip height is that which pro-

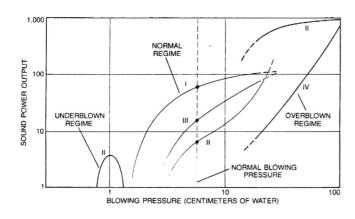

Variation of sound power output with blowing pressure for a typical organ flue pipe. The Roman numerals on the curves indicate the number of the harmonic. Note that the frequency jumps up an octave when the pipe is underblown or overblown. From Fletcher and Thwaites, Ref. 3.

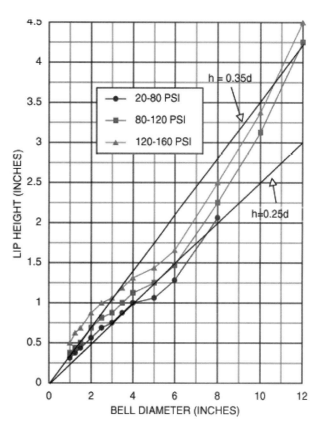

Lunkenheimer's recommendations for optimum lip height vs. bell diameter, with blowing pressure as a parameter, for plain whistles with bell lengths twice the bell diameter. The straight lines indicate the arbitrary criteria $h = 0.35d$ and $h = 0.25d$, as discussed in the text.

duces precisely the phase relationship that maximizes energy transfer from the jet to the gas column. As discussed above, it is difficult to say beforehand what that phase relationship should be, but it is probably rather near the value mandated by Rayleigh's momentum-transfer mechanism. Thus the lip must be inserted approximately where the jet has completed approximately one-half of a complete oscillation, as shown in the figure on page 219. Thus considerations of transit time and phase relationship provide at least some insight into the proper choice of lip height.

Nevertheless, theoretical arguments of type (e) fail completely to explain why the transit time (and therefore the optimum lip height) should depend on the bell diameter *at all*. Arguments (a), (c) and (d) evade the problem by merely *postulating* a first-order dependence on bell diameter. Only argument (b), goofy as it sounds, introduces the bell diameter in an intuitively plausible way. The only other quantity that depends linearly on the bell diameter is the end correction, suggesting that the optimum lip height may somehow reflect details of the acoustic flow and pressure patterns in the mouth of the bell. Is it mere coincidence that the end correction and the optimum lip height are so nearly equal? This is a theoretical problem far too difficult to solve by conventional analysis, and a solution may have to await careful computer simulation.

The transit time does not depend solely on the lip height, however. It also depends on the inlet pressure, which governs the velocity of the jet as it moves downstream. Thus, at fixed lip height, increased pressure shortens the transit time and lessens the effective separation of slot and lip, whereas diminished pressure does the reverse. When the transit time is too short to establish a satisfactory phase relationship at the given lip height, the whistle tends to overblow, and when it is too long the whistle tends to underblow. Overblowing and underblowing are familiar and well studied phenomena in organ pipes. The figure above, left, shows the output level of the first several harmonics of an open pipe as a function of blowing pressure. (Note that the horizontal axis is logarithmic and covers a range of 1000:1 in pressure, and the regime of normal operation extends over a range of ten to one.) It appears that a well-designed organ pipe, like a well-designed whistle, is really quite tolerant of overpressure and underpressure. Note too that when the open pipe overblows or underblows, it does so at the second harmonic, i.e., the octave. But in theory a stopped pipe such as a whistle bell will not support even-numbered harmonics. Therefore an overblown or underblown whistle must sound the next available harmonic, which is the third. Alternatively, it can squeal, i.e., launch an anharmonic oscillation in a mode that is not purely longitudinal.

Let us put aside these theoretical considerations for the moment and see what whistle manufacturers actually recommend. The figure in the right column, previous page, has been prepared from an internal engineering data sheet used by Lunkenheimer to set the lip height of adjustable-bell plain whistles before shipment.[19] It shows the recommended lip height vs. bell diameter for whistles of standard bell length (i.e., twice the bell diameter), for several different ranges of operating pressure. Superimposed on the data are two straight lines, the lower one corresponding to the arbitrary criterion $b = 0.25d$ favored by adherents of arguments (a) and (b), and the upper one corresponding to the value $b = 0.35d$ favored by Swanson. The lower criterion is very well obeyed by whistles 4" in diameter or less, blown at pressures of 80 PSIG or less. At higher pressures the lip must be raised to accommodate higher jet velocities, but a rather good proportionality to bell diameter is still maintained. For whistles between 4" and 8" in diameter there is an unexplained dip in the optimum lip height at all pressures. The magnitude of this dip far exceeds experimental uncertainty in the measurement of lip height, which is specified to 1/32". At still greater pressures the optimum lip height begins to rise again, and actually exceeds Swanson's value at a diameter of 12". At this stage of our understanding, the shapes of these several curves defy explanation. We can only suggest that there exist certain irregularities in the scaling of whistles from one nominal size to another.

Despite these details, however, we are struck once again by the approximate equality of the recommended lip height and the magnitude of the end correction. This is one of several observations that suggest that the bell lengths of plain whistles should be measured from the spreader plate rather than from the lip of the bell itself.

In this light it seems plausible that alteration of the lip height should affect the speaking pitch, and indeed this is the usual method of tuning plain whistles with adjustable bells. Increasing the lip height lowers the pitch, and conversely, lowering the lip raises the pitch. Qualitatively at least, this is what would be expected if the lip height contributes to the effective length. Various quantitative formulas have been suggested for the magnitude of the tuning effect, but none seems to be in good agreement with experiment.[18,20] Once again, this puzzle points up the difficulty of understanding the ambiguous acoustic termination at the open end of a steam whistle bell.

Finally, let us consider the lateral alignment of the lip and the shape of the lip. As with the issue of lip height, there are two aspects to this question: what should whistle manufacturers do, and what do they actually do? With one small exception to be discussed below, there is no body of theory or experimental research on this subject specific to high-pressure whistles. Once again we must turn for guidance to the cumulative experience of organ builders. Traditional organ building practice dictates that the lip should have a

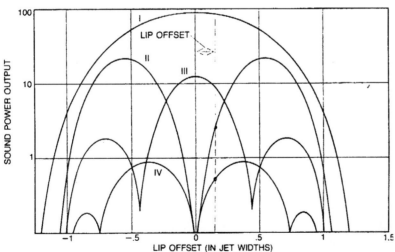

Theoretical harmonic content of the sound from an organ flue pipe as a function of the offset of the lip from the exact center line of the slit. The Roman numerals on the curves indicate the number of the harmonic. Unlike steam whistles, organ pipes are open at both ends; hence harmonics or all orders can be excited. Note that offsetting the lip slightly enriches the harmonic content of the sound. From Fletcher and Thwaites, Ref. 3.

How A Whistle Works

knife-edge profile or nearly so, with the chamfer on the outer side, and the undeflected jet should be directed precisely at this knife edge, or nearly so. The last of these requirements is critical to the voicing of the pipe, unlike the much less stringent requirement on lip height. Moreover, these centuries-old practices have been validated by contemporary acoustic research. The figure on opposite page depicts the harmonic structure of the sound output from a typical organ pipe as a function of the offset of the knife edge from the centerline of the jet. At zero offset, when the knife edge splits the jet precisely in the middle, the fundamental is heard at its loudest, but no harmonic other than the third is present. This gives a dull, flute-like tone that is musically uninteresting. As a result, builders traditionally offset the lip by 10 or 20 percent of the width of the jet, resulting in negligible decrease in the strength of the fundamental but a great increase in the strength of the second and fourth harmonics.

Unlike an organ pipe, a whistle does not ordinarily generate even harmonics, and in general the harmonic content of whistle sound is a matter of indifference to its hearers, who lack the exquisitely refined sensibilities of organ pipe voicers. Nevertheless a whistle is also demonstrably sensitive to radial misalignment of the lip. Furthermore, accidental misalignment occurs more frequently than in organ pipes, because the bell of a plain whistle of conventional design is suspended from its top by the center stud—an arrangement that practically guarantees poor control of centration. Nothing is more common or more distasteful to the ear than a whistle in which the center stud has been slightly bent by accident or abuse, destroying the axial symmetry of excitation and causing the whistle to squeal or overblow.

In contrast to alignment problems, which are real and consequential, the shape of the lip of a whistle appears to have much smaller effect. Insistence on the knife-edge profile used in organ pipes is probably a relic of the now discredited edge-tone model of sound production. A knife edge is unquestionably the best shape for splitting the jet into two systems of vortices, one inside and one outside the whistle bell, but this is irrelevant because the sound has already been produced by the time the jet reaches the lip. It is conceivable, however, that the shape of the lip may affect such secondary matters as the amount of downstream turbulence. In any event, lips of widely differing profile have been successfully employed in steam whistles.

The figure, next page, shows a representative selection of lip profiles and slot alignments among commercially manufactured whistles. Of all manufacturers, Lunkenheimer adheres most closely to the traditions of organ building. The profile of the long-bell Lunkenheimer in (a) shows a converging windway and neatly chamfered lip with narrow land that would not be out of place in an organ flue pipe, even though the mouth extends around the full circumference of the bell. The shortbell Lorain in (b) also has a converging windway, the midline of which precisely bisects the lip of the bell. The bell, however, consists of a length of heavy-wall bronze tubing cut off perfectly square. Nothing could more clearly violate the alleged necessity of a knife-edged lip than this simple and effective design. Single-bell chime whistles tend to have the chamfer, if any, on the inner edge of the bell. An extreme example is furnished by the six-chime steptop of (c). The draft or batter on the edge of the top plate is so slight that it lies within the experimental error in its determination. Thus the undeviated jet would appear to fall well inside the lip of the bell, contrary to every precept of organ-building. Yet steptop whistles of this type are the most widely used and widely imitated of all American locomotive whistles; public acceptance of the design is beyond question. This same alignment, in which the diameter of the bell significantly exceeds the diameter of the steam slot, can be found in numerous other steam whistles. There is some evidence that it worsens conversion efficiency. Its compensatory advantages, if any, have never been clearly set forth.

What is remarkable in all this is the reluctance—one might almost say the refusal—of whistle manufacturers to undertake the investigation of these technical matters in any rigorous or systematic way. The only known exception was Crosby, which in September, 1927, in response to dwindling sales and consumer complaints about its chime whistles, charged an engineer named Kenneth S. M. Davidson to see whether the design could be improved.[21] (It is noteworthy that at this time Crosby was regarded as the nation's premier manufacturer of chime whistles, and

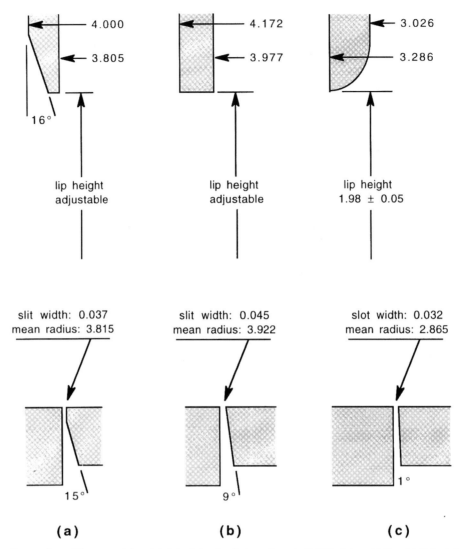

Some representative slit, mouth and lip geometries: (a) 8-inch Lunkenheimer long-bell (3X) plain whistle; (b) 8-inch Lorain short-bell plain whistle; (c) 6-inch Southern Pacific long-bell six-chime whistle. The indicated dimensions are radii from the central axis in inches.

had been making them for fifty years.) Davidson constructed a series of plain whistles in which the height of the lip, the beveling of the lip, and the radius of the steam slot in relation to the radius of the lip could all be varied. He blew these whistles at 80 PSI in various combinations, and then graded their performance in accord with such vague subjective criteria as "clarity of sound" and "sound quality." His judgments were purely auditory; he did not even have a sound level meter, much less the ability to make sound spectrograms. Nevertheless his results basically corroborated the canonical practices of organ flue pipe builders.[22] Inasmuch as Crosby had already adopted these practices, no changes of importance resulted. The Davidson experiments raise the interesting possibility that many com-

mercially manufactured steam whistles, including some of the best known and most highly regarded, had designs which were far from optimum, and might have been substantially improved by systematic research. In particular, one wonders what led the designers of the ubiquitous steptops to situate the lip of the bell so far outside the radius of the steam slot. It would obviously be useful to repeat Davidson's experiments using modern instrumentation, and thus assess the merit of the numerous designs that depart widely from the flue pipe standard. In this way one might eventually approach the question why design rules established at low pressures are so robust, and apparently survive the transition to an altogether different regime of fluid flow.

Appendix A — A Glossary Of Whistle Terms

Compiled by Lin Chapman and Edward Fagen

[**Boldface** type in the description indicates other entries in this Glossary.]

AAR or **A.A.R.** Association of American Railroads, a trade organization whose activities include (among much else) the codification of whistle signals.

absolute pressure The pressure of compressed air or steam measured with respect to a perfect vacuum; a quantity often needed in engineering calculations pertaining to gases and vapors. The absolute pressure is obtained (in English units) by adding 14.7 PSI to the **gauge pressure**. See also **PSIA**.

absolute temperature The temperature measured with respect to the thermodynamic zero of temperature, a quantity often needed in engineering calculations pertaining to gases and vapors. The absolute temperature is obtained by adding 460° to the Fahrenheit temperature, or 273° to the Celsius temperature.

acorn (nut) The ornamental nut that caps the center stud, and holds the bell of a plain whistle or the top plate of a chime whistle in place, so named because it often resembles an inverted acorn. Often erroneously called a **finial.**

adjustable chime (whistle) A **single bell chime whistle** in which the height of the lip can be adjusted to vary the pitch and suit various inlet pressures. See also **petticoat whistle.**

aerodynamic whistle Technical name for a device that generates acoustic signals from the steady pressure of compressed gas in a reservoir, without the aid of moving mechanical parts. See also **whistle.**

air horn A signaling device in which the pressure-induced vibrations of a metallic or phenolic diaphragm are coupled to the air by means of an acoustic horn. Not a true **aerodynamic whistle** because sound production involves a moving mechanical part, although often so called out of habit or ignorance, especially in the context of railroading.

air whistle A whistle intended for operation on compressed air only. In railroad practice the name is often given to a **cab signal** or **peanut** whistle, to distinguish it from the steam whistle mounted on the boiler.

amplifier See **reflector**.

arch The mouth of an individual chamber of a single-bell chime whistle, so named for its shape.

ASME or **A.S.M.E.** American Society of Mechanical Engineers, the professional association that codifies and certifies (among much else) the design and construction of steam boilers, air tanks, and other pressurized vessels.

baby's prick 1. Slang name for the **acorn** used on Lonergan whistles 4" or less in diameter, so named for its appearance. 2. A **dome-top** chime whistle with a vestigial acorn cast integral with the dome, manufactured by Powell around 1903 during a brief transitional period from the flat-top design to the acornless round-top design.

baffle plate See **spreader plate**.

balanced valve A whistle valve for use at high pressures, in which the force of the steam or compressed air on the valve disc is largely counteracted by the force on an opposing piston. See also **equalized valve** and **compound valve**.

baldie or **baldy** Slang name for a round-top whistle without an acorn, as Lunkenheimer whistles prior to 1898 or Powell chime whistles subsequent to 1907.

An unrestored acorn nut of traditional shape and monumental size. Photo by the author.

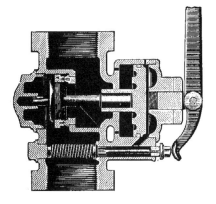

Cross-section of Crosby's version of a balanced valve. The small valve opens first, admitting steam behind the large piston, which counteracts most of the force on the valve disc.

Bowtie fulcrum on a Crane whistle, ca. 1902.

Modern version of a Casey Jones whistle, made by L. G. Simpson ca. 1976.

banshee (whistle) Any shrill whistle with a wailing tone, but especially the distinctive short bell plain whistle built in the shops of the Pennsylvania Rail Road for use on its freight locomotives.

base The lower portion of a whistle, comprising everything between the inlet and the slit. See also **bowl** or **cup** and **extension**.

bastard thread An inlet thread on a whistle which does not conform to the ordinary gas pipe standard. Compare **NPT** and **Santa Fe thread**.

bell cap See **top cap**.

bell The resonating sound chamber of a plain whistle, usually in the form of a cylinder closed at one end. On **single-bell chime** whistles the name is given to the entire assembly of several resonating chambers.

boiler thread A screw thread of 12 turns per inch, independent of diameter, and available in both straight and tapered forms. So called because of widespread use on boiler fittings and accessories, including staybolts, washout plugs, and whistles.

bonnet Alternative name for the **valve cover**, a usage favored by Crosby, a prominent manufacturer.

bootleg whistle A long-bell plain whistle made in the shops of the Southern Railway, possibly in disregard or defiance of company regulations.

bottom plate Alternative name for the **spreader plate**, a usage favored by Crosby, a prominent manufacturer.

bowl The portion of a whistle **base** in which steam or air flows from the inlet to the slit, so named because it is frequently hemispherical in shape.

bowtie fulcrum Popular name for a **double fulcrum** cast integral with the valve body of a whistle, so called because of its shape, and used on early Crane and Lunkenheimer whistles among others.

branch Alternative name for the **manifold** of a multiple-chime whistle, a usage favored by Lunkenheimer.

bull-of-the-woods (whistle) Vernacular name for a two-bell **gong** whistle, so called because of its frequent use in logging and lumbering operations.

button-top (whistle) Popular name for a single-bell chime whistle in which the longest chamber is surmounted by a bulge or extension to increase its effective length. Apparently confined to whistles manufactured in B&O shops. See also **tumor-top** whistle.

caboose whistle 1. A valve closing the far end of a train brake line, containing a small whistle built into the handle for signaling backup movements; 2. A small **gong** whistle of a type often used on cabooses.

cab signal (whistle) A small air-operated whistle mounted in the cab of a locomotive to warn the engineer of malfunction or to convey signals from other members of the train crew.

calliope (Greek: "beautiful voice") An extremely loud musical instrument comprised of chromatically tuned whistles on a common manifold, played from a keyboard and named for the muse of epic poetry. See also **steam piano**.

Casey Jones (whistle) A **chime whistle** resembling a panpipe, comprising three to seven separate flutes mounted on a common bowl in a cylindrical cluster, so named for the celebrated locomotive engineer who had a whistle of this type made to his specification.

center bolt See **center stud.**

centerpiece See **center stud**.

center post See **center stud**.

center rod See **center stud**.

center stem See **center stud**.

center stud On a plain whistle, the long rod threaded at one or both ends which fastens the bell to the base or bowl. A short stud is used on single-bell chime whistles with cast bells.

CFM or **cfm** An abbreviation for "cubic feet per minute," the customary unit of gas flow rate in the English system. The gas is presumed to be at **STP**.

chiff "The consonant before the vowel of speech," said of Baroque organ pipes which produce a brief anharmonic squeak before settling into sustained tone. Possibly related to overblowing in whistles, its physical origin remains a matter of controversy.

chime (whistle) A whistle that sounds two or more notes simultaneously. A chime whistle may comprise several plain whistles mounted on a common manifold, a circular cluster of flutes on a common bowl, or chambers of different lengths contained within a single bell.

Clarion (whistle) The name given to **caboose** or **gong** whistles manufactured by the Westinghouse Air Brake Co. Apparently a generic name, not a trade name, and of obscure origin.

coaxial chime (whistle) See **vertical chime whistle**.

combination whistle Alternative name for a **fire alarm whistle**.

common (whistle) A rarely used name for a **plain whistle**.

compound valve or **compound automatic valve** A valve for use at high pressures in which a small valve, opening first, relieves the pressure of steam or compressed air on the main valve disc. See also **balanced valve**.

CPS or **cps** An abbreviation for "cycles per second," the former unit of frequency. Now obsolete, replaced by **Hertz**, abbreviated **Hz**.

cup Alternative name for the **bowl** of a whistle, a usage favored by Crosby.

cup whistle A plain whistle, usually of 19th century design and manufacture, in which the bell resembles an inverted **egg cup**.

cut-up An alternative term for **lip height**, derived from organ-building practice and usually applied only to organ pipe whistles.

dead man (whistle) A **cab signal** whistle that sounds unless the engineer periodically presses a button or pedal to prevent it from doing so; a test for alertness and a guard against fatigue.

decibel or **deciBel**, abbreviated **db** or **dB.** One-tenth of a Bel (after Alexander Graham Bell); the unit of acoustic intensity. The Bel is a logarithmic unit. One Bel corresponds to an intensity ratio of ten; hence one decibel corresponds to an intensity ratio of the tenth root of ten, or roughly 1.259.

dome-top (whistle) A whistle in which the top cap is hemispherical or nearly so. Also called a **round-top whistle.**

double fulcrum A fulcrum with both upper and lower pivot points, so that the valve actuating lever may be mounted pointing up or down. See also **bowtie fulcrum.**

double whistle Alternative name for a two-bell horizontal **gong whistle**, used in the southern U.S.

drop lever A **vertical valve** mounted in the base of a whistle, with the lever hanging downward.

Dynawhistle Trade name of a horn-loaded **toroidal whistle** of extremely high efficiency, invented by R. J. Weisenberger. See also **Ultrawhistle**.

ears On a step-top or other chime whistle, protruding extensions of the **webs** or **vanes** between the resonating chambers, intended to minimize interaction.

egg cup (whistle) See **cup whistle**.

equalized valve Alternative name for a **balanced valve**.

exhaust whistle A whistle, usually a chime whistle of the panpipe type, inserted in the exhaust pipe of an automobile and engaged by a diverter valve.

explosion whistle A whistle for automotive use, inserted in the spark plug hole of a cylinder, extending or replacing the spark plug itself, and actuated by the exhaust stroke of the engine.

extension The cylindrical prolongation of a whistle **base** below the **bowl**, adapted to contain a vertical valve.

finial An architectural term for the ornamental termination of an arch or column, as on a bedpost; also the **top nut** of a whistle in English usage. U.S. usage favors **acorn** for the top nut and scorns any other name.

fire alarm (whistle) One of the several types of **variable-pitch** whistles, also called a **combination whistle**. In this type the movable piston is actuated by a central rod protruding from the bottom of the valve casting through a steam-tight gland. See also **mockingbird whistle, piston whistle,** and **wildcat whistle**.

flat One of the facets of the **pipe nut**.

flat-top (whistle) A whistle with a flat or nearly flat upper surface on the bell or top plate.

flue pipe A type of organ pipe, also called a labial pipe, in which sound is produced by a jet or sheet of wind issuing from a narrow flue or windway and striking the lip of a resonant column of air, in contrast to lingual pipes in which sound is produced by a vibrating reed. Often invoked as an appropriate model for certain types of whistles.

flute One of the resonant chambers in a **single-bell chime whistle**, or alternatively, one of the cluster of resonators in a **Casey Jones whistle.**

14L The standard American grade crossing signal, so named for the rule which specifies it in the AAR whistle code. It consists of two long blasts, a short blast, and a long blast (i.e., the letter "**Q**" in Morse code), the last

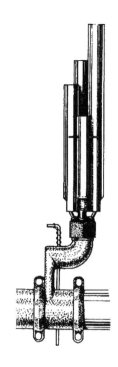

A four-chime Aermore exhaust whistle fitted to the manifold of a Model A Ford.

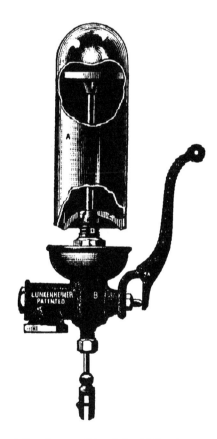

A fire alarm varible-pitch whistle, showing internal construction. Note the offset inlet.

A two-bell Fitts gong whistle, as manufactured by the Union Water Meter Co. ca. 1897.

A one-piece cast iron mailbox whistle, as manufactured by the Bass Foundry ca. 1900.

blast to be prolonged until the locomotive is actually within the crossing. Now called Rule 15L in the most recent versions of the code.

fulcrum The extended pivot on which the valve actuating lever is mounted. Also called the **yoke** or **lever hanger**

gauge pressure The pressure of compressed air or steam measured with respect to atmospheric pressure; the quantity read by a conventional pressure gauge, e.g., in the cab of a locomotive. See also **PSIG**.

gong (whistle) A chime whistle having two opposed bells of the same diameter on a common axis, fed by a bowl assembly with two opposed slits. The name was coined by inventor Abraham Fitts and its origin is obscure.

harmony (whistle) In British or Canadian usage, a two-bell chime, sounding a musical interval.

hooter Vernacular name for a type of exceptionally loud and penetrating plain locomotive whistle of low pitch, especially those manufactured by the Norfolk & Western Railway.

horizontal valve A built-in whistle valve that opens and closes along an axis perpendicular to the main axis of the whistle. Also called **side valve.**

horizontal whistle Alternative name for a **gong whistle**, used in the southern U.S.

Hz or **hz** An abbreviation for "Hertz," the unit of vibrational frequency, replacing the older unit **cycles per second** or **cps**. The name commemorates Heinrich Hertz, 19th century pioneer in the investigation of electromagnetic phenomena.

inlet The steam or compressed air input end of a whistle, often (but not invariably) fitted with a standard pipe thread or coupling flange.

jam nut A nut that fixes the position of a detachable or movable piece; e.g., on a plain whistle, the nut that locks the center stud into the base or bowl, or the nut that fixes the orientation of a rotatable fulcrum.

jet The technical name for the sheet of high-velocity steam or compressed air issuing from the slit of a whistle.

K-4 whistle A standardized and especially melodious three-chime whistle manufactured in the Altoona shops of the Pennsylvania Railroad. Variations of the basic design were fitted to sev-

eral classes of locomotives, of which the most famous was the class K-4 Pacific. Hence the name is often carelessly applied to any chime whistle of PRR origin, regardless of class.

kiloPascal, abbreviated **kPa** The practical unit of pressure in the metric system; one thousand Newtons per square meter. One **PSI** equals 6.895 kPa.

languid See **spreader plate**.

lever 1. On whistle valves, either integral or separate, the handle that opens the valve, causing the whistle to blow. 2. An arm or bar in the cab of a locomotive, part of the mechanical linkage that opens the whistle valve.

lever hanger See **fulcrum**.

lever rod A link or bar connecting the whistle lever on the whistle to the operating lever in the cab of a locomotive.

Liberty ship (whistle) A standardized plain whistle with 8" x 32" bell and integral compound valve, used on Liberty class and Victory class freighters during World War II. Manufacturers included Star Brass, Benson Electric, and Ballou Engineering.

lip height The distance between the spreader plate and the lower lip of a whistle bell. See also **cut-up**.

lip The lower or striking edge of the whistle bell, on which the jet of steam or compressed air impinges.

longbell (whistle) Loosely speaking, a whistle with a bell whose length exceeds twice its diameter.

mailbox (whistle) A one-piece cast iron whistle manufactured under the Barnes patent, U.S. 217,851, having two opposed rectangular mouths, a rectangular cross-section, and a hemicylindrical top, the whole resembling a sidewalk mailbox.

manifold A bronze or iron casting, usually with a single pipe inlet and three or more pipe outlets, on which plain whistles of various sizes are mounted in a linear array to make a multiple-bell chime or calliope rank. Manifolds were often assembled from common pipe fittings, a cheaper if less elegant alternative. See also **branch**.

mockingbird or **Mocking-Bird (whistle)** A type of **variable-pitch** whistle first produced by Lunkenheimer, in which the position of a movable piston inside the bell is controlled by a link chain or wire rope threaded over pulleys mounted on the lip of the bell, and acting against an internal spring. See also **combination whistle, fire alarm whistle, piston whistle,** and **wildcat whistle.**

monkey-tail Slang name for a downward-pointing valve lever with a pronounced reverse curve at the tip.

mouth The opening between the slit of the bowl and the lip of the resonator, usually in the shape of a cylinder or cylindrical segment; the principal source of the sound radiated from a whistle.

Nightingale (whistle) Trade name for a type of variable-pitch whistle resembling an ordinary slide whistle. See also **mockingbird and whippoorwill.**

NOS New old stock, i.e., goods which, for one reason or another, were never put into service after purchase.

NPT An abbreviation for National Pipe Taper, a threaded pipe joint that conforms to the U. S. standard for nominal diameter, pitch, and taper. Other abbreviations sometimes seen are NPS (National Pipe Straight), a thread having the standard diameter and pitch but without taper, and NPTF (National Pipe Taper Dryseal), a thread having a form such that no sealant is required to retard leakage.

nut See **top nut.**

NYAB Abbreviation for the New York Air Brake Co. See also **WABCO.**

OEM Original equipment manufacturer, as distinct from a firm that merely resells goods or products made by other firms.

one-off A unique or non-standard product, not ordinarily manufactured in quantity.

organ pipe (whistle) A single-note whistle resembling a conventional stopped organ flue pipe, characterized by a long narrow bell and one or more mouths which subtend less than the full circumference of the bell.

peanut (whistle) One of several types of small compressed air whistles, manufactured by the Westinghouse Air Brake Co. and used as a **cab signal** in both steam and diesel locomotives, so named for its appearance, or possibly for its aural resemblance to the tiny whistles on the carts of peanut vendors. Sometimes erroneously called a **popcorn whistle.**

petticoat (whistle) A type of chime whistle patented in 1884 and produced in scant numbers by Crosby

Steam Gage & Valve prior to 1917. An adjustable skirt at the lower edge of the bell, fixed by a **jam nut,** adapted the whistle to various inlet pressures. See also **adjustable chime**

pipe nut The massive hexagonal or octagonal portion of the whistle base which surrounds or surmounts the inlet thread, intended to engage a smooth-jaw wrench.

piston whistle Early name for a **variable-pitch** whistle, of the type now known as a **fire alarm whistle.** See also **combination whistle** and **mockingbird whistle.**

plain (whistle) A whistle that sounds a single note rather than a musical interval or chord, although often restricted to whistles with axially symmetric bells. Sometimes erroneously called a **single-chime whistle.** See also **common whistle.**

plenum The air chamber or reservoir that feeds an organ pipe, roughly equivalent in function to the **bowl** of a whistle.

popcorn whistle The small whistle on a steam-powered popcorn vendor's cart, especially one made by Cretors.

PSIA or **psia** An abbreviation for "pounds per square inch absolute," the unit of **absolute pressure** in the English system.

PSIG or **psig** An abbreviation for "pounds per square inch gauge," the unit of **gauge pressure** in the English system.

Q (signal) Name occasionally used for the AAR standard grade crossing signal, so named for its resemblance to the letter "Q" in Morse code. See **14L**

quill 1. *n..* Vernacular name for a steam locomotive whistle, especially one of the **Casey Jones** type. The origin of the name is obscure, but perhaps derives from the use of hollow feather shafts as musical pipes in antiquity. 2. *v.* To produce imitative or musically expressive sounds from a locomotive whistle by artful manipulation of the whistle valve. See also **twill.**

reflector A basin-shaped casting surrounding the mouth of a horizontally mounted whistle to intensify the sound in the forward direction. The best known example is the Hancock 4700 air whistle.

resonator The technical name for the frequency-determining component(s)

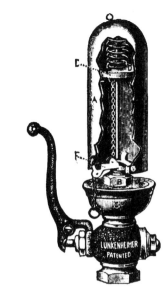

A later model Lunkenheimer mockingbird whistle, showing internal construction.

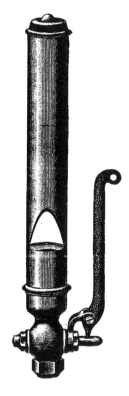

An organ pipe whistle, Star Brass ca. 1904.

Gong Whistle

A horizontal gong whistle made by the Sinker-Davis Co. of Indianapolis, ca. 1910.

A Star Brass cowl siren of the type commonly used on ships.

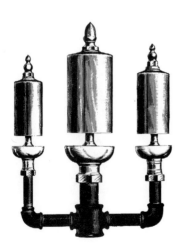

A Crane Co. three- bell chime, ca. 1902.

of a whistle, generally synonymous with **bell**.

reversible lever A valve lever which may be mounted so as to permit actuation by a radial pull perpendicular to the axis of the whistle, or a downward pull parallel to the axis of the whistle.

round-top (whistle) See **dome-top** whistle.

Santa Fe thread A particular type of non-standard or **bastard** pipe thread having greater taper than standard (NPT) pipe thread, and used on the inlet connection of whistles manufactured by the Atchison, Topeka & Santa Fe Railroad.

scale The ratio of the diameter of a whistle bell or organ flue pipe to its length. A small scale indicates a tall skinny whistle, a large scale a short fat one.

scaling law The rule that relates changes in the critical dimensions of a whistle or organ flue pipe, but especially the diameter of the resonator, to changes in its length or speaking pitch.

seat The machined inner surface of a valve body, often conical in shape, against which the **valve stem** or spindle bears.

shop-built whistle A whistle cast in a railroad's own foundry, often (but not invariably) imitative of a commercial design. Well known examples were made by the Pennsylvania, Southern, Southern Pacific, Illinois Central, and Reading railroads, among others.

shortbell (whistle) Loosely speaking, a whistle with a bell whose length is less than twice its diameter.

side valve See **horizontal valve**.

single-bell chime (whistle) A multitone whistle in which a single cylindrical bell is divided by internal partitions into several resonant chambers of different lengths or volumes.

single-chime (whistle) An oxymoron, a self-contradictory misnomer for **plain whistle**. A chime whistle by definition sounds two or more notes.

Sinker-Davis (whistle) A cast iron horizontal version of the Fitts two-bell gong whistle. See also **bull-of-the-woods.**

siren or **syren** A signal or warning device in which a flow of compressed air or steam is interrupted by a rotating perforated disk or cylinder, creating a loud wailing sound. Not a true aerodynamic whistle because it contains a moving mechanical part.

slit In a whistle of conventional design, the annular aperture between the rim of the **bowl** and the **bottom plate** or **spreader plate**, through which the jet of steam or compressed air emerges.

slot See **slit**.

spider A three- or four-armed casting coaxially mounted on the center stud of a plain whistle, in order to support, align, or stabilize the lower portion of the bell.

spindle See **valve stem**.

spreader plate A disc-shaped piece that closes the top of the **bowl** and defines the inner circumference of the **slit**. Also called the **baffle plate, bottom plate,** or **top plate**(!), and occasionally the **languid** or **tongue** by analogy to an organ flue pipe.

spring valve In British usage, a whistle valve which is returned automatically to the closed position by means of an internal spring, in contrast to a quarter-turn valve.

steam horn A signalling device operating on the same principle as an **air horn**, except that the working fluid is steam. Not a true **aerodynamic whistle** although often so called out of habit or ignorance.

steam piano or **steam pianna** Popular name for a **calliope**.

steam roarers Trade name for a line of exceptionally loud plain whistles, patented by W.H. Bailey Ltd. of Manchester, U.K.

steamboat (whistle) A three-chime locomotive whistle of low pitch, especially those manufactured by the Hancock Inspirator Co. after 1938.

steptop (whistle) A single-bell chime whistle without a top cap, so that the ends of the chambers resemble a spiral staircase. Widely used on steam locomotives.

STP An abbreviation for "standard temperature and pressure," a set of conditions used in engineering calculations to normalize the volume or density of a quantity of gas. STP is usually taken to be a temperature of 68°F (20° C) and a pressure of 14.7 PSIA, although other definitions are in use.

three-bell chime (whistle) A chime whistle comprising three individual plain whistles mounted on a common manifold, usually side by side, but occasionally in a triangular array.

three-bell gong (whistle) A **gong whistle** to which a third coaxial plain whistle has been added to produce a three-note chord.

tongue See **spreader plate**.

top cap The upper end of the bell, threading onto or engaging the **center stud**. In plain whistles the top cap may be cast integrally with the bell or brazed, welded, or soldered to the bell cylinder. In flat-top chime whistles the top cap is usually separable and non- functional. Also called the **bell cap** or **top plate**, although the latter name risks confusion with the **spreader plate.**

top lever (whistle) A whistle in which the fulcrum is mounted on top of the bell. The lever operates a vertical valve in the base by means of a push-rod extending coaxially down the center of the bell.

top nut On plain or chime whistles of utilitarian design, the nut which fixes the bell on the center stud. If closed at the top and ornamental in shape, this nut is called an **acorn**.

top plate See **top cap**, also **spreader plate**.

toroidal whistle A whistle in which the resonant chamber has the shape of a squat toroid of rectangular cross section. See also **Dynawhistle** and **Ultrawhistle**.

triller A rare type of 19th century English or European whistle with a freely hinged plate partially occluding the mouth, producing a warbling sound in operation. (see illus. following page)

triple (whistle) Vernacular name for a **three-bell chime.**

Tritone or Tri-tone (whistle) The name applied by Crosby to a top-lever single-bell three-chime whistle of its manufacture. In English usage, any single-bell chime whistle sounding three notes.

Trombone (whistle) Vernacular name for the extremely narrow plain whistles manufactured by the Westinghouse Air Brake Co. and widely used on interurban and light rail vehicles. Apparently a generic name, not a trade name, and of obscure origin, since neither the appearance nor the sound resemble that of an orchestral trombone.

tumor-top (whistle) Slang name for a single-bell chime whistle in which the longest chamber is surmounted by a bulge or extension to increase its effective length. Apparently confined to whistles of B&O manufacture. See also **button-top** whistle.

twill *v.* To produce distinctive sounds from a locomotive whistle, especially rising and falling of pitch, by artful manipulation of the whistle valve. Origin unknown, but possibly echoic. See also **quill**.

two shorts In the AAR whistle code, the universal acknowledgement by the engineer that a signal has been received.

upright valve See **vertical valve**.

valve The device which controls the admission of steam or other pressurized gas to a whistle. Whistles were supplied without valves (**wov**) or with valves built integrally into the base (**wiv**).

valve (access) cover On horizontal valves, the threaded or flanged cap which contains the valve spring and closes the far end of the valve bore. See also **bonnet**.

valve stem In a horizontal valve, the sliding member which cuts off the flow of steam or air. Also called the **spindle**, a usage favored by Crosby.

vane The partition between chambers of a single-bell chime whistle, also called the **web**.

variable pitch whistle A whistle in which the effective length of the bell (and hence the pitch) can be altered during operation by means of an internal piston. See also **combination whistle, piston whistle, wildcat whistle, fire alarm, mockingbird, Nightingale**, and **whippoorwill.**

vertical chime (whistle) A three-note whistle comprising three separate plain whistles mounted coaxially and pointing in the same direction, as distinct from a **three-bell gong** or a **three-bell chime**. Also called a **coaxial chime**.

vertical valve A built-in whistle valve that opens and closes along the same axis as the inlet pipe. The portion of the whistle base which houses a vertical valve is often called the **extension**. See also **drop lever**.

voice aperture English term for the mouth (acoustic source) of a whistle. See also **arch**.

WABCO or **Wabco** Abbreviation for the Westinghouse Air Brake Co. after it became a subsidiary of American Standard. See also **NYAB.**

An exquisitely restored top lever whistle. Photo by Bruce Cynar.

Toroidal whistle of the type invented by R. J. Weisenberger.

washer English term for the **spreader plate.**

web See **vane**.

Whippoorwill 1. Trade name for a type of **variable-pitch whistle**. 2. A whistle call imitative of the song of a whippoorwill, as practiced by whistle artists.

whistle An alarm, signalling, warning, or musical device in which a jet of steam, compressed air, or other pressurized gas impinges at high velocity on the lip of a **bell** or **resonator**, setting the gas contained therein into oscillation. A true **aerodynamic whistle** has no moving mechanical parts, thus distinguishing it from air horns, sirens, and other signalling devices in which sound is generated by diaphragms, rotors, pistons, etc.

whistle blower A device for mechanically operating a whistle valve.

whistle crank A short metal arm attached to the whistle lever in the cab of a locomotive, for imparting motion to the lever or bar that opens the whistle valve.

whistle crank fulcrum A cast-iron bracket in the cab of a locomotive, forming a bearing for the **whistle shaft**.

whistle flange A reinforcing flange riveted around the hole in the boiler shell or steam dome where the whistle is attached.

whistle shaft A short metal rod in the cab of a locomotive, supported by a hanger or fulcrum at each end, and having the whistle lever and whistle crank attached to it.

wildcat (whistle) 1. A type of two-bell vertical chime whistle much favored on Mississippi riverboats. 2. Alternative name for a **variable-pitch whistle**, used in the southern U.S.

willow (whistle) A small narrow whistle resembling an organ flue pipe, used as a **cab signal**.

wiv "with integral valve," an abbreviation often used in whistle catalog descriptions and advertisements.

wov "without valve," an abbreviation often used in whistle catalog descriptions and advertisements.

wsv "with separate valve," an abbreviation often used in whistle catalog descriptions and advertisements.

yoke See **fulcrum**.

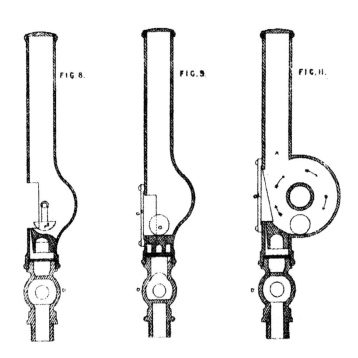

Triller. Unmistakably pregnant steam whistles containing various trilling or warbling mechanisms, from the catalog of Sydney Smith & Sons, London, ca. 1880. Fig. 8 shows a pivoted vane that partially occludes the windway once each revolution. Fig. 5 shows a captive ball that rattles about within a bulge in the bell, much in the manner of the pith ball in a referee's mouth whistle. In Fig. 11 the ball is confined to a circular track. Whistles of this type enjoyed a brief vogue on the continent toward the end of the 19th century. To the best of our knowledge, no comparable types were ever manufactured in North America.

Appendix B — Whistle Patents *

The patent literature is the daily diary of American inventive genius. Within its enormous repository is contained the record of our efforts to create the artifactual world. No resource is more valuable to the industrial archeologist or the historian of technology, and no serious student of these fields can afford to ignore it.

We have endeavored to list here every important U.S. patent related to steam whistles. The search has not been easy. Many whistle-related patents do not contain the word "whistle" in their titles. Whistles can be found under such diverse titles as "low water alarm," "boiler indicator," "boiler accessory," "fog horn," "signaling device," and many others. Conversely, not every title containing the word "whistle" concerns a true aerodynamic whistle, defined as *a device that converts a gas under pressure into acoustical output without the aid of a moving mechanical part*. Thus we have eliminated from the start all devices that embody diaphragms, vibrating reeds, oscillating pistons, revolving rotors, etc. This excludes all horns and sirens, even though these are still traditionally called "whistles" in many applications and contexts. Within this restriction, however, we have attempted to be as thorough as possible.

In order to impose some structure on the mass of material, and assist the student in his or her researches, we have divided the patents into five principal categories, as described below:

Category 1: Steam whistles Patents dealing with the whistle itself, its structure, configuration, operation, method of manufacture, etc. In order to keep the compilation to manageable size we have arbitrarily excluded steam whistles that belong to the kitchen rather than the boiler room, i.e., whistles attached to teakettles and pressure cookers, even though strictly speaking they meet the test for steam whistles. On the other hand, we have included a few patents in which the operating fluid is specified as compressed air rather than steam, on the grounds that steam would serve equally well without essential alteration of the device. This exception, however, does not embrace small whistles blown by mouth ("call whistles"), for which steam is not a plausible replacement. Finally, we have included a number of patents on adjunctive sound reflectors, directional baffles, horns, etc., which, although not strictly necessary for sound production, nevertheless contribute to the acoustic entirety of the device.

Category 2: Alarms Patents dealing with low-water alarms, boiler indicators, relief and safety valves, over- and under-pressure signals, and other devices that automatically give warning of a dangerous situation. These devices employ whistles to sound the alarm, but they embody no substantial improvements to the whistle itself, which is referenced only as prior art.

Category 3: Valves Patents dealing with whistle valves, defined as actuating devices incorporated in, adjacent to, or intimately associated with the steam whistle. This category is subdivided as follows:
3a: Manually operated valves
3b: Hydraulically or pneumatically operated or assisted valves
3c: Electrically operated valves

Category 4: Automatic signals Patents dealing with automatic signaling apparatus and devices, acting upon or used in conjunction with a valve of Category 3, to provide pre-determined signals without human intervention. The whistle itself is not regarded as essential to these patents.

Category 5: Miscellany Patents intimately associated with whistles, but not found in any of the foregoing categories.

It is instructive to plot the rate at which patents were issued within each of these categories. Taken together these plots tell the story of the time evolution of whistle technology. Figures 1 through 4 on page

*Patent Research Group: Bruce Cynar and Edward Fagen, leaders, with the assistance of Harry Barry, Gene Brady, Lin Chapman, Fred Dahlinger, and Richard Weisenberger

239 are graphs (*histograms*) in which the vertical axis is the number of patents issued within each five-year period. Low-water alarms (Category 2) were the first category to blossom, with the rate of invention peaking between 1855 and 1860. Boiler explosions were the curse of the industrialized world in the first half of the nineteenth century, and this is the era in which mechanical engineers and metallurgists undertook a major effort to develop safer boilers. Naturally this effort included devices to remind lazy or inattentive engineers to keep the water level above the crown sheet. Whistles themselves (Category 1) began to develop about 1855, and the rate of invention climbed steadily to a peak in the period 1890 to 1895, a little more than a century ago. Valves and valve refinements (Category 3) continued throughout the period from the Civil War to World War II, with one major peak in the periods 1885 to 1900 and another in the period 1920 to 1935. The first of these peaks reflects the continuing rise in boiler pressures, making conventional disc valves difficult to operate and resulting in the invention of compound and balanced valves. The second peak probably reflects the increasingly complex demands of railroad signaling, requiring automatic valves and valves actuated from remote locations. The last of the four figures, Figure 4, shows the total number of patents issued in all five categories, i.e., the corpus of whistle technology. The three peaks correspond nearly enough to the peaks in low water alarms, whistles, and whistle valves. Note however that two important patents do not appear on any of these graphs because they were issued so recently. These are the ingenious high-efficiency whistle designs of R. J. Weisenberger, Nos. 4,429,656 (1984) and 4,686,928 (1987), which breathed new life into an area that had lain dormant for many decades.

As one penetrates more deeply into the whistle patent literature, one is struck by the disproportion between the number of patents issued and the number of improvements that actually found their way into common use. This appears to bear out Prof. Basalla's thesis that a natural selection process akin to Darwinian "survival of the fittest" operates also in the realm of technological innovation. In any event it is both instructive and amusing to sort whistle-related patents into two classes: first, those seminal inventions that were widely adopted by whistle manufacturers, and second, those inventions of apparently equal merit that simply failed to thrive. Examples of the first class are the fundamental patents on the single-bell chime (Einig, No. 186,718), the date of which is engraved on every important Crosby whistle, the compound automatic valve (Lane, No. 636,907), and the reversible lever (Jones, No. 1,260,775). Examples of the second class are the Barnes "mailbox" whistle (Barnes, No. 217,851), the spherical resonator (Ashley, No. 511,490), and the numerous patents dealing with alignment and support of the lower end of the bell. Even with the advantage of hindsight, it would be a challenge to the scholar and historian of technology to explain retroactively why the former class succeeded in the marketplace and the latter class failed.

In fairness, there should also be two more categories of inventions. The first of these consists of seminal inventions for which no corresponding patent can be found. To the best of our knowledge, certain familiar features of the steam whistle are simply not represented in the patent literature. Chief among these is the steptop configuration, the prevailing type of whistle on American steam locomotives at the zenith of their ascendancy. This design first appeared in the 1907 catalog of the Nathan Mfg. Co., but we are unable to discover any trace of its antecedents in the patent literature. An exceedingly curious 1891 patent by E. S. Gillespie, No. 451,040, appears to presage the steptop configuration, but closer examination shows that the sound-producing elements of this device are vibrating reeds, not whistles! Thus the origins of this important type of whistle do not seem to be represented in the public record.

Finally, with the benefit of hindsight, there should be a category for inventions that ought to have been made but were not. Consider for example the problem of opening a conventional whistle valve against increasingly high steam pressure. In the initial years of steam whistle use this was not a problem, for pressures were relatively low and whistles were operated with quarter-turn ("ground key") valves. The torque required to operate such a valve does not depend on the pressure. On the other hand quarter-turn valves do not lend themselves to rapid operation or to remote operation, both necessary to railroad service. With the advent of the common disc valve, which operates against the inlet pressure, there soon came a point in the development of steam boilers where mechanical leverage alone did

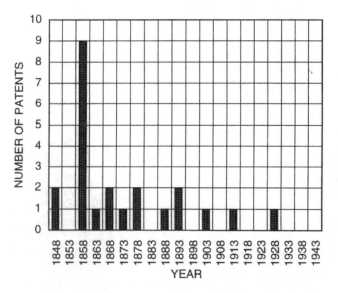

Figure 1. Number of patents issued on low-water alarms (Category 2) within each five-year period, centered on the indicated year.

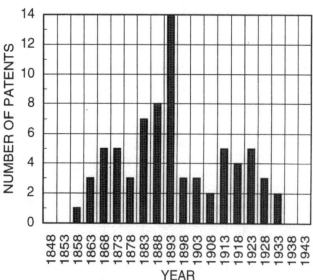

Figure 2. Number of patents issued on steam whistles (Category 1) within each five-year period.

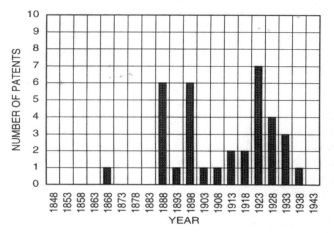

Figure 3. Number of patents issued on whistle valves (Category 3) within each five-year period.

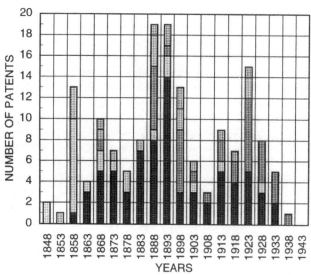

Figure 4. Total number of whistle-related patents issued in all five categories within each five-year period.

not suffice. This led in the 1890's to the invention and patenting of various compound valves, balanced valves, and equalized valves. No one, at this time or subsequently, seems to have thought to apply to steam whistles a type of quick-opening valve in which the forces that operate the valve act at right angles to the force of the steam, wherefore the operation of the valve is not impeded. Yet there was ample precedent for this in the slide valve or "D" valve of steam engines, which had been in use for a century or more. The piston or spool valve was just then coming into use on locomotives, and this too was ignored by whistle manufacturers. It is a puzzle for the historian of technology why so obvious an adaptation was overlooked.

Newcomers to the patent literature frequently assume that the device for which a patent is sought must actually work, and that it must work in the manner the inventor claims. This is not the case. According to law (35 U.S.C. Section 101) "any new and useful process, machine, manufacture, or composition of matter, or any new and useful improvement thereof" may be patented. Thus novelty and utility are the only essential requirements. The word "useful" is often held to imply functionality, but not always; patents have been granted on perpetual motion machines. As for accuracy of description, the literature is strewn with patents of great value on devices and processes whose inventors had either no notion of how their inventions worked, or at best an incorrect or incomplete notion. Two outstanding examples are the oxide-coated cathode for vacuum tubes and the amorphous selenium drum for photocopiers ("Xerox™ machines"), neither of which was correctly elucidated by scientists until decades after their respective patents were issued.

Even within the narrow scope of the whistle patent literature there are patents which either do not work, or do not work in the manner their inventor claims. Consider for example No. 801,081 by J. T. Hoban, assigned by him to the Buckeye Iron and Brass Works. Hoban offers a fine illustration of what is clearly a Buckeye chime whistle of conventional manufacture, except that the lower edges of the webs or partitions between chambers have been relieved so that they do not touch the upper surface of the spreader plate or "apron" as he calls it. What is the purpose of this modification? To quote Hoban ". . .the marginal portion of the apron and the lower edges of the partitions are separated or spaced apart in order to leave such marginal portion wholly free for vibration, by virtue of which I obtain clear distinct, and loud sounds."

The interesting thing about this explanation is that it is utter nonsense. Free vibrations of the spreader plate and chamber partitions, or indeed any portion of the body of a whistle, do not—or at least should not—contribute to its sound output. Moreover, by introducing a slight leak from one chamber to another, precisely at the location of a volume current maximum, Hoban's design promotes mode mixing or mode conversion, and hence a muddying, not a clarification, of whistle tone. It is significant that this invention was never incorporated in whistles of Buckeye manufacture.

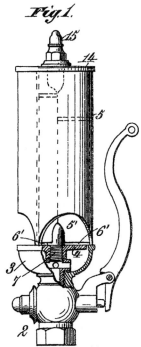

A figure excerpted from U. S. patent 801,081 by J. T. Hoban, showing slight gaps (6' - 6') at the bottom edges of the divider vanes, alleged to promote the clarity and volume of sound.

Do not be too hard on poor Hoban, however. He merely shared in the prevailing ignorance of how a whistle works, a topic that remains somewhat controversial even today. On the other hand, be aware as you scrutinize the patent literature that not everything an inventor says is true, nor is it required to be. A patent, after all, is a license to sell, and thus the claims of inventors should be approached with the same skepticism as the claims of anyone else who has something to sell.

In sum, it appears that the development of the steam whistle and its associated valves and actuators followed a course not unlike many other artifacts of the age of steam. It was invented originally by a gifted mechanic in response to an evident need. In the honorable tradition of his trade, he attached no great importance to what he had done, reckoning it as merely part of his day's work. He kept no detailed records and left future scholars to reconstruct his actions as best they could. His invention was further developed in response to still other needs, an ever-receding horizon of widening applications, higher operating pressures, louder and more distinctive signals, freedom from maintenance, and lower manufacturing costs. The patent applicants themselves ranged from illiterate tinkerers to college professors, and what they invented contained a good deal more dross than gold. But the best of their work survived for more than a century and gave a unique and memorable voice to the industrial age. And when, in the fullness of time, the reciprocating steam engine faded away, the steam whistle faded with it, to linger only in the memories of antiquarians and in the pages of studies such as this one. We will be indebted to readers who bring to our attention errors or omissions in the tabulation that follows.

—EAF

Category 1: Steam Whistles

17,656 **Steam-Boiler Indicator** 06/23/1857
Sylvester W. Warren *Assigned: One-half to D. N. Force*
A whistle with several mouths at various heights to accommodate various inlet pressures, including one to discharge water of condensation.

44,006 **Steam-Boiler Indicator** 08/30/64
Levi E. Lincoln *Assigned: Elizabeth K. Lincoln, Administratrix*
A whistle with several different lip heights on a single bell, to accommodate a variety of inlet pressures. Also contains the first use of a radial-armed spider to steady the bell.

46,910 **Improvement In Steam-Whistles** 03/21/65
C. Kupferle & J. H. Ward
An organ-pipe whistle with a single resonator but two or more different mouths, each fed by its own segment of an annular slit; alleged to produce a novel sound unlike a conventional whistle.

48,921 **Steam-Boiler Indicator** 07/25/65
Abraham Fitts
The original patent on the two-bell chime, incomprehensibly called a "gong" by the inventor. A whistle with two opposed bells surrounding a centered double-sided bowl assembly.

58,875 **Steam-Boiler Indicator** 10/16/66
John Murray
One of the earliest variable-pitch whistles. The position of a sliding sleeve concentric with the bell is controlled by a gimbaled lever pivoted off the center stud.

60,541 **Steam-Boiler Indicator** 12/18/66
John Murray
An improvement in foundry practice. A novel arrangement of patterns and cores permits casting an entire steam whistle in one piece.

64,716 **Steam-Boiler Indicator** 05/14/67
Thomas Shaw
A whistle composed of two concentric bells. Steam enters the inner bell and comes to a partition that directs it through slots into the outer bell. The purpose is unclear.

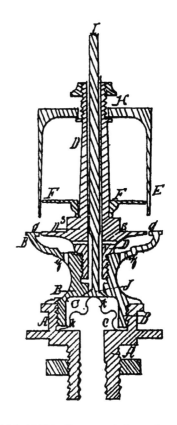

U.S. 44,006. First recorded use of a radial-arm spider (F - F) to stabilize the lower end of the bell.

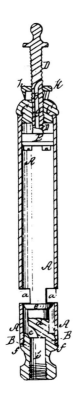

U.S. 84,239. A predecessor of the mockingbird or variable-pitch piston whistle. The position of the piston is fixed by a jam nut, making it difficult or impossible to vary the pitch during use.

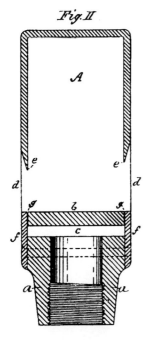

U.S. 217,851. Barnes' original design. Initially, the side cheeks f-f were merely bolted to the main body of the whistle. Later it was found possible to incorporate them in the central casting. The semi-cylindrical top, which give the whistle its popular name, was also a later development.

| 84,239 | **Steam-Boiler Indicator** | 11/17/68 |

Bernhard Weinmann
Another variable-pitch whistle, predecessor of the mockingbird. An internal piston varies the length of the resonator.

| 95,981 | **Whistle** | 10/19/69 |

Thomas Brown
A sheet metal whistle with cylindrical resonator and an adjustable mouth to vary the tone. Claimed to be adaptable to steam—a dubious claim at best.

| 131,176 | **Improvement In Steam-Whistles** | 09/10/72 |

Garrett S. Nevius   *Assigned: One-half to H. T. Baldwin*
Another predecessor of the mockingbird whistle. A movable piston varies the length of the resonator, and carries an external scale that can be marked off with musical notes.

| 141,280 | **Steam-Whistle** | 07/29/73 |

Otto Kromer
An attempt to change the length of the bell in discrete steps by hand-operated baffle plates inserted at various levels along the bell.

| 142,166 | **Steam Whistle** | 08/26/73 |

Otto Kromer
Yet another variable-pitch whistle, this one with a two-part telescoping bell, modeled on an orchestral trombone.

| 166,479 | **Steam-Whistles** | 08/10/75 |

John Rieppel
A top-lever whistle with a contracted bell mouth and a bowl smaller in diameter than the lip of the bell, from which a conical jet issues. Economy of construction and ease of adjustment are claimed.

| 170,274 | **Steam-Whistle** | 11/23/75 |

Henry B. King & C. McKiernan
An extremely simple whistle with an adjustable gauge to control the amount of steam or air that enters. "Less expensive to manufacture, less liable to breakage, and equally powerful in sound."

| 186,718 | **Steam-Whistle** | 01/30/77 |

John Einig
The basic patent on the single-bell chime and the cornerstone of Crosby's fortunes. "A whistle that is divided longitudinally into three or more compartments . . . to produce simultaneously . . . three or more harmonious sounds." The date of this patent appears on every Crosby single-bell chime larger than two inches in diameter.

| 213,272 | **Steam-Whistle** | 03/11/79 |

Frederick A. Wood
Another variable-pitch whistle with a movable piston, its position controlled by means of two rods emerging from the top of the whistle and connected by a cross-bar.

| 217,851 | **Steam-Whistle** | 07/29/79 |

Joshua B. Barnes
The basic patent on the so-called mailbox whistle, as subsequently manufactured by Bass Foundry & Machine. Barnes claimed a lower cost of manufacture by forming the bowl and principal parts from a single casting.

239,264 **Steam Whistle** 03/22/81
John Miller & Isaac Smith
A two-chambered organ pipe whistle with three valves, one for each chamber and a third to admit steam to both. Also two variants with mechanical "warblers." From Hyson Green Works, Nottingham.

253,701 **Steam Whistle Blank** 02/14/82
Wilbur F. Heath
A practical method for preparing foundry molds and cores for the casting of a complete whistle, requiring a minimum of subsequent machining.

264,606 **Steam Whistle** 09/19/82
William Barnett
The basic patent on the three-bell coaxial chime. Each whistle is fed from the one below it by a centrally located supply pipe.

285,639 **Steam Whistle** 09/25/83
Frank McCabe
"A steam-whistle of inexpensive construction . . . a hollow whistle slotted at one side . . . with an adjustable lip plate."

286,420 **Steam Whistle** 10/09/83
James E. Gause
An improvement on the variable-pitch piston whistle, with a top-mounted lever.

299,497 **Whistle** 05/27/84
Edward E. Swett
A bell in the shape of an inverted frustum of a cone, claimed to use less steam and to be capable of producing a variety of pitches, depending on the rate at which steam is admitted.

304,511 **Steam Whistle** 09/02/84
John Einig
A chime whistle with an adjustable skirt that changes the length of the chambers, threaded onto the bottom of the bell and locked by a jam ring. The basis of the Crosby "petticoat" whistle. (see next page)

337,098 **Signal-Horn** 03/02/86
Charles A. Volke
A single or double organ pipe whistle with adjustable flaps or baffles over the mouth(s) to entrain additional atmospheric air and vary the pitch.

359,775 **Chime Steam Whistle** 03/22/87
Richard T. Crane
A two-bell coaxial chime in which the bowl of the upper whistle is an integral part of the top plate of the lower whistle.

364,830 **Steam Whistle** 06/14/87
Wilham G. Losch & L. B. Harner   *Assigned: One-third to S. A. Losch*
Openings of various sizes are made in the base of the bell to create "simultaneous distinct sounds . . . either in accord or discord."

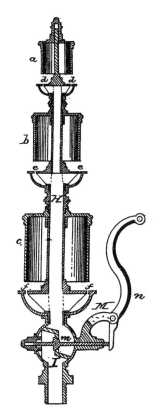

U.S. 264,606. The first three-bell coaxial chime. Note that all three bells open downward, distinguishing it from the three-bell gong.

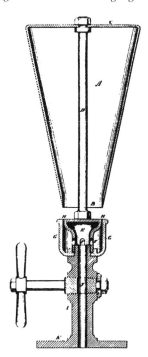

U.S. 299,497. The first of many efforts to economize the use of steam by using a slot smaller in diameter than the bell. Swett's design enjoyed a brief commercial success.

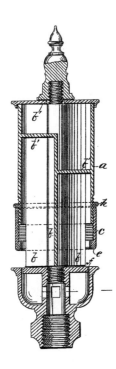

U.S. 304,511. The inventor of the single-bell chime also invented the "petticoat" whistle, with adjustable skirt. Not assigned to Crosby, but manufactured exclusively by them.

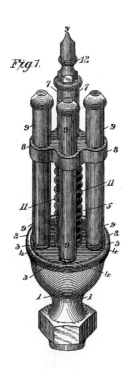

U.S. 405,622. An early panpipe, which almost certainly went out of tune when adjusted. The assignee, Eaton, Cole & Burnham, was a jobber, not a whistle manufacturer.

| 405,330 | **Steam Whistle** | 06/18/89 |
| Henry V. Smith | | *Assigned: One-half to E. G. Burnham* |

A panpipe or "Casey Jones" whistle, a cluster of tubes surrounding a central bowl. The steam impinges on the lips of these tubes at 45º, allegedly for greater efficiency.

| 405,622 | **Steam-Whistle** | 06/18/89 |
| Edwin R. Tomlinson | | *Assigned: One-half to Eaton, Cole & Burnham* |

Another panpipe or "Casey Jones" whistle. The entire tube assembly can be raised or lowered on a screw thread to alter the sound.

| 407,067 | **Whistle** | 07/16/89 |
| James R. Eldridge | | *Assigned: One-half to R. McKinnon* |

A steam whistle fitted with an umbrella-like sound deflector to direct its sound horizontally over a large surface area.

| 427,059 | **Steam Whistle** | 05/06/90 |
| William B. Dunning | | |

A group of whistles mounted on a cylindrical reservoir with a rotating inner tube delivering steam to different whistles in succession.

| 431,007 | **Steam Whistle** | 06/24/90 |
| E. F. Quinlan & J. G. Knebel | | |

A single-bell chime of peculiar inverted construction, intended to replace the bell of a plain steam whistle.

| 448,127 | **Steam Whistle** | 03/10/91 |
| Richard T. Crane | | |

A top-lever variable-pitch whistle in which the internal piston and the vertical valve are mechanically linked. Opening the valve simultaneously raises the pitch.

| 466,403 | **Steam Whistle** | 01/05/92 |
| Henry R. Frisbie | | *Assigned: One-half to F. Kinsley* |

A chime whistle comprising two or more separate pie-wedge-shaped whistles grouped around a common bowl and secured by a top cap. Advantages in maintenance are claimed.

| 466,404 | **Chime Whistle** | 01/05/92 |
| Henry R. Frisbie | | *Assigned: One-half to F. Kinsley* |

A chime whistle in which the longitudinal chambers are not defined by fixed partitions, but by adjustable vanes that pivot around the center stud.

| 468,793 | **Steam Chime Whistle** | 02/16/92 |
| Frank M. Curran | | |

A single-bell chime whistle in which the chambers are tuned by sliding wooden plugs at their upper ends.

| 471,171 | **Steam Whistle** | 03/22/92 |
| Henry R. Frisbie | | |

Various improvements to plain whistles, including support for the lower end of the bell, a valve seat which can be reground *in situ*, and a lever fulcrum which can be oriented to any angle.

472,946 **Chime Whistle** 04/12/92
Henry R. Frisbie *Assigned: One-half to F. Kinsley*
A single-bell chime whistle in which the pitches of the several chambers are obtained by adjusting their angular width rather than their length.

476,472 **Steam Whistle** 06/07/92
Edmund Lunkenheimer
Four improvements in one patent: (1) bell bolts to spider and spider screws into bowl; (2) same but bowl stud goes into spider; (3) a single-bell chime in which the longest chamber opens into a domed top, and (4) a piston whistle of the type commonly known as a "fire alarm."

480,078 **Steam Whistle** 08/02/92
John Einig
A single-bell chime in which the inside of the bell is threaded, as are the edges of the baffles, so that the entire bell assembly may be screwed up and down to accommodate various inlet pressures.

493,920 **Steam Whistle** 03/21/93
Henry R. Frisbie
A scheme for fabricating the whistle body in parts, rather than casting it as one large piece. Advantages in cost and maintenance are claimed.

503,547 **Steam Whistle** 08/15/93
Edmund H. Lunken *Assigned: The Lunkenheimer Company*
Further improvements in the piston whistle. Here the piston is actuated by a cable running over pulleys, making it intermediate between the mockingbird and fire alarm types. The inventor is the former Edmund Lunkenheimer, who shortened his name in 1892.

511,490 **Steam Whistle** 12/26/93
Frank M. Ashley
Bells of novel shapes, with novel means of support, alignment, and axial adjustment.

520,418 **Steam Chime Whistle** 05/29/94
Henry R. Frisbie & F. Kinsley
The basic patent on the Kinsley four-chime whistle. Chambers of equal length are made to resonate at different frequencies by ingeniously twisted and tapered internal partitions. The outer shell is an adjustable sleeve of brass tubing.

535,658 **Revolving Steam Whistle** 03/12/95
Joseph F. Batchelor
A chime whistle fitted with a "humming sphere" which, as it revolves, cuts out certain of the resonant chambers.

550,240 **Whistle** 11/26/95
Frank M. Ashley
An attempt to overcome the thermally induced cracking of cast bells by supporting the bell from the top with long extensions from the base.

571,357 **Whistle** 11/17/96
Henry R. Frisbie *Assigned: Eastwood Wire Manufacturing*
An attempt to economize the use of steam by forming the jet into a conically expanding stream, issuing from a bowl significantly smaller in diameter than the bell itself.

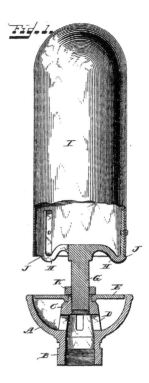

U.S. 476,472. Lunkenheimer's version of a plain whistle bell supported at its lower end by a spider, rather than at its upper end by a center stud.

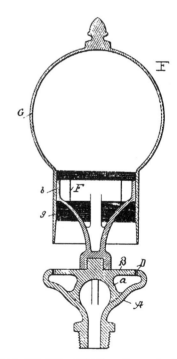

U.S. 511,490. Whistle with a spherical bell, approximating a Helmholtz resonator. This is merely one of Ashley's highly innovative (but commercially unsuccessful) designs.

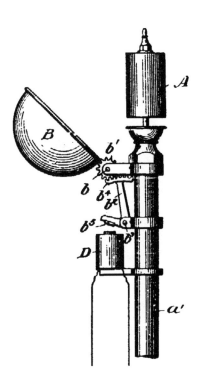

U.S. 630,166. Closing an electrical circuit causes a solenoid to flip one of several reflecting bowls into position around the mouth of the whistle.

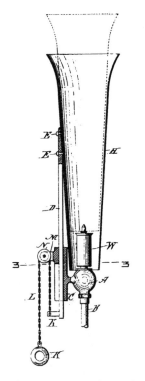

U.S. 987,038. Despite claims, the horn would appear to direct the sound uselessly upward.

606,668   **Fog Whistle**   07/05/98
Silar H. Hunter
A steam whistle mounted inside a large horn, the horn serving to direct and amplify the sound.

630,166   **Sound Deflector**   08/01/99
Joseph F. Batchelor   *Assigned: Eliza J. Boyden*
A hemispherical bowl mounted at the base of a whistle in order to deflect the sound preferentially in one direction. Includes also a plurality of bowls, one of which is selected electromagnetically.

742,375   **Chime Whistle**   10/27/1903
Isaac Anderson   *Assigned: Saginaw Whistle Company*
A two-tone chime-whistle with two mouths, in which all of the parts are integral and made in one solid casting.

766,129   **Steam Whistle**   07/26/04
Isaac Anderson & R. Ayres
An elaboration of No.742,375 embodying certain economies of manufacture. Greater efficiency and increased loudness are also claimed.

801,081   **Steam Whistle**   10/03/05
John T. Hoban   *Assigned: Buckeye Iron & Brass Works*
A chime whistle in which the bottom edges of all parts of the bell touching the bowl are slightly relieved in order to promote their free vibration.

844,254   **Megaphone Attachment for Steam Whistles**   02/12/07
Robert H. Courtney, Jr.
A conical horn with an adapter that can be clamped around the mouth of a whistle.

936,253   **Chime Whistle**   10/05/09
Frank Parizek   *Assigned: Quincy Brass Works*
Improvements in the construction of a compact four-note chime. Probably intended as an auto exhaust whistle.

981,604   **Chime Whistle**   01/17/11
John A. Anderson
A variation on the construction of the Kinsley four-chime whistle, permitting the interior parts of the bell to be fabricated from sheet metal rather than by casting.

987,038   **Convertible Whistle and Fog Horn**   03/14/11
Reinold Berrenberg
A large horn that may be lowered at will over a conventional whistle, allegedly turning it into a fog horn.

992,487   **Whistle**   05/16/11
Horace Ellison
A low pressure whistle modeled on an organ flue pipe. The airway is formed by an internal wedge, and an adjustable opening on the side of the bell adjusts the tone.

1,047,890   **Whistle**   12/17/12
Reuben L. Hohnan   *Assigned: E. E. Gross*
A compressed air whistle in which the bell is aligned and adjusted by radial supports springing from the rim of the bowl.

| 1,053,275 | **Chime-Whistle** | 02/18/13 |

Arthur Cameron *Assigned: Ivory Safety Razor Company*

A four-note auto exhaust whistle of compact and economical construction.

| 1,288,798 | **Whistle** | 12/24/18 |

Jerome J. Aull *Assigned: Lunkenheimer Company*

A cast iron chime with a top lever pivoting on the upper shoulder of the bell and the lever hanging down next to the bell. This patent is the basis of the Lunkenheimer "Tritone" line. (see next page)

| 1,315,019 | **Whistle** | 09/02/19 |

William A. Heyer

". . . a whistle which will automatically regulate itself to the pressure of the actuating fluid so that it will sound under all conditions."

| 1,328,639 | **Whistle** | 01/20/20 |

Frank Parizek

Primarily an explosion whistle for use on automobiles. Screws into cylinder, and when the driver opens a diverter valve, the cylinder exhausts through the whistle.

| 1,357,248 | **Whistle and Mounting** | 11/02/20 |

Frank Parizek

An improvement on the previous patent. An altered mounting permits the spark plug to remain in place.

| 1,440,698 | **Whistle** | 01/02/23 |

Valentine C. Rocholl

A train whistle with a short radial horn or directional baffle surrounding the mouth to direct sound upward, away from the region where "the resiliency of the air has been destroyed." *(sic)*

| 1,449,211 | **Whistle** | 03/20/23 |

Norman G. Baker

A modified bowl and bell support for calliope whistles, " . . . to insure more direct and uniform pressure of the air discharged from the cup of the whistle. . ."

| 1,500,100 | **Exhaust Whistle** | 07/08/24 |

Robert C. Anderson & F. F. Rike *Assigned: Buckeye Iron & Brass Works*

An automobile exhaust whistle of improved construction, subsequently manufactured by Buckeye as an alarm for use on fire engines.

| 1,515,471 | **Locomotive Whistle and Mounting** | 11/11/24 |

Arthur L. Foley

A paraboloidal reflector to direct the sound primarily in the forward direction with maximum efficiency. The basic patent on the Hancock 4700 air whistle.

| 1,530,899 | **Whistle Operated by Steam** | 03/24/25 |

Francois Limon

Describes a number of novel bell designs in which the resonant chamber is annular or toroidal in shape, and steam escapes through a central orifice. Some permit the incorporation of horns or directional baffles. (see next page)

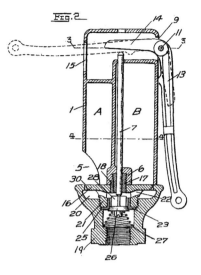

U.S. 1,288,798 Economic considerations govern the design of this single-bell chime for Lunkenheimer. Note that the top lever is reversible.

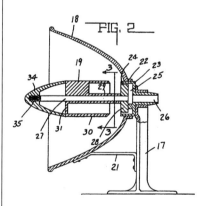

U.S.1,515,471. Prof. Foley's original embodiment of the Hancock air whistle. The shape of the reflector is acoustically correct; one wonders why Hancock changed it.

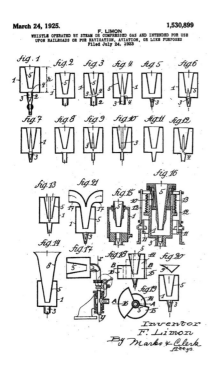

March 24, 1925.   1,530,899
F. LIMON
WHISTLE OPERATED BY STEAM OR COMPRESSED GAS AND INTENDED FOR USE
UPON RAILROADS OR FOR NAVIGATION, AVIATION, OR LIKE PURPOSES
Filed July 24, 1923

U.S. 1,530,899. M. Limon of Versailles seems to have anticipated almost every imaginable combination of whistle, horn, and directional baffle.

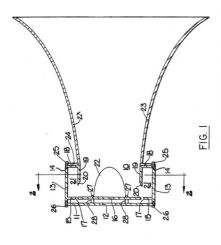

U.S. 4,686,928. A horn-loaded variant of the toroidal whistle.

1,602,839   **Whistle**   10/12/26
Valentine C. Rocholl
An ellipsoidal reflector surrounding the lower end of the bell directs the sound upward, allegedly out of the path of stack gases. See also US 1,440.698.

1,650,526   **Locomotive Whistle Amplifier**   11/22/27
David Lindsay
A metal case that surrounds the whistle and has two horn-shaped openings to direct the sound of the whistle forward and backward.

1,786,122   **Locomotive Whistle**   12/23/30
Charles T. McElvaney, Jr. & P. G. Golding
Another directional baffle for increasing sound distribution in the forward direction.

1,826,129   **Whistle**   10/06/31
Albin W. Gronquist   *Assigned: Isaac Ginsburg*
An inexpensive and unusually strong and simple whistle in which pushing down on the bell opens the valve.

1,890,212   **Whistle and the Like**   12/06/32
Arthur L. Bridgham   *Assigned: Charles H. Sherburne*
Basic patent on the Sherburne caboose whistle. Utmost economy in the use of compressed air is achieved by entraining supplementary atmospheric air in the windstream.

2,678,625   **Resonant Sound Signal Device**   05/18/54
Harry H. Hall & Otmar E. Teichmann   *Assigned: Robert H. Morse, Jr.*
A variant of Limon, US 1,530,899, in which steam exhausts through an exponential horn, increasing efficiency and directionality. A predecessor of Weisenberger, US 4,686,928, and cited by him.

4,429,656   **Toroidal Shaped Closed Chamber Whistle**   02/07/84
Richard J. Weisenberger
A whistle of unusually high efficiency in which the resonant chamber has the shape of a squat toroid of rectangular cross-section. A two-bell vertical chime is also described.

4,686,928   **Toroidal Whistle**   08/18/87
Richard J. Weisenberger
Similar to the above but heavily horn loaded, providing still higher efficiency and directionality.

Category 2: Alarms

4,541   **Steam-Boiler Indicator**   05/28/1846
Matthias W. Baldwin
A safety valve that exhausts through a steam whistle. The earliest whistle-related U.S. patent, The inventor was the founder of the Baldwin Locomotive Works.

7,808   **Steam-Boiler Indicator**   12/03/50
Joseph Dilks
The first combined low water alarm and visual indicator. A floating ball-cock opens the whistle valve and moves an indicator showing the water level in the boiler.

20,726   **Steam-Boiler Indicator**   06/29/58
Alex. Miller
A low water alarm in which a float valve activates a steam whistle.

21,040   **Steam-Boiler Indicator**   07/27/58
Jos. Whitmore
A device with integral whistle that bolts to the side of a boiler to measure the water level.

21,699   **Steam-Boiler Indicator**   10/05/58
Martin Robbins & Jno. L. Frisbie
A device with integral whistle that bolts to the top of the boiler to measure the water level.

22,287   **Steam-Boiler Indicator**   12/14/58
Geo. W. Grader & Benjn. F. Cowan
Novel construction of an alarm gauge for steam and water level that obviates the need for stuffing boxes or packing.

22,313   **Steam-Boiler Indicator**   12/14/58
Thomas Stubblefield
Another float-actuated device, with improvements intended to prevent false alarms.

23,761   **Steam-Boiler Indicator**   04/26/59
Selah Dustin
The ball-cock and the valve mechanism are entirely contained inside the boiler, obviating the need for stuffing boxes or packing.

24,017   **Steam-Boiler Indicator**   05/17/59
John L. Frisbie
The ball-cock lever is connected to the valve via a geared pivot, permitting adjustment of the set point without interruption of service.

28,165   **Steam-Boiler Indicator**   05/08/60
Selah Dustin
The low water alarm mechanism and signal device (whistle or bell) are situated entirely outside the boiler and connected thereto by a pair of sensing tubes.

29,455   **Steam-Boiler Indicator**   08/07/60
Charles H. Brown
A whistle actuated by the thermal expansion of a long iron rod in a steam chamber.

45,680   **Steam-Boiler Indicator**   12/27/64
Thomas Shaw   *Assigned: Philip S. Justice*
Another alarm actuated by thermal expansion of an iron rod, this one adapted for marine vessels.

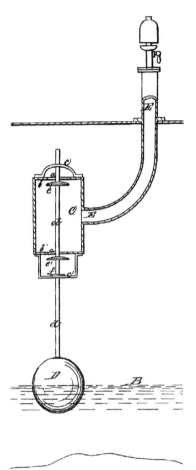

U.S. 23,761. A gland-free low water alarm. But why is there a shutoff cock on the whistle?

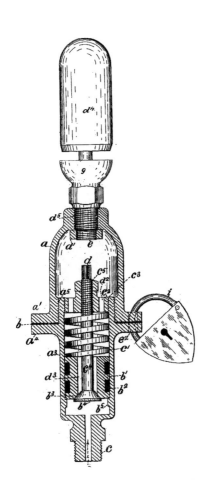

U S. 334,519. A thoroughly worked-out version of this sensible combination.

62,150   **Steam-Boiler Indicator**   02/19/67
Stewart B. Palmer
A complex low water alarm that first makes a "crackling noise," then sounds the whistle.

67,506   **Steam-Boiler Indicator**   08/06/67
Richard T. Crane
An arrangement of pipes or bars that fills with steam when the water level drops, bulging out and opening a valve that sounds the alarm whistle.

162,795   **Low-water Indicator**   5/04/75
James Harding Brown
A low-water alarm that combines an audible alarm, a visual indicator, and an automatic governor for pumping more water into the boiler.

214,186   **Alarm-Whistle for Steam Engines**   04/08/79
J. A. & S. E. Pelphrey   *Assigned: One-third to Elder J. Pelphrey*
A whistle activated by the melting of a rod of low melting point alloy. A height adjustment permits the fusible rod to be used repeatedly.

227,539   **Duplex Whistle for Steam-Boilers**   05/11/80
Juan Vila Y Jove
A high or low water alarm where the cock (valve) has both large and small openings. High water gives one sound, low water gives another, so that pitch and intensity vary with water level.

334,519   **Alarm Whistle For Steam Boilers**   01/19/86
David P. Dobbins
A safety valve with an integral steam whistle, including a means of padlocking the setting.

525,206   **Low Pressure Alarm**   08/28/94
George Heffner
A low-pressure alarm whistle for railway airbrake systems. Ingenious piping connects the alarm directly to the reservoir rather than to the train line, preventing false or delayed alarms.

532,224   **Low Pressure Alarm**   01/08/95
Benjamin C. Whelan   *Assigned: One-half to Adelbert R. Gibson*
Another low-pressure alarm for railway airbrake systems.

716,568   **Steam Boiler Indicator**   12/23/1902
Earnest G. Moore
A safety valve that uses the escaping gas to sound an integral whistle located above the valve.

1,030,454   **Train Air Signal Indicator**   06/25/12
Thomas F. Bellhouse   *Assigned: One-half to L. S. Pratt*
A railway low-pressure signal device that provides a visual cue to the engineer in addition to sounding a whistle.

1,779,795   **Abnormal Steam Pressure Signal**   10/28/30
Joseph Backstatter
The combination of a relief valve and whistle, applied to automobile radiators.

Category 3a: Whistle Valve, Manual Actuation

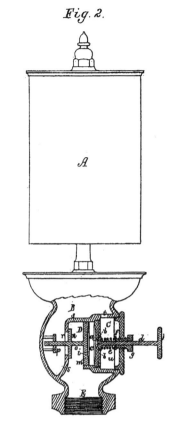

109,388   **Steam Whistle**   11/22/1870
William S. Cooper   *Assigned: Cooper, Jones & Cadbury*
A vertical valve actuated by a camshaft rotating on a horizontal axis, rather than by direct application of an axial force.

334,766   **Railway-Car Signal**   01/26/86
Sands Forman
A two-way valve for operating a whistle from several different locations in a train.

353,785   **Car Signal**   12/07/86
Sands Forman
An improvement to his two-way valve patent, US 334,766.

357,702   **Whistle**   02/15/87
George H. Crosby
Crosby's fundamental patent on the compound valve, in which the opening of a small valve relieves the pressure on the main valve.

U.S. 357,702. George Crosby's invention of the compound automatic valve opened the way to the manufacture and sale of large whistles for use on high pressures.

406,454   **Steam Whistle**   07/09/89
Charles D. Lynch
Another compound valve made of two concentric disks, a smaller disk that opens first and diminishes the effort needed to open the main disk.

616,197   **Valve for Steam-Whistles**   12/20/98
Wilhelm Moller
Valve incorporating automatic condensate drain.

636,907   **Whistle Valve**   11/14/99
Frederick Lane   *Assigned: Crosby Steam Gage & Valve Co.*
Another basic patent on the compound automatic valve. A smaller auxiliary valve, opened by the lever, allows steam to push open the main valve normally held closed by steam pressure.

1,000,012   **Steam-Whistle**   08/08/1911
Amet T. Jolma
A mechanical apparatus for reliable operation of a whistle valve from long distances, as in logging and lumbering camps.

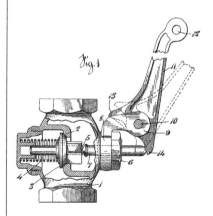

1,260,775   **Reversible Lever for Steam Whistles**   03/26/1918
David C. Jones   *Assigned: Lunkenheimer Co.*
A lever which can be mounted to extend horizontally or vertically, combined with a fulcrum which can rotate 360 degrees. Used on every Lunkenheimer whistle after this date.

1,392,773   **Whistle Operating Connection**   10/04/21
Joseph E. Lemoine & Clement O'Neal
Another device for remote actuation of a whistle valve, as in logging camps. Attaching the signal rope to a wheel permits pulling from any direction.

U.S. 1,260,775. A simple idea, but surprisingly slow to arrive: a lever which can be actuated by a pull in any direction.

1,396,096   **Steam-Whistle-Operating Mechanism**   11/08/21
Tommy J. Converse
Yet another device to facilitate remote actuation of a whistle valve, as in logging camps.

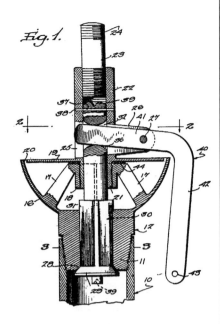

Fig. 1.

U.S. 1,665,671. The advantages of this configuration are far from self-evident; nevertheless it was adopted by at least two whistle manufacturers, Prime and Port Huron.

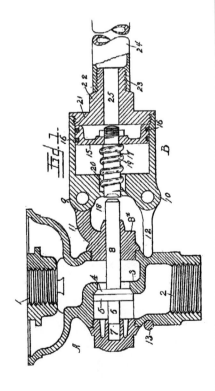

U.S. 615,398. A representative early pneumatic valve, predecessor of the modern Viloco valve.

| 1,486,252 | **Locomotive Whistle** | 03/11/24 |

John Kruttschnitt

A balanced valve in which the full boiler pressure is largely cancelled by opposing pressure on an auxiliary piston.

| 1,536,508 | **Whistle-Controlling Mechanism** | 05/05/25 |

Alexander Lilja

A spring-loaded return device installed along the manually operated rope or wire to the whistle. Intended for unusually long runs in logging camps, etc.

| 1,665,671 | **Locomotive Whistle** | 04/10/28 |

Ralph C. Morehouse

A vertical valve in which the actuating lever is neither above nor below the whistle, but intrudes between the bell and the bowl.

| 1,703,028 | **Whistle** | 02/19/29 |

Elmer R. Emerson & F. M. Dever

An improved version of the usual vertical valve, in which a close-fitting piston and a cylinder with bypass passages minimize steam leaks.

| 1,820,558 | **Whistle** | 08/25/31 |

Roger W. Clifford

A complex form of balanced valve in which the auxiliary balancing piston is entirely contained within the boiler shell.

| 1,898,54 | **Signal Controlling Device** | 02/21/33 |

Cecil S. Kelley   Assigned: Westinghouse Air Brake Co.

A pneumatic valve for use on unusually long lines. Automatically vents the line after closing to prevent the sluggish cutoff due to air trapped in the line.

Category 3b: Whistle Valve with Hydraulic or Pneumatic Actuation

566,245   **Apparatus For Operating Locomotive Whistles** 08/18/1896

John W. Thomas, Jr.

A valve mechanism that operates both by compressed air from the engineer's cab and mechanically in case of compressed air failure.

| 596,257 | **Steam Whistle** | 12/28/97 |

La Roy Bartlett

A vertical valve operated by a pneumatic piston, adapted to actuation by either steam or compressed air.

| 615,398 | **Means for Operating Steam-Whistles** | 12/06/98 |

Walter R. Lyons

Compressed gas acts on a spring-loaded piston that opens a conventional valve in the bowl of the whistle.

998,159 **Device For Blowing Whistles On Vessels** 07/18/1911
John S. Clarke *Assigned: One-third each to A. H. Langell, & C. R. Wedler*
A pneumatically or hydraulically actuated mechanism for blowing whistles on long ships such as ore carriers, where the whistle is front-mounted but controlled from a rear bridge.

1,313,251 **Steam-Whistle** 08/19/19
Douglas Brews
Another fluid-actuated valve mechanism for use on lengthy ships, eliminating the need for a chain or cord.

1,518,107 **Fluid Operated Whistle Valve** 12/02/24
Charles D. Rafferty
Still another fluid-actuated valve for whistle-blowing from a remote location.

1,530,691 **Whistle-Operating Mechanism** 03/24/25
Forrest J. Parsons
An attachment to an ordinary whistle valve that permits pneumatic as well as manual actuation.

1,561,412 **Whistle Operating Mechanism** 11/10/25
Glenn L. Davis & Frank W. Lampton
A whistle valve incorporating a piston for actuation by compressed air or steam.

1,689,509 **Device For Operating Locomotive Whistles** 10/30/28
Harry Vissering
A pneumatic piston operates the steam valve so the whistle may be located in front of the stack for efficient sound projection.

1,705,627 **Controlling Mechanism for Locomotive Whistles** 03/19/29
Harry Vissering
A combination valve permitting actuation manually or pneumatically.

1,842,813 **Signal Connection** 01/26/32
Alberto 1. Woodring *Assigned: National Safety Devices Company*
A compressed air actuator interposed between the locomotive cab and the whistle.

2,213,488 **Whistle Valve** 09/03/40
Thomas Dowrick & James F. Chase
A balanced valve actuated by compressed air and integrated with the whistle base.

Category 3c: Whistle Valve with Electrical Actuation

352,044 **Electro-Mechanical Whistle** 11/02/1886
Harry B. Cox
A modified telegraph sounder opens and closes a rotary valve.

363,079 **Electrical Device For Operating Steam Whistles** 05/17/87
William M. Pease
A weighted iron rod passes through an enormous solenoid atop the bell and holds the vertical valve closed. When energized, the solenoid lifts the rod and opens the valve.

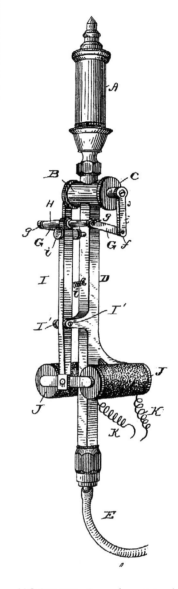

U.S. 352,044. An exuberant (and not altogether practical) example of mechanical ingenuity in the late 19th century.

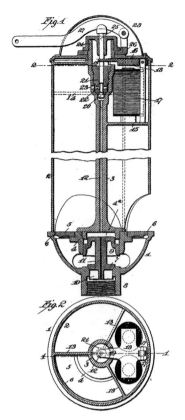

U.S. 951,877. The inventor has thoughtfully provided a manual lever in case the electro-magnet fails to work.

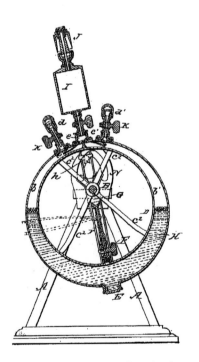

U.S. 66,459. Note the smaller whistles a - a' on either side of the main whistle. These can be detached "for use in the lifeboats in the case of shipwreck."

522,694   **Electrically-Controlled Whistle and Valve**   07/10/94

Charles E. Ongley   *Assigned: George J. Schoeffel*

An electrically controlled valve admits steam to operate a much larger main valve, which in turn blows the whistle. The entire assembly bypasses the usual manual valve.

608,955   **Steam-Whistle**   08/09/98

Forrest A. Davey   *Assigned: One-half to John G. Patterson*

A compound valve actuated by an external electromagnet.

787,422   **Whistle Valve**   04/18/1905

Frank L. Wolfe   *Assigned: Crosby Steam Gage & Valve Co.*

An improvement to Lane, US 636,907, in which the auxiliary valve is opened by a solenoid.

951,877   **Chime Whistle**   03/15/10

Henry W. Aylward   *Assigned: The Signal And Control Company*

A chime whistle with an electromagnet hidden in the inactive volume above the shorter chambers. The magnet activates a top-mounted lever.

Category 4: Automatic Signaling Devices

13,668   **Musical Instrument**   10/09/1855

Joshua C. Stoddard

The fundamental patent on the steam calliope. The essential feature is balanced valves actuated by push rods from a studded drum, similar to a music box. Whistles are mentioned only as prior art.

14,562   **Automatic Steam-Whistle On Locomotives**   04/01/56

Jas. Harrison, Jr.

A spiral cam for delivering pre-programmed whistle blows along a train journey.

15,085   **Fog Signal**   06/10/56

Rufus Porter

A "Sonorific Beacon," anchored in a shoal, which converts the rocking motion of waves into air pressure to blow whistles.

20,596   **Locomotive Signal**   06/15/58

A. E. Turnbull

Track-mounted cams and a series of arms and levers on the locomotive operate the whistle.

66,459   **Atmospheric Alarm Whistle**   07/09/67

Samuel G. Cabell

A device to convert the rolling motion of a small craft into gas pressure to blow an alarm whistle.

156,374 **Improvement in Fire-Extinguishers** 10/27/74
Henry S. Parmelee
The melting of the fusible plug in a sprinkler system permits water pressure to actuate the valve of a conventional steam whistle.

244,036 **Automatic Steam and Air Whistle** 07/12/81
James H. Crosby *Assigned: One-half to Frank S. Lee*
A steam-operated device of Rube Goldberg complexity for automatically creating a regulated series of short, intermittent blasts.

379,641 **Automatic Whistle Attachment** 03/20/88
Marine Gage
A track-mounted cam actuates lever on locomotive to sound whistle at grade crossings. (See page 256 for illustration.)

401,377 **Whistle-Actuating Mechanism** 04/16/89
William Rymer
A steam-driven rotary cam, its motion amplified by levers, pulls the whistle valve at predetermined intervals.

414,337 **Automatic Railway-Signal** 11/05/89
Abraham B. Snyder
A signal device activated by the train wheel passing over and pressing down on a lever that pumps air to a whistle.

553,900 **Electrical Whistle-Controlling Device** 02/04/96
Arthur E. Colgate *Assigned: George J. Schoeffel*
A motor-driven cam operates an electromagnetic valve to sound the whistle at predetermined intervals. Intended primarily for marine signaling in fog.

585,882 **Whistle For Buoys** 07/06/97
Edward C. Bates *Assigned: Crosby Steam Gage & Valve Co.*
An air receiver is charged when the buoy rises on a swell, and a whistle sounds when the buoy falls into a wave trough.

766,334 **Automatic Steam-Whistle** 08/02/1904
Herman A. Ewald
A roller arm riding on a steam-driven rotary cam operates a conventional valve.

1,515,888 **Electric Steam-Whistle Installation For Boats** 11/18/24
Frank L. Saunders
An electrically operated valve combined with a clockwork-driven contact wheel for automatic blowing of predetermined signals.

1,549,824 **Apparatus for Actuating Whistle and Bell Signals** 08/18/25
Alberto I. Woodring *Assigned: National Safety Devices Company*
A rotary cam driven by a compressed air motor, and fitted with cam followers that simultaneously blow the whistle and ring the bell of a locomotive throughout predetermined periods.

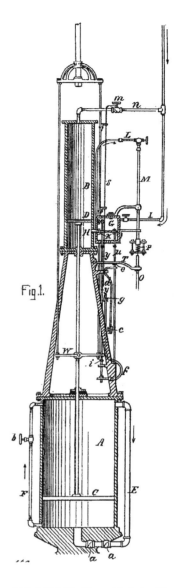

U.S. 244,036. The whistle itself, not shown, sits atop this huge pile of apparatus.

Category 5: Miscellany

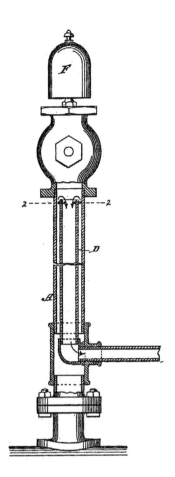

U.S. 527,000. Coaxial inlet and drain pipes provide dry steam at all times.

86,195   **Steam Whistle Drain Valve**   06/26/1869
Thomas Wendell & John H. Dorst
A combination vacuum-breaker and drain valve for the release of condensate.

414,336   **Air Whistle**   11/05/89
Sinclair Smith
A cylinder with weighted piston is interposed between whistle valve and whistle, allegedly to prevent the release of condensate and divorce the working fluid from the actuating fluid.

527,000   **Non-Condensing Apparatus for Steam Whistles**   10/02/94
John George Hermes
A circulating return pipe and continuous flow of steam prevent condensate buildup in a whistle feed pipe.

532,088   **Steam Whistle**   01/08/95
Frank W. Ofeldt   *Assigned: Marine Vapor Engine Co.*
Despite the title, the patent is concerned primarily with boiler improvements to provide an ever-ready source of steam for blowing a whistle.

584,445   **Steam Generator for Whistles**   06/15/97
Paul A. N. Winand
Exhaust gases from an internal combustion engine boil water to provide steam to blow a whistle(!) The notion of using the exhaust gases themselves seems not to have occurred to the inventor.

989,936   **Steam Whistle**   04/18/1911
James Henry Yates
A scheme of utmost simplicity for continuously blowing off condensate in the standpipe of a steam whistle.

1,311,355   **Steam Whistle Diaphragm**   07/29/19
John Kropacz
A device to retard the passage of steam at low pressure and permit high-pressure steam to pass.

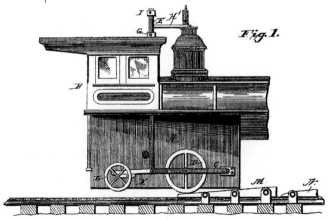

U.S. 379,641. Merrily we roll along, relieved of all necessity to remember to blow the whistle by the inventor's system of cams and rollers.

Notes

Chapter 1. Introduction

1. Lewis Mumford, *Technics and Civilization* (Harcourt, Brace, New York, 1934), p. 156.

2. Lucius Beebe & Charles Clegg, *The American West: The Pictorial Epic of a Continent* (Dutton, New York, 1952); also Lucius Beebe, *Trains in Transition* (Appleton-Century, New York, 1941) p. 3.

3. Henry Adams, *The Education of Henry Adams* (Modern Library, New York, 1931), p. 379.

7. William Wordsworth, "On the Projected Kendal and Windermere Railway" [Quoted by Henry Petroski, *To Engineer is Human* (Vintage, New York, 1992), p. 58.]

8. Henry David Thoreau, *Walden* (Heritage Press, New York, 1939) p. 198.

9. Frank Norris, *The Octopus* (Doubleday, Page & Co., New York, 1924) p. 51.

Chapter 2. The Steam Whistle in Historical Context

1. There are literally hundreds of books dealing with the development of the steam engine. An excellent although decidedly Anglocentric account can be found in Asa Briggs, *The Power of Steam,* (University of Chicago Press, Chicago, 1982). See also the references contained therein. For a witty and well illustrated popular account of the origins of the railway, once can scarcely do better than Oliver Jensen, *The American Heritage History of Railroads in America*, (American Heritage, New York, 1975), especially Ch. 1, pp. 12-29.

2. For more than a century, a steam engine was called a "fire" engine, naming it after the source of its energy rather than its working fluid. This rather sensible practice is consistent with our present day use of "gas" or "gasoline" engine for an internal combustion engine running on the Otto cycle.

3. The one indispensable reference is Charles E. Lee, "Adrian Stephens: Inventor of the Steam Whistle," *Transactions of the Newcomen Society*, Vol. XXVII (Courier Press, London, 1956) p. 163. Our account is drawn almost exclusively from this paper.

4. Basalla, George, *The Evolution of Technology*, (Cambridge University Press, Cambridge, 1988).

5. John H. White, Jr., *American Locomotives: An Engineering History, 1830-1880*, (Johns Hopkins Press, Baltimore, 1968), p. 214.

6. John H. Morrison, *History of American Steam Navigation*, (W. F. Sametz, New York, 1903) p. 238. For the use of steam whistles as fog horns, see pp. 576, 580, and 601-605.

Chapter 3. The Applications of Steam Whistles

1. Basalla, *op. cit.* (Ref. 4, Ch. 2).

2. For a very brief but authoritative discussion of 19th century railroad whistles in the U.S., see John H. White, *loc. cit.* (Ref. 5, Ch. 2). The best popular account of the development of the locomotive whistle is M. Figen, "The Locomotive Whistle", *Railroad Magazine*, December, 1942, p. 60. "The Romance of Locomotive Whistles" (author unidentified), *Railroad Magazine*, July, 1978, p. 12, is derived largely from Figen, and inferior to it in every way. Charles F. H. Allen, "The Steam Locomotive Whistle", Bulletin No. 106 of The Railway & Locomotive Historical Society, Inc. (RLHS, Boston, 1962) is disappointingly brief and superficial. Numerous short accounts can be found in popular "railfan" books, e.g Henry B. Comstock, *The Iron Horse* (Crowell, New York, 1971) p. 93.

3. White, *loc. cit.* (Ref. 5, Ch. 2).

4. Deane Ellsworth, "Whistle Engineering," *Live Steam Magazine*, April, 1976, p. 10.

5. Peter Ommundsen, private communication.

6. E. A. Fagen, "The Harmonic Analysis of Chime Chords," *Horn & Whistle*, No. 80 (Summer, 1998), p. 15; No. 81 (Fall, 1998), p. 6.

7. A. L. Foley, "Study of Locomotive Whistles," *Railway Age,* December 3, 1925; "The Whistle", *Railway & Locomotive Engineering,* October, 1925, p. 295; "C&E.I. Experiments With Front End Whistles," *Railway Age*, July 30, 1927, p. 204.

8. At first glance it seems odd that a manufacturer of water meters would also manufacture very large factory

whistles, but there is a hidden connection. One of the founders of the Union Water Meter Co. was Benaiah Fitts, brother of Abraham Fitts, inventor of the Fitts gong.

9. The content of this section is drawn in large part from Steven Espenschied, *A History of the American Steam Calliope*, (Vantage Press, New York, 1986). See also Morrison, *op. cit.* (Ref. 6, Ch. 2), pp. 627-630, and David Bowers, *Encyclopedia of Automatic Musical Instruments*, (Vestal Press, Vestal, NY, 1972) pp. 838-844. Among periodicals, see *Live Steam Magazine*, September, 1973, pp. 12-15, and September, 1975, p. 49; *Contemporary Keyboard*, March, 1977, pp. 14 ff.; and Oliver Jensen, "Don't Boil the Calliope Player, or Good News for Music Lovers," *American Heritage*, August, 1980, p. 30.

10. The name "calliope," meaning "beautiful voice," comes from classical Greek mythology. Kalliope herself was the chief of the Muses, presiding over eloquence and heroic poetry. Her name is properly pronounced in four syllables with the accent on the second: kal-EYE-oh-pee. Rivermen, circus performers, and others professionally associated with the instrument regarded this pronunciation as an affectation, and invariably called it a KAL-ee-ope. Even this was too pretentious for its millions of unlettered hearers, who simply called it a "steam pie-anna."

11. Worcester, Massachusetts seems to have been a busy place in terms of steam whistle development. Recall that this was the home of Abraham Fitts, who invented the Fitts gong at roughly the same time, and subsequently the home of the Union Water Meter Co., which manufactured it.

12. *Puppet* vs. *poppet*: The Oxford English Dictionary recognizes no difference between a "puppet valve" and a "poppet valve." Both signify a valve controlled by some external mechanism or agency, as in the everyday sense of the word "puppet." "Puppet valve" was the prevailing usage throughout the 19th century, but is now rare.

13. *The American Organist Magazine*, vol. 38, no. 12 (December, 1955).

14. For the mathematically inclined, this is called a *self-affine* transformation.

15. E. A. Fagen, "Whistle Science 3: The scaling of bells," *Horn & Whistle*, No. 54 (Nov/Dec 1992), p. 21.

16. *Live Steam Magazine*, June, 1977, pp. 6-10; Conrad Milster, "How I built my calliope," *Horn & Whistle*, No. 93 (Fall, 2001) pp. 8-13.

Chapter 4. The Steam Whistle in Popular Culture

1. Henry David Thoreau, *Walden* (Heritage Press, New York, 1939) p. 123.

2. Albert Murray, *Train Whistle Guitar* (McGraw-Hill, New York, 1974) p. 50.

3. Lewis Mumford, *op. cit..* (Ref. 1, Ch. 1) pp. 12 ff.

4. William Humphrey, "The Farmer's Daughter," in *September Song* (Seymour Lawrence/Houghton Mifflin, Boston, 1992), p. 24.

5. Murray, *op. cit*, p. 8, p. 15.

6. *American Machinist,* April 24, 1880, p. 9.

7. Edward S. Morse, "The Steam Whistle a Menace to Public Health," paper read before the Massachusetts Association of Boards of Health at Boston, January 27, 1905, and subsequently published as a pamphlet by the author. I am indebted to Bruce Cynar for the discovery of this gem.

8. Thomas Wolfe, *Of Time and the River* (Charles Scribner's Sons, New York, 1971) pp. 23, 76, 86, 401, *passim.*

9. Mabel O'Donnell, *Engine Whistles*, The Alice and Jerry Books Reading Foundation Series, (Row, Peterson & Co., Evanston, Illinois, 1942). As above, I am indebted to Bruce Cynar for the discovery and gift of this book.

10. Michael Broggie, *Walt Disney's Railroad Story: The Small-Scale Fascination that Led to a Full-Scale Kingdom* (Pentrex, Pasadena, CA, 1998).

11. Nicolai Cikovsky, Jr., "George Inness's *The Lackawanna Valley*: 'Type of the Modern,'" in *The Railroad in American Art,* Susan Danly & Leo Marx, eds., (MIT Press, Cambridge, 1988) pp. 71-91.

12. The essential reference is an enormous and thoughtfully annotated bibliography by Philip Pacey of the University of Central Lancashire. Entitled "Music and Railways," it is available on the Internet at <www.uclan.ac.uk/library/musrail.htm>. I am indebted to Alexander D. Mitchell IV for bringing this resource to my attention.

13. Katie Letcher Lyle, *Scalded to Death by the Steam* (Algonquin Press, Chapel Hill, 1983).

14. "The Wedding of the Rails," copyright 1990 by Lorraine S. Wilkinson.

Chapter 5. Whistle Manufacturers and Their Products

1. In one of the least fortunate choices of logo in American corporate history, Crane Co. cast steel products were marked in the 1920's with a swastika.

2. James A. Laux, "The one great name in valves: a history of the Lunkenheimer Company," *Queen City Heritage, Journal of the Cincinnati Historical Society,* Spring, 1983, pp. 17-38.

3. For an astonishing demonstration of octave pitch ambiguity, listen to the "Shepard scales" (R. N. Shepard, "Circularity in judgments of relative pitch," *J. Acoust. Soc. Am.* **36**, 2346 (1964)). These can be heard on "Auditory Demonstrations," A. J. M. Houtsma *et al.*, a compact disc (Philips 1126-061) prepared at the Institute for Perception Research, Eindhoven, and available as item AD-CB-BK from ASA Publications, Box 1020, Sewickley, PA 15143.

Chapter 6. Collecting Steam Whistles

1. Werner Muensterberger, *Collecting: An Unruly Passion* (Harcourt Brace, San Diego, 1995), a searching (and more than a little unsettling) psychological analysis of the impulse to collect.

2. Mitch Tuchman, *Magnificent Obsessions* (Chronicle Press, San Francisco, 1994).

3. C. Mackay, *Extraordinary Popular Delusions and the Madness of Crowds,* (Noonday Press, New York, 1965) p. 91.

4. Muensterberger, *op. cit.,* pp. 73 ff.

5. *Collectable* vs. *collectible.* The -*able*/-*ible* controversy is so vexed that Fowler (*Modern English Usage*) devotes four pages to it. Nevertheless the rule is clear in this instance: the suffix -*able* is preferred when adjectives denoting worthiness, suitability, etc. are formed from transitive verbs. The Oxford English Dictionary and The American Heritage Dictionary, however, both list *collectible* as an acceptable substitute. American usage is about evenly divided between the two spellings, with some tendency to use *collectable* for the adjective and *collectible(s)* for the noun. This supposed distinction is superfluous and without grammatical or etymological foundation.

6. As we saw in Ch. 5, Buckeye, Crosby and Kinsley whistles were all numbered, but it is not clear that this number is a serial number.

7. Muensterberger, *op cit.,* p. 4.

8. I am indebted to Prof. George Basalla of the University of Delaware for this information. See also G. Phillips Bevan, ed., *British Manufacturing Industries,* (Edward Stanford, London, 1876), and William G. Lathrop, *The Brass Industry in Connecticut,* (W. G. Lathrop, Shelton, CT, 1909).

9. By contrast, the market for certain other items of railroad hardware, especially locomotive number plates and builder's plates, is full of perils. Plates are relatively easy to reproduce. Their simple castings require little or no machining, and because of their uniqueness they can command prices comparable to most locomotive whistles. Hence the inducements to fakery are numerous and persuasive. Tourist railroads and railroad clubs occasionally sell reproductions of plates as a fund-raising device, but these reputable organizations have been most conscientious about marking them as replicas. As further protection, the castings are sometimes executed in aluminum or plastic resin, so that they can never be mistaken for the bronze or cast iron originals. Alternatively, they are sometimes reproduced at less than their original size.

Chapter 7. Conserving Steam Whistles

1. "Cleaning and Finishing of Copper and Copper Alloys," F. B. Rote *et al.*, ASM Committee on Finishing of Copper and Copper Alloys, *Metals Handbook,* 8th edition, (American Society for Metals, Metals Park, Ohio, 1964), Volume 2, pp. 635-647. For a later version, see the article under the same title by Robert M. Paine and Bob Srinivasan, *Metals Handbook,* 9th edition (1982), Volume 5, pp. 611-627.

2. John H. White, Jr., *op. cit.* (Ref. 5, Ch. 2), Appendix F, p. 468. Reprinted from *Railroad Gazette,* December 8, 1882.

Chapter 8. Blowing Steam Whistles

1. This table and the technical bulletin from which it came were reprinted in *Horn & Whistle,* No. 38 (March/April, 1989), p. 22. An obvious misprint for the 2" diameter whistle has been corrected.

2. A fourth row has been added to each of these tables, a normalized flow rate obtained by dividing the air consumption by the *absolute* pressure, i.e., the flow rate per unit of absolute pressure. This number is

proportional to the cross-sectional area of the windway, and does not depend on the blowing pressure. These normalized flow rates have been analyzed by the author in an effort to discover the scaling laws used by the manufacturer. See E. A. Fagen, "Whistle Science 2: Air consumption vs. size," *Horn & Whistle* No. 53 (Sept/Oct 1992), p. 3. The surprising result is that there is no regularity which extends throughout either product line. According to an internal company memorandum, the same is true of Crosby whistles.

3. E. A. Fagen, "Whistle Science 1: How to estimate air consumption," *Horn & Whistle*, No. 46 (July/Aug 1991), p. 16. See also E. A. Fagen, "Blowing the *Titanic's* whistle," *Horn & Whistle,* No. 90 (Winter 2000-2001), p. 14.

Chapter 9. How a Whistle Works

1. This anecdote comes from James Gleick, *Genius* (Pantheon Books, New York, 1992) p. 137.

2. N. H. Fletcher & T. D. Rossing, *The Physics of Musical Instruments* (Springer-Verlag, New York, 1991). See especially Sec. 8.3 and Chs. 16 and 17. Potential readers are warned that the book is dense with mathematics and likely to daunt those without a degree in physics or engineering.

3. N. H. Fletcher & S. Thwaites, "The Physics of Organ Pipes," *Scientific American* **248**, 1 (January, 1983), pp. 94-103.

4. John William Strutt, Baron Rayleigh, *Theory of Sound,* (Dover Publications, New York, 1945), Vol II, Ch. XXI, Sec. 365, pp. 376-381.

5. For the mathematically inclined, the divergence of the velocity no longer vanishes.

6. H. Levine and J. Schwinger, *Phys. Rev.* **73**, 383 (1948). See also L. A. Weinstein, *Doklady Akad. Nauk SSSR II,* **S. 58**, 1957 (1947); *J. Tech. Phys. (U.S.S.R.)* **XIX**, 911 (1949). The mathematics is formidable, and thorough acquaintance with function theory is needed to follow the argument. R. E. Swanson favored the value $0.35d$ for the end correction on the basis of his experiments. Lord Rayleigh's widely quoted theoretical value, $0.41d$, (Rayleigh, *op cit.*, App. A, pp 487-491) applies only to pipes fitted with infinite baffles at their mouths, so that they open into half-space (2π steradians).

7. P. Ommundsen, "Whistle size and whistle sounds," *Horn & Whistle*, No. 91 (Spring, 2001) p. 7.

8. A modern video clip of the oscillating jet at the mouth of an organ flue pipe is available on the Internet at <http://aol.member.com/ReinerJank/klgd-ani.htm>. The

technique by which this video was made is described at <http://aol.member.com/ReinerJank/em-legen.htm>. The accompanying text is in German.

9. The case for the organ flue pipe as a modified edge-tone oscillator was forcefully propounded by W. Blocker, "Theory of Edge-Tone Oscillators," *J. Acoust. Soc. Am.* **55**, 2, (February, 1974) p. 458. Unfortunately, this citation is merely the abstract of a contributed oral paper; the paper itself was never published. A slightly revised version of the paper appeared on the Internet 26 years later at (http://209.211.36.9/users/wblocker/index. htm). The role of the acoustic crosswind from the mouth of the pipe is ignored, making the applicability of this theory to flue pipes doubtful at best. An incompressible fluid is assumed throughout.

10. J. W. Coltman, "Jet drive mechanisms in edge tones and organ pipes," J. Acoust. Soc. Am. **60**, 3 (September, 1976), p. 725.

11. For the details of these studies, see the comprehensive bibliography at the end of Chapter 16 of Fletcher & Rossing, *op. cit.*

12. J. W. Coltman, "Sounding mechanism of the flute and organ pipe,"*J. Acoust. Soc. Am.* **44**, 4 (October, 1968), p. 983.

13. Bernoulli's Law (Daniel Bernoulli, 1700-1782) of incompressible fluid flow is merely a restatement of the law of the conservation of energy. It says that the difference in pressure between a stationary fluid and a moving fluid is equal to the kinetic energy density of the moving fluid. See any text on elementary fluid mechanics, e.g. P. Bradshaw, *Experimental Fluid Mechanics,* 2nd ed. (Pergamon, Oxford, 1970), pp. 18-21.

14. For a series expansion of Bernoulli's Law in powers of the compressiblility, see A. Shapiro, *The Dynamics and Thermodynamics of Compressible Fluid Flow*, Vol. 2, (Ronald Press, New York,) p. 94. The expansion fails, however, at pressures far below the usual operating pressures of steam whistles.

15. Conventional wisdom has maintained for centuries that the jet of an organ flue pipe is laminar. This widely held belief is belied by the actions of organ builders themselves, however, who throughout the 18th and 19th centuries cut tiny nicks in the languids of their flue pipes in order to promote prompt speech—a practice strongly denigrated by Baroque purists. We now know that nicking promotes turbulent flow, which in turn stabilizes the jet at higher operating pressures, just as the dimples on a golf ball stabilize its flight through the air, This brought an important advantage to organ builders as they continually raised operating pressures in search of greater volume of sound. Today the weight of evidence suggests that the jet is turbulent in most existing organ pipes, or if not initially turbulent when it

emerges from the flue, then it soon becomes so as it moves downstream. Laminar flow jets are likely to be found only in the oldest and smallest Baroque organs, voiced at the lowest pressures.

16. R. C. Chanaud, "Aerodynamic whistles," *Scientific American* **222**, 1 (January, 1970) p. 40.

17. S. A. Elder, "On the mechanism of sound production in organ pipes," *J. Acoust. Soc. Am.* **54**, 6 (December, 1973), p. 1554. Cf. also Fletcher & Rossing, *op. cit.*, p. 436.

18. R. E. Swanson, undated and unpublished internal memorandum of Railway Appliance Research Ltd. Swanson's remarks were subsequently published by Deane H. Ellsworth in "Whistle Engineering," *Live Steam Magazine*, April, 1976, p. 10. Readers are cautioned that formulas in the printed version are polluted with typographic errors. Swanson's original memo is not error-free either.

19. Lunkenheimer Standard Practise Sheet SP-40, dated March 2, 1962.

20. P. Ommundsen, "Effect of the whistle mouth on frequency," *Horn & Whistle* No. 92 (Summer, 2001), p. 14.

21. This study was discovered and made available by Craig Bliss, a contemporary employee of Crosby Valve. The study was of course entirely internal, and never appeared in the open literature.

22. A review of Davidson's results has been published by P. Ommundsen, "The Davidson experiments of 1927," *Horn & Whistle,* No. 90 (Winter, 2000) p. 18.

Index

A

D

N

T

Talking. *See* Whistle talk
Tangley Co., 55
Tashmoo [steamer], 145
Telescoping whistles, 114
Temperature, absolute, 214, **229**
TGV [music], 76
Theft, 161-162
Thermodynamics, 16
    and engines, 7, 16
    and physics of whistles, 221
    single-phase *vs.* two-phase systems, 199
Thomas Register of American Manufacturers [publication],
    81–82
Thoreau, Henry David, 17, 62, 66
Three-bell chime whistles, *234. See also* Multiple-bell chime
    whistles
Three-bell gong whistles, **234–235.** *See also* Gong whistles
3M. *See* Minnesota Mining & Manufacturing Co. (3M)
Thwaites, ?, 219
TIG welding. *See* Welding
Timekeepers
    whistles as, 62–64
Tin, 180-181. *See also* Alloys; Bronze
Tinnitus, 194
Titanic [ocean liner], 44, 65, 145
Titfield Thunderbolt, The [movie], 68
Tongues. *See* Spreader plates
"Tonight" show, 71
Tools for conservation, 168
Top caps, **235**
Top-lever whistles, 26, 35, *96,* 119, **235**
Top nuts, 170, **235.** *See also* Acorns
Top plates. *See* Spreader plates; Top caps
Torches, 169, 176, 178, 179, 183, 184
Toroidal whistles, *222, 223,* **235**
Townsend, S. H., 53
Toy boxes, 68, 78
Trademarks. *See* Logos of whistle manufacturers
Train, The [movie], 68
Train Whistle Guitar [novel], 62, 65
Trains [publication], 151
Transient states, 220
Trespassing, 146
Trevithick, Richard, 8–9, 15–16
Triads, 30, 31, 33, 34, 40, 116, 156. *See also* Harmony
Trillers, **235**
Triple whistles, **235.** *See also* Multiple-bell chime whistles
Tritone whistles, 34, 105, 119–*120,* **235**
Trombone air whistles, *134,* **235**
Tumor-top whistles, *37,* **235**
Tuning
    of calliopes, 55, 57–58
    of whistles, 38, 110, 202, 226
Turbulent flow, 14, 213, 221. *See also* Fluid dynamics

Turner, J. M. W., 72
Turner, Thomas, 12–15, 24
Twain, Mark, 77
Twentieth Century Limited [train], 145
Twilling, **235.** *See also* Quilling; Whistle talk
Two shorts, **235.** *See also* Whistle codes
Tyfon Co., 44

U

Ultrawhistles. *See* Toroidal whistles
Underblowing, 204, 225–*226*
Union Brass Works, 113, 127–128, 145
Union Pacific [movie], 68
Union Pacific Railroad
    collecting whistles used by, 145, 156
    harmony of chime whistles used on, 33
    markings on whistles used by, 158
Union [steamboat], 53
Union Water Meter Co., 82*t,* 84, 86
    gong whistles by, 48, *192*
Unions, 115-116
United Brass Co., 127
United Brass Works, 127
Upright valves. *See* Vertical valves

V

Valve covers, 88, 128-*129,* 171, **235**
Valve seats. *See* Seats, valve
Valve stems, 88, 171, **235**
Valves, **235.** *See also* Safety valves; Patents; individual manu-
    facturers of whistles
    balanced, **21,** 28, *45-46,* 52, 119, 129-*130, 132,* **229**
    compound automatic, **21,** *28,* 87, 88, 99, 102,*104,*122-123,
        132, **231,** 238, 240, 251, 254
    conservation of, 175
    equalized, **21, 231**
    horizontal, **21,** 28, 30-31, 34-35, 87, 89, 102, 121, **232**
    solenoid, 46, 55, 58
    spring, 28, 35, **234**
    vertical, **21,** 28, 31, 34-35, *37,* 87, 89, 104, 121, **235**
Van Duzen Foundry, 54
van Gogh, Vincent, 140, 158
Vanderbilt, Cornelius, 105
Vanes, **235.** *See also* Ears
Variable-pitch whistles, **235.** *See also* Fire-alarm whistles;
    Mockingbird whistles; Piston whistles; Telescoping
    whistles; Wildcat whistles
Veeing, 171, 172, *176,* 183
Velocity
    of fluids, 213, 216–217, 218-221, 225-226
    of sound, 199, 214, 214, 220
Vertical chime whistles, *48,* 96, **235**
Vertical valves, **21,** 28, 31, 34-35, **235**
    and shop-built whistles, 34

Y

Z